# The JUNIOR CLASSICS

## VOLUME NINE · SPORT AND ADVENTURE

Warren Chappell

*Christian gave orders to lower the boat.*

[See page 369]

# *The* JUNIOR CLASSICS

Edited *by* MABEL WILLIAMS *and* MARCIA DALPHIN.

*With Introduction by* WILLIAM ALLAN NEILSON, *Former*

*President of Smith College; Introduction to First Edition by*

CHARLES W. ELIOT, *Former President of Harvard University*

Popular Edition

*ILLUSTRATED*

VOLUME
NINE

SPORT AND
ADVENTURE

P. F. COLLIER & SON CORPORATION

"Stover Plays Football," from "The Varmint," copyright, 1910, by Little, Brown & Company. "The Winning Bug," from "Split Seconds," copyright, 1926, by Jackson Scholz; copyright, 1927, by William Morrow & Company, Inc. "Billy Topsail and the Devilfish," from "The Adventures of Billy Topsail," copyright, 1906, by Fleming H. Revell Company. "The Two-Twenty Low Hurdle Race," from "The Human Comedy," copyright, 1943, by Harcourt, Brace and Company, Inc. "Head Over Heels," copyright, 1942, by B. J. Chute. "Knapsack of Salvation," from "I'll Take the High Road," copyright, 1939, by Wolfgang Langewiesche. "Chased by the Trail," copyright, 1907, by Perry Mason Company. "The Prospector," from "They of the High Trails," copyright, 1902, by Hamlin Garland; copyright, 1916, by Harper & Brothers. "Tom Chist and the Treasure Chest," from "Howard Pyle's Book of Pirates," copyright, 1921, by Harper & Brothers. "Dick Turpin," from "Highwaymen," copyright, 1923, by Robert M. McBride & Company. "New York to Paris," from "We," copyright, 1927, by Charles A. Lindbergh. "Flying over the North Pole," from "Skyward," copyright, 1928, by Richard E. Byrd. "Dawn Over Zero," from "Dawn Over Zero," copyright, 1946, by Alfred A. Knopf, Inc. "The Making of an Explorer," from "Ends of the Earth," copyright, 1929, by Roy Chapman Andrews. "With Helmet and Hose," from "Exploring with Beebe," copyright, 1932, by William Beebe. "Summit of the World: The Fight for Everest," from "High Conquest," copyright, 1941, by James Ramsey Ullman. "Adrift on an Ice Pan," copyright, 1909, by Wilfred Thomason Grenfell. "The Race for the South Pole," from "The Last Continent of Adventure," copyright, 1930, by Walter B. Hayward. "The Lone Voyagers," from "The Book of the Gloucester Fishermen," copyright, 1927, by James Brendan Connolly. "An Adventure with a Whale," from "The Cruise of the Cachalot," copyright, 1925, by D. Appleton & Company. "Rounding the Cape in a Windjammer," copyright, 1931, by National Geographic Society.

Acknowledgments of permissions given by authors and publishers for the use of copyright
material appear in Volume X.

CT

# CONTENTS

v

# CONTENTS

(The sources of the stories in this volume will be found listed on page 389)

# STOVER PLAYS FOOTBALL

## By OWEN JOHNSON

### I

WHY, look at the Dink!" said Lovely Mead the next afternoon, as Stover emerged in football togs which he had industriously smeared with mud to conceal their novelty.

"He must be going out for the 'Varsity!" said Fatty Harris sarcastically.

"By request," said the Gutter Pup.

"Why, who told you?" said Stover.

"You trying for the 'Varsity?" said Lovely Mead incredulously. "Why, where did you play football?"

"Dear me, Lovely," said Stover, lacing his jacket, "thought you read the newspapers."

"Huh! What position are you trying for?"

"First substitute scorer," said Stover, according to Finnegan's theory. "Any more questions?"

Lovely Mead, surprised, looked at Stover in perplexity and remained silent.

Dink, laughing to himself at the ease of the trick, started across the Circle for the 'Varsity football field, whither already the candidates were converging to the first call of the season.

He had started joyfully forth from the skeptics on the steps, but once past the chapel and in sight of the field his gait abruptly changed. He went quietly, thoughtfully, a little alarmed at his own daring, glancing at the padded figures that overtopped him.

The veterans with the red L on their black sweaters were apart, tossing the ball back and forth and taking playful tackles at one-another. Stover, hiding himself modestly in the common herd, watched with entranced eyes the lithe, sinuous forms of Flash Condit and Charlie DeSoto—greater to him than the faint heroes of mythology—as they tumbled the Waladoo Bird gleefully on the ground. There was Butcher Stevens of the grim eye and the laconic word, a man to follow and emulate; and the broad span of Turkey Reiter's shoulders, a mark to grow to. Meanwhile, Garry Cockrell, the captain, and Mr. Ware, the new coach from the Princeton championship eleven, were drawing nearer on their tour of inspection and classification. Dink knew his captain only from respectful distances—the sandy hair, the gaunt cheek bones and the deliberate eye, whom governors of states alone might approach with equality, and no one else. Under the dual inspection the squad was quickly sorted, some sent back to their House teams till another year brought more weight and experience, and others tentatively retained on the scrubs.

"Better make the House team, Jenks," said the low, even voice of the captain. "You want to harden up a bit. Glad you reported, though."

Then Dink stood before his captain, dimly aware of the quick little eyes of Mr. Ware quietly scrutinizing him.

"What form?"

"Third."

The two were silent a moment studying not the slender, wiry figure, but the look in the eyes within.

"What are you out for?"

"End, sir."

"What do you weigh?"

"One hundred and fifty—about," said Dink.

A grim little twinkle appeared in the captain's eyes. "About one hundred and thirty-five," he said, with a measuring glance.

"But I'm hard, hard as nails, sir," said Stover desperately.

"What football have you played?"

Stover remained silent.

"Well?"

"I—I haven't played," he said unwillingly.

"You seem unusually eager," said Cockrell, amused at this strange exhibition of willingness.

"Yes, sir."

"Good spirit; keep it up. Get right out for your House team——"

"I won't!" said Stover, blurting it out in his anger and then flushing: "I mean, give me a chance, won't you, sir?"

Cockrell, who had turned, stopped and came back.

"What makes you think you can play?" he said not unkindly.

"I've got to," said Stover desperately.

"But you don't know the game."

"Please, sir, I'm not out for the 'Varsity," said Stover confusedly. "I mean, I want to be in it, to work for the school, sir."

"You're not a Freshman?" said the captain, and the accents of his voice were friendly.

"No, sir."

"What's your name?" said Cockrell, a little thrilled to feel the genuine veneration that inspired the "sir."

"Stover—Dink Stover."

"You were down at the Green last year, weren't you?"

"Yes, sir," said Stover, looking down with a sinking feeling.

"You're the fellow who tried to fight the whole House?"

"Yes, sir."

"Well, Dink, this is a little different—you can't play football on nothing but nerve."

"You can if you've got enough of it," said Stover, all in a breath. "Please, sir, give me a chance. You can fire me if I'm no good. I only want to be useful. You've got to have a lot of fellows to stand the banging and you can bang me around all day. I do know something about it, sir; I've practiced tackling and falling on the ball all summer, and I'm hard as nails. Just give me a chance, will you? Just one chance, sir."

Cockrell looked at Mr. Ware, whose eye showed the battling spark as he nodded.

"Here, Dink," he said gruffly, "I can't be wasting any more time over you. I told you to go back to the House team, didn't I?"

Stover, with a lump in his throat, nodded the answer he could not utter.

"Well, I've changed my mind. Get over there in the squad."

The revulsion of feeling was so sudden that tears came into Stover's eyes.

"You're really going to let me stay?"

"Get over there, you little nuisance!"

Dink went a few steps, and then stopped and tightened his shoelaces a long minute.

"Too bad the little devil is so light," said Cockrell to Mr. Ware. "Best player I ever played against had no right on a football field."

"But one hundred and thirty-five!"

"Yes, that's pretty light."

"What the deuce were you chinning so long about?" said Cheyenne Baxter to Dink, as he came joyfully into the squad.

"Captain wanted just a bit of general expert advice from me," said Dink defiantly. "I've promised to help out."

The squad, dividing, practiced starts. Stover held his own, being naturally quick; and though Flash Condit and Charlie DeSoto distanced him, still he earned a good word for his performances.

Presently Mr. Ware came up with a ball and, with a few words of introduction, started them to falling on it as it bounded grotesquely over the ground, calling them from the ranks by name.

"Hard at it, Stevens."

"Dive at it."

"Don't stop till you get it."

"Oh, squeeze the ball!"

Stover, moving up, caught the eye of Mr. Ware intently on him, and rose on his toes with the muscles in his arms strained and eager.

"Now, Stover, hard!"

The ball with just an extra impetus left the hand of Mr. Ware. Stover went at it like a terrier, dove and came up glorious and muddy with the pigskin hugged in his arms. It was the extent of his football knowledge, but that branch he had mastered on the soft summer turf.

Mr. Ware gave a grunt of approval and sent him plunging after another. This time as he dove the ball took a tricky bounce and slipped through his arms. Quick as a flash Dink, rolling over, recovered himself and flung himself on it.

"That's the way!" said Mr. Ware. "Follow it up. Can't always get it the first time. Come on, Baxter."

The real test came with the tackling. He waited his turn, all eyes, trying to catch the trick, as boy after boy in front of him went cleanly or awkwardly out to down the man who came plunging at him. Some tackled sharply and artistically, their feet leaving the ground and taking the runner off his legs as though a scythe had passed under him; but most of the tackling was crude, and often the runner slipped through the arms and left the tackler prone on the ground to rise amid the jeers of his fellows.

"Your turn, Stover," said the voice of the captain. "Wait a minute." He looked over the squad and selected McCarty, saying: "Here, Tough, come out here. Here's a fellow thinks all you need in this game is nerve. Let's see what he's got."

Dink stood out, neither hearing nor caring for the laugh that went up. He glanced up fifteen yards away where Tough McCarty stood waiting the starting signal. He was not afraid, he was angry clean through, ready to tackle the whole squad, one after another.

"Shall I take it sideways?" said Tough, expecting to be tackled from the side as the others had been.

"No, head on, Tough. Let's see if you can get by him," said Cockrell. "Let her go!"

McCarty, with the memory of past defiances, went toward Stover head down, full tilt. Ordinarily in practice the runner slackens just before the tackle; but McCarty, expecting slight resistance from a novice, arrived at top speed.

Stover, instead of hesitating or waiting the coming, hurled himself recklessly forward. Shoulder met knee with a crash that threw them both. Stunned by the savage impact, Stover spilled head over heels, dizzy and furious, instinctively flung himself from his knees upon the prostrate body of McCarty, as he had followed the elusive ball a moment before.

"That's instinct, football instinct," said Mr. Ware to Cockrell, as they approached the spot where Dink, still dazed, was clutching Tough McCarty's knees in a convulsive hug.

"Let go! Let go there, you little varmint," said Tough McCarty, considerably shaken. "How long are you going to hold me here?"

Some one touched Dink on the shoulder; he looked up through the blur to see the captain's face.

"All right, Dink, get up."

But Stover released his grip not a whit.

"Here, you young bulldog," said Cockrell with a laugh, "it's all over. Let go. Stand up. Sort of groggy, eh?"

Dink, pulled to his feet, felt the earth slip under him in drunken reelings.

"I missed him," he said brokenly, leaning against Mr. Ware.

"H'm, not so bad," said the coach gruffly.

"How do you feel?" said Garry Cockrell, looking at him with his quiet smile.

Dink saw the smile and misjudged it.

"Give me another chance," he cried furiously. "I'll get him."

"What! Ready for another tackle?" said the captain, looking at him intently.

"Please, sir."

"Well, get your head clear first."

"Let me take it now, sir!"

"All right."

"Hit him harder than he hits you, and grip with your hands," said the voice of Mr. Ware in his ear.

Dink stood out again. The earth was gradually returning to a state of equilibrium, but his head was buzzing and his legs were decidedly rebels to his will.

The captain, seeing this, to give him time, spoke to McCarty with just a shade of malice.

"Well, Tough, do you want to take it again?"

"Do I?" said McCarty sarcastically. "Oh, yes, most enjoyable! Don't let me interfere with your pleasure. Why don't you try it yourself?"

"Would you rather watch?"

"Oh, no, of course not. This is a real pleasure, thank you. The little devil would dent a freight train."

"All ready, Stover?" said Cockrell.

The players stood in two lines, four yards apart. No one laughed.

They looked at Stover, thrilling a little with his communicated recklessness, grunting forth their approval.

"Good nerve."

"The real stuff."

"Pure grit."

"Little devil."

Stover's face had gone white, the eyes had dwindled and set intensely, the line of the mouth was drawn taut, while on his forehead the wind lifted the matted hair like a banner. In the middle of the lane, crowding forward, his arms out, ready to spring, his glance fixed on McCarty, he waited like a champion guarding the pass.

"All right, Stover?"

Someone near him repeated the question.

"Come on!" he answered.

McCarty's one hundred and seventy pounds came rushing down. But this time the instinct was strong. He slacked a bit at the end as Stover, not waiting his coming, plunged in to meet him. Down they went again, but this time it was the force of Stover's impact that threw them.

When Cockrell came up, Dink, altogether groggy, was entwined around one leg of McCarty with a gaunt grin of possession.

They hauled him up, patted him on the back and walked him up and down in the cool breeze. Suddenly, after several minutes, the mist rose. He saw the fields and heard the sharp cries of the coaches prodding on the players.

Then he looked up to find Garry Cockrell's arm about him.

"All right now?" said the captain's voice.

Stover hastily put the arm away from him.

"I'm all right."

"Did I give you a little too much, youngster?"

"I'm ready again," said Stover instantly.

Cockrell laughed a short, contented laugh.

"You've done enough for today."

"I'll learn how," said Dink doggedly.

"You know the real things in football now, my boy," said the captain shortly. "We'll teach you the rest."

Dink thought he meant it sarcastically.

"You will give me a chance, won't you?" he said.

"Yes," said the captain, laying his hand on his shoulder with a smile. "You'll get chance enough, my boy. Fact is, I'm going to start you in at end on the scrub. You'll get all the hard knocks you're looking for there. You won't get any credit for what you do—but you boys are what's going to make the team."

"Oh, sir, do you mean it?"

"I'm in the habit of meaning things."

"I'll—I'll——" began Stover, and then stopped before the impossibility of expressing how many times his life should be thrown to the winds.

"I know you will," said the captain, amused. "And now, you young bulldog, back to your room and shake yourself together."

"But I want to go on; I'm feeling fine."

"Off the field," said the captain with terrific sternness.

Dink went like a dog ordered home, slowly, unwillingly, turning from time to time in hopes that his captain would relent.

When he had passed the chapel and the strife of the practice had dropped away he felt all at once sharp, busy pains running up his back and over his shoulders. But he minded them not. At that moment with the words of the captain—*his* captain forever now—ringing in his ears, he would have gone forth gratefully to tackle the whole team, one after another, from wiry little Charlie DeSoto to the elephantine P. Lentz.

Suddenly a thought came to him.

"Gee, I bet I shook up Tough McCarty, anyhow," he said grimly. And refreshed by this delightful thought he went briskly across the Circle.

At the steps Finnegan, coming out the door, hailed him excitedly:

"Hi, Dink, we've got a Freshman who's setting up to jiggers and éclairs. Hurry up!"

"No," said Dink.

"What?" said Dennis faintly.

"I can't," said Dink, bristling; "I'm in training."

## II

"Oh, we'll push her over
  Or rip the cover—
    Too bad for the fellows that fall!
They must take their chances
  Of a bruise or two
    Who follow that jolly football."

So SANG the group on the Kennedy steps, heralding the twilight; and beyond, past the Dickinson, a chorus from the Woodhull defiantly flung back the challenge. For that week the Woodhull would clash with the Kennedy for the championship of the houses.

The football season was drawing to a close, only the final game with Andover remained, a contest awaited with small hopes of victory. For the season had been disastrous for the 'Varsity; several members of the team had been caught in the toils of the octopus examination and, what was worse among the members, ill-feeling existed due to past feuds.

Stover, in the long grueling days of practice, had won the respect of all. Just how favorable an impression he had made he did not himself suspect. He had instinctive quickness and no sense of fear— that was something that had dropped from him forever. It was not that he had to conquer the impulse to flinch, as most boys do; it simply did not exist with him. The sight of a phalanx of bone and muscle starting for his end to sweep him off his feet roused only a sort of combative rage, and true joy of battle. He loved to go plunging into the unbroken front and feel the shock of bodies as he tried for the elusive legs of Flash Condit or Charlie DeSoto.

This utter recklessness was indeed his chief fault; he would rather charge interference than fight it off, waiting for others to break it up for him and so make sure of his man.

Gradually, however, through the strenuous weeks, he learned the deeper lessons of football—how to use his courage and the control of his impulses.

"It's a game of brains, youngster, remember that," Mr. Ware would repeat day after day, hauling him out of desperate plunges.

"That did no good; better keep on your feet and follow the ball. Above all, study the game."

His first lesson came when, at last being promoted to end on the scrub, he found himself lined up against Tough McCarty, the opposing tackle. Stover thought he saw the intention at once.

"Put me against Tough McCarty, eh?" he said, digging his nails into the palms of his hands. "Want to try out my nerve, eh? I'll show 'em!"

Now McCarty did not relish the situation either; foreseeing as he did the long weeks of strenuous contact with the one boy in the school who was vowed to an abiding vengeance. The fact was that Tough McCarty, who was universally liked for his good nature and sociable inclination, had yielded to the irritation Stover's unceasing enmity had aroused and had come gradually into something of the same attitude of hostility. Also, he saw in the captain's assigning Stover to his end a malicious attempt to secure amusement at his expense.

For all which reasons, when the scrub first lined up against the 'Varsity, the alarum of battle that rode on Stover's pugnacious front was equaled by the intensity of his enemy's coldly-calculating glance.

"Here's where I squash that fly," thought McCarty.

"Here's where I fasten to that big stuff," thought Dink, "and sting him until the last day of the season!"

The first direct clash came when the scrubs were given the ball and Dink came in to aid his tackle box McCarty for the run that was signaled around their end.

Tough made the mistake of estimating Stover simply by his lack of weight, without taking account of the nervous, dynamic energy which was his strength. Consequently, at the snap of the ball, he was taken by surprise by the wild spring that Stover made directly at his throat and, thrown off his balance momentarily by the frenzy of the impact, tripped and went down under the triumphant Dink, who, unmindful of the fact that the play had gone by, remained proudly fixed on the chest of the prostrate tackle.

"Get off," said the muffled voice.

Stover, whose animal instincts were all those of the bulldog, pressed down more firmly.

"Get off me, you little blockhead," said McCarty, growing furious, as he heard the jeers of his teammates at his humiliating reversal.

"Hurry up there, you Stover!" cried the voice of the captain, unheeded, for Dink was too blindly happy with the thrill of perfect supremacy over the hated McCarty to realize the situation.

"Stover! ! !"

At the shouted command Dink looked up and at last perceived the play was over. Reluctantly he started to rise, when a sudden upheaval of the infuriated McCarty caught him unawares and Tough's vigorous arm flung him head over heels.

Down went Dink with a thump and up again with rage in his heart. He rushed up to McCarty and struck him a resounding blow.

The next moment not Tough, but Cockrell's own mighty hand caught him by the collar and swung him around.

"Get off the field!"

"What?" said Dink, astounded, for in his ignorance he had expected complimentary pats on his back.

"Off the field!"

Dink, cold in a minute, quailed under the stern eye of the supreme leader.

"I did sling him pretty hard, Garry," said Tough, taking pity at the look that came into Dink's eyes at this rebuke.

"Get off!"

Dink, who had stopped with a sort of despairing hope, went slowly to the side-lines, threw a blanket over his head and shoulders and squatted down in bitter, utter misery. Another was in his place, plunging at the tackle that should have been his, racing down the field under punts that made the blood leap in his exiled body. He did not understand. Why had he been disgraced? He had only shown he wasn't afraid—wasn't that why they had put him opposite Tough McCarty, after all?

The contending lines stopped at last their tangled rushes and straggled, panting, back for a short intermission. Dink, waiting under the blanket, saw the captain bear down upon him and, shivering like a dog watching the approach of his punishment, drew the folds tighter about him.

"Stover," said the dreadful voice, loud enough so that everyone could hear, "you seem to have an idea that football is run like a slaughterhouse. The quicker you get that out of your head the better. Now, do you know why I fired you? Do you?"

"For slugging," said Dink faintly.

"Not at all. I fired you because you lost your head; because you forgot you were playing football. If you're only going into this to work off your private grudges, then I don't want you around. I'll fire you off and keep you off. You're here to play football, to think of eleven men, not one. You're to use your brains, not your fists. Why, the first game you play in someone will tease you into slugging him and the umpire will fire you. Then where'll the team be! There are eleven men in this game on your side and on the other. No matter what happens don't lose your temper, don't be so stupid, so brainless—do you hear?"

"Yes, sir," said Dink, who had gradually retired under his blanket until only the tip of the nose showed and the terror-stricken eyes.

"And don't forget this. You don't count. It isn't the slightest interest to the team whether some one whales you or mauls you! It isn't the slightest interest to you, either. Mind that! Nothing on earth is going to get your mind off following the ball, sizing up the play, working out the weak points—nothing. Brains, brains, brains, Stover! You told me you came out here because we needed someone to be banged around—and I took you on your word, didn't I? Now, if you're going out there as an egotistical, puffed-up, conceited individual who's thinking only of his own skin, who isn't willing to sacrifice his own little, measly feelings for the sake of the school, who won't fight for the team, but himself——"

"I say, Cap, that's enough," said Dink with difficulty; and immediately retired so deep that only the mute, pleading eyes could be discerned.

Cockrell stopped short, bit his lip and said sternly: "Line up now. Get in, Stover, and don't let me ever have to call you down again. Tough, see here." The two elevens ran out. The captain continued:

"Tough, every chance you get today give that little firebrand a jab, understand? So it can't be seen."

The 'Varsity took the ball and for five minutes Dink felt as though he were in an angry sea, buffeted, flung down and whirled about by massive breakers. Without sufficient experience his weight was powerless to stop the interference that bore him back. He tried to meet it standing up and was rolled head over heels by the brawny shoulders of Cheyenne Baxter and Doc Macnooder. Then, angrily, he tried charging into the offenses and was drawn in and smothered while the back went sweeping around his unprotected end for long gains.

Mr. Ware came up and volunteered suggestions:

"If you're going into it dive through them, push them apart with your hands—so. Keep dodging so that the back won't know whether you're going around or through. Keep him guessing and follow up the play if you miss the first tackle."

Under this coaching Dink, who had begun to be discouraged, improved and when he did get a chance at his man he dropped him with a fierce, clean tackle, for this branch of the game he had mastered with instinctive delight.

"Give the ball to the scrubs," said the captain, who was also coaching.

Stover came in close to his tackle. The third signal was a trial at end. He flung himself at McCarty, checked him, and, to his amazement, received a dig in the ribs. His fists clenched, went back and then stopped as, remembering, he drew a long breath and walked away, his eyes on the ground; for the lesson was a rude one to learn.

"Stover, what are you doing?" cried the captain, who had seen all.

Dink, who had expected to be praised, was bewildered as well as hurt.

"What are you stopping for? You're thinking of McCarty again, aren't you? Do you know where your place was? Back of your own half. Follow up the play. If you'd been there to push there'd been an extra yard. Think quicker, Stover."

"Yes, sir," said Stover, suddenly perceiving the truth. "You're right, I wasn't thinking."

"Look here, boy," said the captain, laying his hand on his shoulders. "I have just one principle in a game and I want you to tuck it away and never forget it."

"Yes, sir," said Dink reverently.

"When you get in a game get fighting mad, but get cold mad—play like a fiend—but keep cold. Know just what you're doing and know it all the time."

"Thank you, sir," said Dink, who never forgot the theory, which had a wider application than Garry Cockrell perhaps suspected.

"You laid it on pretty strong," said Mr. Ware to Cockrell, as they walked back after practice.

"I did it for several reasons," said Garry; "first, because I believe the boy has the makings of a great player in him; and second, I was using him to talk to the team. They're not together and it's going to be hard to get them together."

"Bad feeling?"

"Yes, several old grudges."

"What a pity, Garry," said Mr. Ware. "What a pity it is you can't only have second and third formers under you!"

"Why so?"

"Because they'd follow you like mad dervishes," said Mr. Ware, thinking of Dink.

Stover, having once perceived that the game was an intellectual one, learned by bounds. McCarty, under instructions, tried his best to provoke him, but met with the completest indifference. Dink found a new delight in the exercise of his wits, once the truth was borne in on him that there are more ways of passing beyond a windmill than riding it down. Owing to his natural speed he was the fastest end on the field to cover a punt, and once within diving distance of his man he almost never missed. He learned, too, that the scientific application of his one hundred and thirty-eight pounds, well timed, was sufficient to counterbalance the disadvantage in weight. He never loafed, he never let a play go by without being in it, and at retrieving fumbles he was quick as a cat.

Meanwhile the house championships had gone on until the Woodhull and the Kennedy emerged for the final conflict. The experience gained in these contests, for on such occasions Stover played with his House team, had sharpened his powers of analysis and given him a needed acquaintance with the sudden, shifting crises of actual play.

Now, the one darling desire of Stover, next to winning the fair opinion of his captain, was the rout of the Woodhull, of which Tough McCarty was the captain and his old acquaintances of the miserable days at the Green were members—Cheyenne Baxter, the Coffee-colored Angel and Butsey White. This aggregation, counting as it did two members of the 'Varsity, was strong, but the Kennedy, with P. Lentz and the Waladoo Bird and Pebble Stone, the Gutter Pup, Lovely Mead and Stover, all of the scrub, had a slight advantage.

Dink used to dream of mornings, in the lagging hours of recitation, of the contest and the sweet humiliation of his ancient foes. He would play like a demon, he would show them. Tough McCarty and the rest, what it was to be up against the despised Dink—and dreaming thus he used to say to himself, with suddenly tense arms:

"Gee, I only wish McCarty would play back of the line so I could get a chance at him!"

But on Tuesday, during the 'Varsity practice, suddenly as a scrimmage ended and sifted open a cry went up. Ned Banks, left end on the 'Varsity, was seen lying on the ground after an attempt to rise. They gathered about him with grave faces, while Mr. Ware bent over him in anxious examination.

"What is it?" said the captain, with serious face.

"Something wrong with his ankle; can't tell yet just what."

"I'll play Saturday, Garry," said Banks, gritting his teeth. "I'll be ready by then. It's nothing much."

The subs carried him off the field with darkened faces—the last hopes of victory seemed to vanish. The gloom spread thickly through the school, even Dink, for a time, forgot the approaching hour of his revenge in the great catastrophe. The next morning a little comfort was given them in the report of Doctor Charlie that there was no sprain but only a slight wrenching, which, if all went well, would allow him to start the game. But the consolation was scant. What chance had Banks in an Andover game? There would have to be a shift; but what?

"Turkey Reiter will have to go from tackle to end," said Dink, that afternoon, as in football togs they gathered on the steps before the game, "and put a sub in Turkey's place."

"Who?"

"I don't know."

"I guess you don't."

"Might bring Butcher Stevens back from center."

"Who'd go in at center?"

"Fatty Harris, perhaps."

"Hello—here's Garry Cockrell now," said P. Lentz. "He don't look particular cheerful, does he?"

The captain, looking indeed very serious, arrived, surveyed the group and called Stover out. Dink, surprised, jumped up, saying:

"You want me, sir?"

"Yes."

Cockrell put his arm under his and drew him away.

"Stover," he said, "I've got bad news for you."

"For me?"

"Yes. I'm not going to let you go into the Woodhull game this afternoon."

Stover received the news as though it had been the death of his entire family, immediate and distant. His throat choked, he tried to say something and did not dare trust himself.

"I'm sorry, my boy—but we're up against it, and I can't take any risks now of your getting hurt."

"It means the game," said Dink at last.

"I'm afraid so."

"We've no one to put in my place—no one but Beekstein Hall," said Stover desperately. "Oh, please, sir, let me play; I'll be awfully careful. It's only a House game."

"Humph—yes, I know these House games. I'm sorry, but there's no help for it."

"But I'm only a scrub, sir," said Stover, pleading hard.

"We're going to play you at end," said Cockrell suddenly, seeing he did not understand, "just as soon as we have to take Banks out; and Heaven only knows when that'll be."

Dink was aghast.

"You're not going—you're not going——" he tried to speak, and stopped.

"Yes, we've talked it over and that seems best."

"But—Turkey Reiter—I—I thought you'd move him out."

"No, we don't dare weaken the middle; it's bad enough now."

"Oh, but I'm so light."

The captain watched the terror-stricken look in his face and was puzzled.

"What's the matter? You're not getting shaky?"

"Oh, no, sir," said Dink. "It's not that. It—it seems so awful that you've got to put me in."

"You're better, my boy, than you think," said Cockrell, smiling a little, "and you're going to be better than you know now. Now you understand why you've got to keep on the side-lines this afternoon. You're too fragile to take risks on."

"Yes, I understand."

"It comes hard, doesn't it?"

"Yes, sir, it does; very hard."

When the Kennedy and Woodhull lined up for play an hour later little Pebble Stone was at end in place of Stover, who watched from his post as linesman the contest that was to have been his opportunity. He heard nothing of the buzzing comments behind, of the cheers or the shouted entreaties. Gaze fixed and heart in throat, he followed the swaying tide of battle, imprisoned, powerless to rush in and stem the disheartening advance.

The teams, now more evenly matched, both showed the traces of tense nerves in the frequent fumbling that kept the ball changing sides and prevented a score during the first half.

In the opening of the second half, by a lucky recovery of a blocked kick, the Kennedy scored a touchdown, but failed to kick the goal, making the score four to nothing. The Woodhull then began a determined assault upon the Kennedy's weak end. Stover, powerless, beheld little Pebble Stone, fighting like grim death, carried back and back five, ten yards at a time as the Woodhull swept up the field.

"It's the only place they can gain," he cried in his soul in bitter iteration.

He looked around and caught the eye of Captain Cockrell and sent him a mute, agonizing fruitless appeal.

"Kennedy's ball," came the sharp cry of Slugger Jones, the umpire.

Dink looked up and felt the blood come back to his body again— on the twenty-five yard line there had been a fumble and the advance was checked. Twice again the battered end of the Kennedy was forced back for what seemed certain touchdowns, only to be saved by loose work on the Woodhull's part. It was getting dark and the half was ebbing fast—three minutes more to play. A fourth time the Woodhull furiously attacked the breach, gaining at every rush over the light opposition, past the forty-yard line, past the twenty-yard mark and triumphantly, in the last minute of play, over the goal for a touchdown. The ball had been downed well to the right of the goalposts and the trial for goal was an unusually difficult one. The score was a tie, everything depended on the goal that, through the dusk, Tough McCarty was carefully sighting. Dink, heartbroken, despairing, leaning on his linesman's staff, directly behind the ball, waited for the long, endless moments to be over. Then there was a sudden movement of McCarty's body, a wild rush from the Kennedy and the ball shot high in the air and, to Stover's horror, passed barely inside the farther goalpost.

"No goal," said Slugger Jones. "Time up."

Dink raised his head in surprise, scarcely crediting what he had heard. The Woodhull team were furiously disputing the decision, encouraged by audible comments from the spectators. Slugger Jones, surrounded by a contesting, vociferous mass, suddenly swept them aside and began to take the vote of the officials.

"Kiefer, what do you say?"

Cap Kiefer, referee, shook his head.

"I'm sorry, Slugger, it was close, very close, but it did seem a goal to me."

"Tug, what do you say?"

"Goal, sure," said Tug Wilson, linesman for the Woodhull.

At this, jeers and hoots broke out from the Kennedy.

"Of course he'll say that!"

"He's from the Woodhull."

"What do you think?"

"Justice!"

"Hold up, hold up, now," said Slugger Jones, more excited than anyone. "Don't get excited; it's up to your own man. Dink, was it a goal or no goal?"

Stover suddenly found himself in a whirling angry mass—the decision of the game in his own hands. He saw the faces of Tough McCarty and the Coffee-colored Angel in the blank crowd about him and he saw the sneer on their faces as they waited for his answer. Then he saw the faces of his own teammates and knew what they, in their frenzy, expected from him. He hesitated.

"Goal or no goal?" cried the umpire, for the second time.

Then suddenly, face to face with the hostile mass, the fighting blood came to Dink. Something cold went up his back. He looked once more above the riot, to the shadowy posts, trying to forget Tough McCarty, and, with a snap to his jaws, he answered: "Goal."

### III

DINK RETURNED to his room in a rage against everything and everyone, at Slugger Jones for having submitted the question, at Tough McCarty for having looked as though he expected a lie, and at himself for ever having acted as linesman.

If it had not been the last days before the Andover match he would have found some consolation in rushing over to the Woodhull and provoking McCarty to the long-deferred fight.

"He thought I'd lie out of it," he said furiously. "He did; I saw it. I'll settle that with him, too. Now I suppose everyone in this house'll be down on me; but they'd better be mighty careful how they express it."

For as he had left the field he had heard only too clearly how the Kennedy eleven, in the unreasoning passion of conflict, had expressed itself. At present, through the open window, the sounds of violent words were borne up to him from below. He approached and looked down upon the furious assembly.

"Damn me up and down, damn me all you want," he said, doubling up his fists. "Keep it up, but don't come up to me with it."

Suddenly, back of him, the door opened and shut and Dennis de Brian de Boru Finnegan stood in the room.

"I say, Dink——"

"Get out," said Stover furiously, seizing a pillow.

Finnegan precipitately retired and, placing the door between him and the danger, opened it slightly and inserted his freckled little nose.

"I say, Dink——"

"Get out, I told you!" The pillow struck the door with a bang. "I won't have anyone snooping around here!"

The next instant Dennis, resolved on martyrdom, stepped inside, saying:

"I say, old man, if it'll do you any good, take it out on me."

Stover, thus defied, stopped and said:

"Dennis, I don't want to talk about it."

"All right," said Dennis, sitting down.

"And I want to be alone."

"Correct," said Dennis, who didn't budge.

They sat in moody silence, without lighting the lamp.

"Pretty tough," said Dennis at last.

Stover's answer was a grunt.

"You couldn't see it the way the umpire did, could you?"

"No, I couldn't."

"Pretty tough!"

"I suppose," said Dink finally, "the fellows are wild."

"A little—a little excited," said Dennis carefully. "It was tough— pretty tough!"

"You don't suppose I wanted that gang of muckers to win, do you?" said Stover.

"I know," said Dennis sympathetically.

The Tennessee Shad now returned from the wars, covered with mud and the more visible marks of the combat.

"Hello," he said gruffly.

"Hello," said Stover.

The Tennessee Shad went wearily to his corner and stripped for the bath.

"Well, say it," said Stover, who, in his agitation, had actually picked up a textbook and started to study. "Jump on me, why don't you?"

"I'm not going to jump on you," said the Tennessee Shad, who weakly pulled off the heavy shoes. "Only—well, you couldn't see it as the umpire did, could you?"

"No!"

"What a day—what an awful day!"

Dennis de Brian de Boru Finnegan, with great tact, rose and hesitated:

"I'm going—I—I've got to get ready for supper," he said desperately. Then he went lamely over to Stover and held out his hand: "I know how you feel, old man, but—but—I'm glad you did it!"

Whereupon he disappeared in blushing precipitation.

Stover breathed hard and tried to bring his mind to the printed lesson. The Tennessee Shad, sighing audibly, continued his ablutions, dressed and sat down.

"Dink."

"What?"

"Why did you do it?"

Then Stover, flinging down his book with an access of rage cried out:

"Why? Because you all, every damn one of you, expected me to *lie!*"

. . . . . .

The next day Stover, who had firmly made up his mind to a sort of modified ostracism, was amazed to find that over night he had become a hero. By the next morning the passion and the bitterness of the struggle having died away, the house looked at the matter in a calmer mood and one by one came to him and gripped his hand with halting, blurted words of apology or explanation.

Utterly unprepared for this development, Stover all at once realized that he had won what neither courage nor wit had been able to bring him, the something he had always longed for without being quite able to name it—the respect of his fellows. He felt it in the looks that followed him as he went over to chapel, in the nodded recognition of Fifth Formers, who had never before noticed him, in The Roman himself who flunked him without satire or aggravation. And not yet knowing himself, his impulses or the strange things that lay dormant beneath the surface of his everyday life, Stover was a little ashamed, as though he did not deserve it all.

That afternoon as Dink was donning his football togs, preparing for practice, a knock came at the door which opened on a very much embarrassed delegation from the Woodhull—the Coffee-colored Angel, Cheyenne Baxter and Tough McCarty.

"I say, is that you, Dink?" said the Coffee-colored Angel.

"It is," said Stover, with as much dignity as the state of his wardrobe would permit.

"I say, we've come over from the Woodhull, you know," continued the Coffee-colored Angel, who stopped after this bit of illuminating news.

"Well, what do you want?"

"I say, that's not just it; we're sent by the Woodhull I meant to say, and we want to say, we want you to know—how white we think it was of you!"

"Old man," said Cheyenne Baxter, "we want to thank you. What we want to tell you is how white we think it was of you."

"You needn't thank me," said Stover gruffly, pulling his leg through the football trousers. "I didn't want to do it."

The delegation stood confused, wondering how to end the painful scene.

"It was awful white!" said the Coffee-colored Angel, tying knots in his sweater.

"It certainly was," said Cheyenne.

As this brought them no further along the Coffee-colored Angel exclaimed in alarm:

"I say, Dink, will you shake hands?"

Stover gravely extended his right.

Cheyenne next clung to it, blurting out:

"Say, Dink, I wish I could make you understand—just—just how white we think it was!"

The two rushed away leaving Tough McCarty to have his say. Both stood awkwardly, frightened before the possibility of a display of sentiment.

"Look here," said Tough firmly, and then stopped, drew a long breath and continued: "Say, you and I have sort of formed up a sort of vendetta and all that sort of thing, haven't we?"

"We have."

"Now, I'm not going to call that off. I don't suppose you'd want it either."

"No, I wouldn't."

"We've got to have a good, old slam-bang fight sooner or later and then, perhaps, it'll be different. I'm not coming around asking you to be friends, or anything like that sort of rot, you know, but what I want you to know is this—is this—what I want you to understand is just how darned *white* that was of you!"

"All right," said Stover frigidly, because he was tremendously moved and in terror of showing it.

"That's not what I wanted to say," said Tough, frowning terrifically and kicking the floor. "I mean—I say, you know what I mean, don't you?"

"All right," said Stover gruffly.

"And I say," said Tough, remembering only one line of all he had come prepared to say, "if you'll let me, Stover, I should consider it an honor to shake your hand."

Dink gave his hand, trembling a little.

"Of course, you understand," said Tough who thought he comprehended Stover's silence, "of course we fight it out some day."

"All right," said Stover gruffly.

Tough McCarty went away. Dink, left alone, clad in his voluminous football trousers, sat staring at the door, clasping his hands tensely between his knees, and something inside of him welled up, dangerously threatening his eyes—something feminine, to be choked instantly down.

He rose angrily, flung back his hair and filled his lungs. Then he stopped.

"What the deuce are they all making such a fuss for?" he said. "I only told the truth."

He struggled into his jersey, still trying to answer the problem. In his abstraction he drew a neat part in his hair before, perceiving the *faux pas,* he hurriedly obliterated the effete mark.

"I guess," he said, standing at the window still pondering over the new attitude toward himself—"I guess, after all, I don't know it all. Tough McCarty—well, I'll be damned!"

Saturday came all too soon and with it the arrival of the stocky Andover eleven. Dink dressed and went slowly across the campus— every step seemed an effort. Everywhere was an air of seriousness and apprehension, strangely contrasted to the gay ferment that usually announced a big game. He felt a hundred eyes on him as he went and knew what was in everyone's mind. What would happen when Ned Banks would have to retire and he, little Dink Stover, weighing one hundred and thirty-eight, would have to go forth to stand at the end of the line. And because Stover had learned the lesson of football, the sacrifice for an idea, he too felt not fear but a sort of despair that the hopes of the great school would have to rest upon him, little Dink Stover, who weighed only one hundred and thirty-eight pounds.

He went quietly to the Upper, his eyes on the ground like a guilty man, picking his way through the crowds of Fifth Formers, who watched him pass with critical looks, and up the heavy stairs to Garry Cockrell's room, where the team sat quietly listening to the final instructions. He took his seat silently in an obscure corner, studying the stern faces about him, hearing nothing of Mr. Ware's staccatto periods, his eyes irresistibly drawn to his captain, wondering how suddenly older he looked and grave.

By his side Ned Banks was listening stolidly and Charlie DeSoto, twisting a paper-weight in his nervous fingers, fidgeting on his chair with the longing for the fray.

"That's all," said the low voice of Garry Cockrell. "You know what you have to do. Go down to Charlie's room; I want a few words with Stover."

They went sternly and quickly, Mr. Ware with them. Dink was alone, standing stiff and straight, his heart thumping violently, waiting for his captain to speak.

"How do you feel?"

"I'm ready, sir."

"I don't know when you'll get in the game—probably before the first half is over," said Cockrell slowly. "We're going to put up to you a pretty hard proposition, youngster." He came nearer, laying his hand on Stover's shoulder. "I'm not going to talk nerve to you, young bulldog, I don't need to. I've watched you and I know the stuff that's in you."

"Thank you, sir."

"Not but what you'll need it—more than you've ever needed it before. You've no right in this game."

"I know it, sir."

"Tough McCarty won't be able to help you out much. He's got the toughest man in the line. Everything's coming at you, my boy, and you've got to stand it off, somehow. Now, listen once more. It's a game for the long head, for the cool head. You've got to think quicker, you've got to out-think every man on the field and you can do it. And remember this: No matter what happens never let up—get your man back of the line if you can, get him twenty-five yards beyond you, get him on the one-yard line—but get him!"

"Yes, sir."

"And now one thing more. There's all sorts of ways you can play the game. You can charge in like a bull and kill yourself off in ten minutes, but that won't do. You can go in and make grandstand plays and get carried off the field, but that won't do. My boy, you've got to last out the game."

"I see, sir."

"Remember there's a bigger thing than yourself you're fighting for, Stover—it's the school, the old school. Now, when you're on the sidelines don't lose any time; watch your men, find out their tricks, see if they look up or change their footing when they start for an end run. Everything is going to count. Now, come on."

They joined the eleven below and presently, in a compact body, went out and through Memorial and the chapel, where suddenly the field appeared and a great roar went up from the school.

"All ready," said the captain.

They broke into a trot and swept up to the cheering mass. Dink remembered seeing the Tennessee Shad, in his shirt sleeves, frantically leading the school and thinking how funny he looked. Then someone pulled a blanket over him and he was camped among the substitutes, peering out at the gridiron where already the two elevens were sweeping back and forth in vigorous signal drill.

He looked eagerly at the Andover eleven. They were big, rangy fellows and their team worked with a precision and machine-like rush that the red and black team did not have.

"Trouble with us is," said the voice of Fatty Harris, at his elbow, "our team's never gotten together. The fellows would rather slug each other than the enemy."

"Gee, that fellow at tackle is a monster," said Dink, picking out McCarty's opponent.

"Look at Turkey Reiter and the Waladoo Bird," continued Fatty Harris. "Bad blood! And there's Tough McCarty and King Lentz. We're not together, I tell you! We're hanging apart!"

"Lord, will they ever begin!" said Dink, blowing on his hands that had suddenly gone limp and clammy.

"We've won the toss," said another voice. "There's a big wind, we'll take sides."

"Andover's kick-off," said Fatty Harris.

Stover sunk his head in his blanket, waiting for the awful moment to end. Then a whistle piped and he raised his head again. The ball had landed short, into the arms of Butcher Stevens, who plunged ahead for a slight gain and went down under a shock of blue jerseys.

Stover felt the warm blood return, the sinking feeling in the pit of his stomach left him, he felt, amazed, a great calm settling over him, as though he had jumped from out his own body.

"If Flash Condit can once get loose," he said quietly, "he'll score.

They ought to try a dash through tackle before the others warm up. Good!"

As if in obedience to his thought Flash Condit came rushing through the line, between end and tackle, but the Andover left half-back, who was alert, caught him and brought him to the ground after a gain of ten yards.

"Pretty fast, that chap," thought Dink. "Too bad, Flash was almost clear."

"Who tackled him?" asked Fatty Harris.

"Goodhue," came the answer from somewhere. "They say he runs the hundred in ten and a fifth."

The next try was not so fortunate, the blue line charged quicker and stopped Cheyenne Baxter without a gain. Charlie DeSoto tried a quarter-back run and some one broke through between the Wala-doo Bird and Turkey Reiter.

"Not together—not together," said the dismal voice of Fatty Harris.

The signal was given for a punt and the ball lifted in the air went soaring down the field on the force of the wind. It was too long a punt for the ends to cover, and the Andover back with a good start came twisting through the territory of Ned Banks who had been blocked off by his opponent.

"Watch that Andover end, Stover," said Mr. Ware. "Study out his methods."

"All right, sir," said Dink, who had watched no one else.

He waited breathless for the first shock of the Andover attack. It came with a rush, compact and solid, and swept back the Lawrence-ville left side for a good eight yards.

"Good-bye!" said Harris in a whisper.

Dink began to whistle, moving down the field, watching the backs. Another machine-like advance and another big gain suc-ceeded.

"They'll wake up," said Dink solemnly to himself. "They'll stop 'em in a minute."

But they did not stop. Rush by rush, irresistibly the blue left their own territory and passed the forty-five yard line of Lawrenceville. Then a fumble occurred and the ball went again with the gale far out of danger, over the heads of the Andover backs who had mis-judged its treacherous course.

"Lucky we've got the wind," said Dink, calm amid the roaring cheers about him. "Gee, that Andover attack's going to be hard to stop. Banks is beginning to limp."

The blue, after a few quick advances, formed and swept out toward Garry Cockrell's end.

"Three yards lost," said Dink grimly. "They won't try him often. Funny they're not on to Banks. Lord, how they can gain through the center of the line. First down again." Substitute and coach, the frantic school, alumni over from Princeton, kept up a constant storm of shouts and entreaties.

"Oh, get together!" "Throw 'em back!" "Hold 'em!" "First down again!" "Hold 'em, Lawrenceville!" "Don't let them carry it seventy yards!" "Get the jump!" "There they go again!" "Ten yards around Banks!"

Stover alone, squatting opposite the line of play, moving as it moved, coldly critical, studied each individuality.

"Funny nervous little tricks that Goodhue's got—blows on his hands—does that mean he takes the ball? No, all a bluff. What's he do when he does take it? Quiet and looks at the ground. When he doesn't take it he tries to pretend he does. I'll tuck that away. He's my man. Seems to switch in just as the interference strikes the end about ten feet beyond tackle, running low—Banks is playing too high; better, perhaps, to run in on 'em now and then before they get started. There's going to be trouble there in a minute. The fellows aren't up on their toes yet—what is the matter, anyhow? Tough's getting boxed right along, he ought to play out further, I should think. Hello, some one fumbled again. Who's got it? Looks like Garry. No, they recovered it themselves—no, they didn't. Lord, what a butter-fingered lot—why doesn't he get it? He has—Charlie DeSoto—clear field—can he make it?—he ought to—where's that Goodhue? looks like a safe lead; he'll make the twenty-yard line at least—yes, fully that, if he doesn't stumble—there's that Goodhue now—someone ought to block him off, good work—that's it—that makes the touchdown—lucky—very lucky!"

Some one hit him a terrific clap on the shoulder. He looked up in surprise to behold Fatty Harris dancing about like a crazed man. The air seemed all arms, hats were rising like startled coveys of birds. Some one flung his arms around him and hugged him. He flung him off almost indignantly. What were they thinking of—that was only one touchdown—four points—what was that against the blue team and the wind at their backs, too? One touchdown wasn't going to win the game.

"Why do they get so excited?" said Dink Stover to John Stover, watching deliberately the ball soaring between the goalposts; "6 to 0 —they think it's all over. Now's the rub."

Mr. Ware passed near him. He was quiet, too, seeing far ahead.

"Better keep warmed up, Stover," he said.

"Biting his nails, that's a funny trick for a master," thought Dink. "He oughtn't to be nervous. That doesn't do any good."

The shouts of exultation were soon hushed; with the advantage of the wind the game quickly assumed a different complexion. Andover had found the weak end and sent play after play at Banks, driving him back for long advances.

"Take off your sweater," said Mr. Ware.

Dink flung it off, running up and down the side-lines, springing from his toes.

"Why don't they take him out?" he thought angrily, with almost a hatred of the fellow who was fighting it out in vain. "Can't they see it? Ten yards more, oh, Lord! This ends it."

With a final rush the Andover interference swung at Banks, brushed him aside and swept over the remaining fifteen yards for the touchdown. A minute later the goal was kicked and the elevens again changed sides. The suddenness with which the score had been tied impressed everyone—the school team seemed to have no defense against the well-massed attacks of the opponents.

"Holes as big as a house," said Fatty Harris. "Asleep! They're all asleep!"

Dink, pacing up and down, waited the word from Mr. Ware, rebelling because it did not come.

Again the scrimmage began, a short advance from the loosely-knit school eleven, a long punt with the wind and then a quick, business-like line-up of the blue team and another rush at the vulnerable end.

"Ten yards more; oh, it's giving it away!" said Fatty Harris.

Stover knelt and tried his shoelaces and rising, tightened his belt.

"I'll be out there in a moment," he said to himself.

Another gain at Banks's end and suddenly from the elevens across the field the figure of the captain rose and waved a signal.

"Go in, Stover," said Mr. Ware.

He ran out across the long stretch to where the players were moving restlessly, their clothes flinging out clouds of steam. Back of him something was roaring, cheering for him, perhaps, hoping against hope.

Then he was in the midst of the contestants, Garry Cockrell's arm about his shoulders, whispering something in his ear about keeping cool, breaking up the interference if he couldn't get his man, following up the play. He went to his position, noticing the sullen expressions of his teammates, angry with the consciousness that they were not doing their best. Then taking his stand behind Tough McCarty, he saw the Andover quarter and the backs turn and study him curiously. He noticed the half-back nearest him, a stocky, close-cropped, red-haired fellow, with brawny arms under his rolled-up jersey, whose duty it would be to send him rolling on the first rush.

"All ready?" cried the voice of the umpire. "First down."

The whistle blew, the two lines strained opposite each other. Stover knew what the play would be—there was no question of that. Fortunately the last two rushes had carried the play well over to his side—the boundary was only fifteen yards away. Dink had thought out quickly what he would do. He crept in closer than an end usually plays and at the snap of the ball rushed straight into the starting interference before it could gather dangerous momentum. The back, seeing him thus drawn in, instinctively swerved wide around his interference, forced slightly back. Before he could turn forward his own speed and the necessity of distancing Stover and Condit drove him out of bounds for a four-yard loss.

"Second down, nine yards to go!" came the verdict.

"Rather risky, going in like that," said Flash Condit, who backed up his side.

"Wanted to force him out of bounds," said Stover.

"Oh—look out for something between tackle and guard now."

"No—they'll try the other side now to get a clean sweep at me," said Stover.

The red-haired halfback disappeared in the opposite side and, well protected, kept his feet for five yards.

"Third down, four to gain."

"Now for a kick," said Stover, as the Andover end came out opposite him. "What the deuce am I going to do to this coot to mix him up. He looks more as though he'd like to tackle me than to get past." He looked over and caught a glance from the Andover quarter. "I wonder. Why not a fake kick? They've sized me up for green. I'll play it carefully."

At the play, instead of blocking, he jumped back and to one side, escaping the end who dove at his knees. Then, rushing ahead, he stalled off the half and caught the fullback with a tackle that brought him to his feet, rubbing his side.

"Lawrenceville's ball. Time up for first half."

Dink had not thought of the time. Amazed, he scrambled to his feet, half angry at the interruption, and following the team went over to the room to be talked to by the captain and the coach.

It was a hang-dog crowd that gathered there, quailing under the scornful lashing of Garry Cockrell. He spared no one, he omitted no names. Dink, listening, lowered his eyes, ashamed to look upon the face of the team. One or two cried out:

"Oh, I say, Garry!"

"That's too much!"

"Too much, too much, is it?" cried their captain, walking up and down, striking the flat of his hand with the clenched fist. "By heavens, it's nothing to what they're saying of us out there. They're ashamed of us, one and all! Listen to the cheering if you don't believe it! They'll cheer a losing team, a team that is being driven back foot by foot. There's something glorious in that, but a team that stands up to be pushed over, a team that lies down and quits, a team that hasn't one bit of red fighting blood in it, they won't cheer; they're ashamed of you! Now, I'll tell you what's going to happen to you. You're going to be run down the field for just about four touchdowns. Here's Lentz being tossed around by a fellow that weighs forty pounds less. Why, he's the joke of the game. McCarty hasn't stopped a play, not one. Waladoo's so easy that they rest up walking through him. But that's not the worst, you're playing wide apart as though there wasn't man within ten miles of you; not one of you is helping out the other. The only time you've taken the ball from them is when a little shaver comes in and uses his head. Now, you're not going to win this game, but by the Almighty you're going out there and going to hold that Andover team! You've got the wind against you; you've got everything against you; you've got to fight on your own goal line, not once, but twenty times. But you've got to hold 'em; you're going to make good; you're going to wipe out that disgraceful, cowardly first half! You're going out there to stand those fellows off! You're going to make the school cheer for you again as though they believed in you, as though they were proud of you! You're going to do a bigger thing than beat a weaker team! You're going to fight off defeat and show that, if you can't win, you can't be beaten!"

Mr. Ware, in a professional way, passed from one to another with a word of advice. "Play lower, get the jump—don't be drawn in by a fake plunge—watch Goodhue."

But Dink heard nothing; he sat in his corner, clasping and unclasping his hands, suffering with the moments that separated him from the fray. Then all at once he was back on the field, catching the force of the wind that blew the hair about his temples, hearing the half-hearted welcome that went up from the school.

"Hear that cheer!" said Garry Cockrell bitterly.

From Butcher Stevens' boot the ball went twisting and veering down the field. Stover went down, dodging instinctively, hardly knowing what he did. Then as he started to spring at the runner an interferer from behind flung himself on him and sent him sprawling, but not until one arm had caught and checked his man.

McCarty had stopped the runner, when Dink sprang to his feet, wild with the rage of having missed his tackle.

"Steady!" said the voice of his captain.

He lined up hurriedly, seeing red. The interference started for him, he flung himself at it blindly and was buried under the body of the red-haired half. Powerless to move, humiliatingly held under the sturdy body, the passion of fighting rose in him again. He tried to throw him off, doubling up his fist, waiting until his arm was free.

"Why, you're easy, kid," said a mocking voice. "We'll come again."

The taunt suddenly chilled him. Without knowing how it happened, he laughed.

"That's the last time you get me, old rooster," he said, in a voice that did not belong to him.

He glanced back. Andover had gained fifteen yards.

"That comes from losing my head," he said quietly. "That's over."

It had come, the cold consciousness of which Cockrell had spoken, strange as the second wind that surprises the distressed runner.

"I've got to teach that red-haired coot a lesson," he said. "He's a little too confident. I'll shake him up a bit."

The opportunity came on the third play, with another attack on his end. He ran forward a few steps and stood still, leaning a little forward, waiting for the red-haired back who came plunging at him. Suddenly Dink dropped to his knees, the interferer went violently over his back, something struck Stover in the shoulder and his arms closed with the fierce thrill of holding his man.

"Second down, seven yards to gain," came the welcome sound.

Time was taken out for the red-haired halfback, who had the wind knocked out of him.

"Now he'll be more respectful," said Dink, and as soon as he caught his eye he grinned. "Red hair—I'll see if I can't get his temper."

Thus checked and to use the advantage of the wind Andover elected to kick. The ball went twisting, and, changing its course in the strengthening wind, escaped the clutches of Macnooder and went bounding toward the goal where Charlie DeSoto saved it on the twenty-five-yard line. In an instant the overwhelming disparity of the sides was apparent.

A return kick at best could gain but twenty-five or thirty yards. From now on they would be on the defensive.

Dink came in to support his traditional enemy, Tough McCarty. The quick, nervous voice of Charlie DeSoto rose in a shriek: "Now, Lawrenceville, get into this, 7—52—3."

Dink swept around for a smash on the opposite tackle, head down, eyes fastened on the back before him, feeling the shock of resistance and the yielding response as he thrust forward, pushing, heaving on, until everything piled up before him. Four yards gained.

A second time they repeated the play, making the first down.

"Time to spring a quick one through us," he thought.

But again DeSoto elected the same play.

"What's he trying to do?" said Dink. "Why don't he vary it?"

Someone hauled him out of the tangled pile. It was Tough McCarty.

"Say, our tackle's a stiff one," he said, with his mouth to Stover's ear. "You take his knees; I'll take him above this time."

Their signal came at last. Dink dove, trying to meet the shifting knees and throw him off his balance. The next moment a powerful arm caught him as he left the ground and swept him aside.

"Any gain?" he asked anxiously as he came up.

"Only a yard," said McCarty. "He got through and smeared the play."

"I know how to get him next time," said Dink.

The play was repeated. This time Stover made a feint and then dove successfully after the big arm had swept fruitlessly past. Flash Condit, darting through the line, was tackled by Goodhue and fell forward for a gain.

"How much?" said Stover, rising joyfully.

"They're measuring."

The distance was tried and found to be two feet short of the necessary five yards. The risk was too great, a kick was signaled and the ball was Andover's, just inside the center of the field.

"Now, Lawrenceville," cried the captain, "show what you're made of."

The test came quickly, a plunge between McCarty and Lentz yielded three yards, a second four. The Andover attack, with the same precision as before, struck anywhere between the tackles and found holes. Dink, at the bottom of almost every pile, raged at Tough McCarty.

"He's doing nothing, he isn't fighting," he said angrily. "He doesn't know what it is to fight. Why doesn't he break up that interference for me?"

When the attack struck his end now it turned in, slicing off tackle, the runner well screened by close interference that held him up when Stover tackled, dragging him on for the precious yards. Three and four yards at a time, the blue advance rolled its way irresistibly toward the red and black goal. They were inside the twenty-yard line now.

Cockrell was pleading with them. Little Charlie DeSoto was running along the line, slapping their backs, calling frantically on them to throw the blue back.

And gradually the line did stiffen, slowly but perceptibly the advance was cut down. Enmities were forgotten with the shadow of the goalposts looming at their backs. Waladoo and Turkey Reiter were fighting side by side, calling to each other. Tough McCarty was hauling Stover out of desperate scrimmages, patting him on the back and calling him "good old Dink." The fighting blood that Garry Cockrell had called upon was at last there—the line had closed and fought together. And yet they were borne back to their fifteen-yard line, two yards at a time, just losing the fourth down.

Stover at end was trembling like a blooded terrier, on edge for each play, shrieking:

"Oh, Tough, get through—you must get through!"

He was playing by intuition now, no time to plan. He knew just who had the ball and where it was going. Out or in, the attack was concentrating on his end—only McCarty and he could stop it. He was getting his man, but they were dragging him on, fighting now for inches.

"Third down, one yard to gain!"

"Watch my end," he shouted to Flash Condit, and hurling himself forward at the starting backs dove under the knees, and grabbing the legs about him went down buried under the mass he had upset.

It seemed hours before the crushing bodies were pulled off and someone's arm brought him to his feet and someone hugged him, shouting in his ear: "You saved it, Dink, you saved it!"

Someone rushed up with a sponge and began dabbing his face.

"What the deuce are they doing that for?" he said angrily.

Then he noticed that an arm was under his and he turned curiously to the face near him. It was Tough McCarty's.

"Whose ball is it?" he said.

"Ours."

He looked to the other side. Garry Cockrell was supporting him.

"What's the matter?" he said, trying to draw his head away from the sponge that was dripping water down his throat.

"Just a little wind knocked out, youngster—coming to?"

"I'm all right."

He walked a few steps alone and then took his place. Things were in a daze on the horizon, but not there in the field. Everything else was shut out except his duty there.

Charlie DeSoto's voice rose shrill:

"Now, Lawrenceville, up the field with it. This team's just begun to play. We've got together, boys. Let her rip!"

No longer scattered, but a unit, all differences forgot, fighting for the same ideal, the team rose up and crashed through the Andover line, every man in the play, ten—fifteen yards ahead.

"Again!" came the strident cry.

Without a pause the line sprang into place, formed and swept forward. It was a privilege to be in such a game, to feel the common frenzy, the awakened glance of battle that showed down the line. Dink, side by side with Tough McCarty, thrilled with the same thrill, plunging ahead with the same motion, fighting the same fight; no longer alone and desperate, but nerved with the consciousness of a partner whose gameness matched his own.

For thirty yards they carried the ball down the field, before the stronger Andover team, thrown off its feet by the unexpected frenzy, could rally and stand them off. Then an exchange of punts once more drove them back to their twenty-five-yard line.

A second time the Andover advance set out from the fifty-yard line and slowly fought its way to surrender the ball in the shadow of the goalposts.

Stover played on in a daze, remembering nothing of the confused shock of bodies that had gone before, wondering how much longer he could hold out—to last out the game as the captain had told him. He was groggy, from time to time he felt the sponge's cold touch on his face or heard the voice of Tough McCarty in his ear.

"Good old Dink, die game!"

How he loved McCarty fighting there by his side, whispering to him: "You and I, Dink! What if he is an old elephant, we'll put him out of the play."

Still, flesh and blood could not last forever. The half must be nearly up. "Two minutes more time."

"What was that?" he said groggily to Flash Condit.

"Two minutes more. Hold 'em now!"

It was Andover's ball. He glanced around. They were down near the twenty-five-yard line somewhere. He looked at McCarty, whose frantic head showed against the sky.

"Break it up, Tough," he said, and struggled toward him.

A cry went up, the play was halted. "He's groggy," he heard voices say, and then came the welcome splash of the sponge.

Slowly his vision cleared to the anxious faces around him.

"Can you last?" said the captain.

"I'm all right," he said gruffly.

"Things cleared up now?"

"Fine!"

McCarty put his arm about him and walked with him.

"Oh, Dink, you will last, won't you?"

"You bet I will, Tough!"

"It's the last stand, old boy!"

"The last."

"Only two minutes more we've got to hold 'em! The last ditch, Dink."

"I'll last."

He looked up and saw the school crouching along the line—tense drawn faces. For the first time he realized they were there, calling on him to stand steadfast.

He went back, meeting the rush that came his way, half knocked aside, half getting his man, dragged again until assistance came. DeSoto's stinging hand slapped his back and the sting was good, clearing his brain.

Things came into clear outline once more. He saw down the line and to the end where Garry Cockrell stood.

"Good old captain," he said. "They'll not get by me, not now."

He was in every play, it seemed to him, wondering why Andover was always keeping the ball, always coming at his end. Suddenly he had a shock. Over his shoulder were the goalposts, the line he stood on was the line of his own goal.

He gave a hoarse cry and went forward like a madman, parting the interference. Someone else was through; Tough was through; the whole line was through flinging back the runner. He went down clinging to Goodhue, buried under a mass of his own tacklers. Then, through the frenzy, he heard the shrill call of time.

He struggled to his feet. The ball lay scarcely four yards away from the glorious goalposts. Then, before the school could sweep them up; panting, exhausted, they gathered in a circle with incredulous, delirious faces, and leaning heavily, wearily on one another, gave the cheer for Andover. And the touch of Stover's arm on McCarty's shoulder was like an embrace.

# THE WINNING BUG

*By JACKSON SCHOLZ*

*Illustration by Warren Chappell*

A S the quarter-milers swung into the last turn, something peculiar happened which set me to thinking. It might easily have been an accident, with no significance at all, because a twelve-lap board track offers a ticklish bit of navigation, even for the experienced runner, and I had to admit that Sax was pretty green at this sort of thing.

But, at the same time, it's part of a coach's business to watch for just such little happenings of this kind, which might make or break an athlete if they're allowed to pass unnoticed.

It looked as though Sax had deliberately fouled Chris Leighton with his elbow as they swung into the last turn. Of course there were any number of things which might have caused him to lurch in Chris's direction, such as a loose board, plain leg weariness or inexperience, and, anyway, it didn't make a great deal of difference, because Chris had weathered too many rough races to be bothered by a little thing like that. He held his stride, without breaking, and they came into the home stretch shoulder to shoulder. Sax cracked about fifteen yards from the finish, and Chris romped home with a good lead.

I hadn't intended for them to make a race of it, because we'd only been on the boards a little over a week. We train for the indoor season on a twelve-lap board track, built just outside the gym. It was my idea to get away from the narrow, dangerous curves of the inside track, so after yelling my head off for a couple of years, they finally gave me an outdoor track, just to keep me quiet. More later concerning this.

I had sent Sax and Chris out with specific instructions to turn me in a sixty-second quarter, but, as it often happens with colts and athletes when you give them their heads, this pair got started, and before I knew what it was all about, they were running their fool legs off. I could have yelled to them to cut it down, but I'll frankly admit I was curious to see how it would come out. I enjoy a good race as much as anybody.

I wasn't curious about Chris. He'd been my top-notch quarter-miler for the last two years, and I knew pretty well what stuff he had. But this was Saxon Demming's first season in competition, so I figured that this was about as good an opportunity as any to learn the material I had to work upon. The result of the race convinced me that he had plenty of natural speed, endurance, which could be developed, and a good supply of courage. But the little incident on the last turn caused me to discredit all these till I was a little surer of my ground.

Saxon Demming was still a rather unknown quantity. He had done a little track work as a freshman, but, inasmuch as he hadn't shown a great deal of promise at the time, I hadn't paid a great deal of attention to him. This year, however, he looked like the real stuff. He had filled out a lot, grown some, and had taken on the keen, alert appearance of a man who knows what he wants. I liked his eyes.

And I learned, too, that he was pretty popular on the campus. He was dabbling a bit in politics, which was a tribute to his ability for making friends, and, from reliable sources, available to all coaches, I learned that he was one of the best-liked men in his class.

I proceeded to bawl out Chris and Sax for the exhibition they had staged against my orders. I laid it on pretty thick, merely for the sake of discipline, and for the benefit of the rest of the squad standing around. Chris had heard the same thing before, so he didn't pay much attention to it; and Sax, standing hunched over with his hands on his knees, was still too winded to care much what happened. I sent them both to the showers and transferred my attention to the hurdlers.

When I went down to the varsity room a little later, Sax was just lacing his shoes. I told him to drop into my office on his way out. I was waiting for him when he came up a few minutes later, and I didn't waste any words.

"What was the idea of staging a race out there today?"

Sax flushed a little, but didn't try to avoid the question or pass the buck.

"Why, I—I don't know, coach," he said. "I just didn't seem to be able to help it. I had no intention of racing when we started, but I was feeling so good, and—well, I guess I went a little faster than I intended. When I started to run I forgot myself altogether."

I let that pass, because it was a pretty good indication of the natural-born racer.

"How about the little mix-up on the last turn?" I asked pointedly. "Why did you foul Leighton?"

Naturally I expected him to deny this, or at least to offer some good excuse, but instead he regarded me with a sort of lost, puzzled look in his eyes.

"I don't know," he said simply.

"You don't know?" I gasped. Sax shook his head dully. "But you knew you did it," I insisted.

He nodded.

"Then why?" I demanded.

The expression in his eyes became stubborn and a trifle sullen.

"I—I don't know," he repeated, and, before I had a chance to question him further, he turned and hurried out of the office. I let him go.

The funny part of it was that I believed the kid, as much as I hated to do so. He had absolutely no idea why he had fouled Leighton on the turn. The whole thing was a mystery to him, and worried him all the more for that reason. If he had asked me for a solution, I could have told him, although I don't believe it would have helped a great deal. A coach, after twenty years of experience, gathers a lot of wisdom in spite of himself, and I don't suppose I'm any exception to the rule.

Sax Demming's trouble was not a common one among athletes, but every coach runs up against it now and then. For convenience I'll call it "the winning bug." By that I mean that whenever an athlete is bitten by this bug, the one idea uppermost in his mind is to win, regardless of all consequences. He attaches so much importance to victory that everything else dwindles to nothing by comparison.

It doesn't necessarily indicate a crooked streak in a man's character, because in every other way he may be square shooting and fine, except that under the excitement of competition he is really not himself. But, if such a thing is allowed to run, it may become such a fixture in a person's character that it pokes its head up in some of the problems of everyday life.

Athletics with such men is generally a passion, and when aroused to the fever pitch of competition they are not responsible for their actions, inasmuch as their ideas are all centered on winning, and anything they do immediately before or during a race may be laid to some automatic impulse.

I don't often preach on the subject of sportsmanship, because it's not becoming for a coach to shout about morals, ethics and such things. He's paid to deliver the goods, not talk about them, so the more he concentrates on the matter in hand the fatter and more regular will be his pay check.

He's paid to win, but at the same time there are various ways of winning, and I find that my men will win more regularly if they are right mentally, before and after a race. It pays in the long run to keep the minds of the boys clean and square. I teach my boys to give their last breath and to fight to the last inch, but to fight fair all the way.

In that way victories mean a lot more, and defeats hurt a lot less. If a man runs the best race that's in him and loses, he hasn't much to regret, but if he runs a crooked race and wins, well—think it over. If they lose they've learned to grin and keep their mouths shut. No excuses, you understand.

Then, of course, there's the selfish, personal satisfaction I get out of developing a piece of raw material. The athletic field is a wonderful workshop, and a man can be analyzed there to a finer point than in any classroom in the world.

Some winning bugs are never cured. They continue their way through life, fouling on the turns. It's one of the most pathetic problems I'm faced with on the track. and I sure hated to see the symptoms cropping out in young Demming, because I certainly liked the kid. So, because I realized what the trouble was and Sax didn't, I felt the responsibility to be mostly mine. Maybe I was assuming an obligation out of the line of duty, but I couldn't see it that way. It seems to me that a coach's first duty is to the athlete himself, even though the school is paying his salary.

I was still mulling the matter over, when some one rapped at the door. I yelled "Come in!" and a couple of slick-haired, sailor-panted lads came in with their hats respectfully in their hands. They were clean-cut youngsters, and a trifle ill at ease, so I grinned and invited them to relieve their minds of whatever was bothering them.

"Well, it's this way, coach," one of them began, "we represent the Scroll and Quill—membership committee, you know, investigation and all that sort of stuff. We're considering Saxon Demming for membership, and—we thought we'd better talk to you before deciding on him definitely. Can you recommend him, coach? Is he the sort of man we want?

Now can you beat that? Of all the times in the world for the Scroll and Quill to take me into their confidence! It's true, they always ask my advice on any track man they consider taking in, and I've always tried to play square with them, and to advise them honestly on the man in question. But Sax Demming, just at this time —huh!

The Scroll and Quill, by the way, is a second-term sophomore organization which is composed of the most influential men in the class. The members are chosen irrespective of any other connection, and are considered for their capabilities alone. It's a mighty fine organization, perhaps the best in school, with its ideals based exclusively on the welfare of the college. It is nonpolitical, but has an admittedly tremendous influence on school life, particularly toward the development of the lower classmen. To be a member of the Scroll and Quill is pretty much of an honor, and gives a man a good running start for his entire college career.

You see, I realized what this membership would be to a boy, but, at the same time, I was unable to shake off the uncomfortable vision of two flying figures, coming into the last turn of the quarter, the deliberate foul, and—well, I wanted to be fair to both parties so the only thing I could do was to stall for a time.

"Well, now, I'll tell you, boys," I said, "it was mighty good of you to come to me for advice, but I'm afraid I'm not in a position now to give it. You see I haven't had a chance to see much of the boy yet, but if you can wait till a little later in the indoor season, I can tell you definitely, one way or the other."

This seemed to be agreeable to them, although I'm afraid they had a hunch that something was wrong. At any rate they decided to let it go at that, and left me alone once more to wrestle with my conscience, and a few other minor and major difficulties.

I told you before that I'd had a lot of trouble getting my outdoor board track, but I didn't mention any of the details, or the ticklish position in which the acquisition of this feature had placed me. Track athletics, in the first place, were none too popular with some of the old fossils in the faculty, but there was one old duck who was particularly rabid about the money spent for my track, inasmuch as he had wanted it spent for an original painting, by somebody or other, to hang in the library.

At any rate, he raised a lot of fireworks, by virtue of the fact that he'd been on the faculty for so many years, and when the money was finally appropriated for the track, this old boy, "Doc" Brown by name, had managed in some way or other to make my job hinge upon the big indoor meet. He figured that, as we'd been winning consistently in previous years with the old track, to spend all that money for a new track and lose besides, would be just cause for a new coach. The sad part of it was that he had rallied enough support among the other athletic-hating members of the faculty board to make my job hang by a thread.

Of course I didn't help things a lot by telling him a few of my own personal views on the matter, which were pointed enough to cause the old boy to turn a dangerous shade of purple. At the end of our little interview he swore a half dozen assorted kinds of vengeance. I'd have felt kind of sorry for him if I hadn't known that he'd accumulated enough money in his life to permit him to retire in comfort and quit pestering other people.

Anyway, I didn't think much of his ravings at the time, but later I had reason to believe that the old cuss had meant every word of it, and was out for blood after all.

We worked out regularly every afternoon. Sometimes the weather was pretty chilly, and sometimes we had to sweep the snow from the track, but the boys were all supplied with sweat suits, and I made them limber up well indoors before taking a chance of pulling a muscle on the outdoor track.

I had a good likely bunch of material that year, and was bringing them all around in pretty fine shape. The outdoor work seemed to agree with them, and it sure looked as though the Indoor Valley Conference would be a repetition of the last few years. I didn't see how we could be whipped. But then, I figured without old Doc Brown.

I should have been warned when I noticed him snooping around the track several afternoons of the week. He seemed to have taken a sudden keen interest in athletics, and he used to stand in the shelter of the wide gym door, his old knit muffler wrapped around his neck, and his sharp little eyes peering from the sides of a hooked nose, for all the world like a vulture perched hungrily on a rock.

I wouldn't have been surprised to hear him croak, or whatever vultures do. At any rate, he sure devoted a lot of time to hate. A nice pleasant disposition. He worried me some, and I often wondered what friendly thoughts were fermenting in his fertile old brain.

But I had other worries, too, and I don't mind admitting that Sax Demming was my principal one. Every time I'd run him in any sort of a race or a trial, he'd go plumb hog wild and do almost anything to cross the finish first. It was a case with him of win or bust, and there wasn't much danger of his busting. In fact, he developed into the fastest four-forty man on the squad. That was the irony of the thing, because, good or bad, I won't let a man compete for me if he doesn't shoot square.

I suppose I should have kicked him off the squad, but that would have ruined his whole career in school, and might have had a serious effect on his life. Anyway, I liked the kid, and had a feeling deep down in me that there was some way out. I talked to him on several occasions, and he was always repentant and humble as the deuce.

But that's all the good it seemed to do. The rest of the squad liked him in spite of his tactics on the track, so I just let him stick around and worried my head off, trying to figure out some solution. Finally I hit on one which I thought might work.

Our indoor schedule was light this year, and aside from a few club meets, in which I entered a few individual stars, the Valley Conference was the first big meet of the season. It came earlier, this year, than usual, because the Colosseum in Kansas City, where it was always held, was only available on this date.

The meet, through years of popularity, had come to be a pretty big affair—almost a social function—and all the seats were sold weeks in advance. True, we had won the meet for the last several years, but there had been some mighty tight squeaks, and the crowd always got their money's worth. It was the biggest track event, indoor or outdoor, on our sport calendar, so naturally we went after it with everything we had.

I held tryouts for this meet one week ahead, a regular track meet on a small scale, in which my boys fought for places on the team. I had started working them, a week before the tryouts, in smooth-soled shoes, because the owners of the colosseum refused to let us chew the floor up with spikes.

Some indoor meets, you see, are run in spiked shoes—tiny spikes which grip the boards and add a lot to the runner's speed—but in some meets spikes are prohibited and we have to use a flat-soled running shoe. As I said, I made the boys wear the plain-soled shoe a couple of weeks before a big meet, so they would be used to the things. I was trying out a new kind of shoe this year with little rubber pimples on the sole. They seemed to hold the boards fine.

We had a good day for the tryouts, and there was a fair-sized crowd on hand to watch the boys do their stuff. I had four pretty good quarter-milers, but one of them, Davis, also ran the half, so it made no difference whether he qualified for the four-forty or not. Therefore, as I had to have four men for the mile relay I had to pick three other quarter-milers from the tryouts. I had made the statement that I expected to take but four quarter-milers along.

Sax was, of course, the fastest man I had. The other two were Chris Leighton and Jack Wallace. These last two I called into my office just before they went on the track. We had a short talk, and both boys protested at what I told them to do until I'd explained the matter and they saw things from my angle. They were grinning when I sent them out to warm up.

Six men started the quarter. Three were to be chosen for the team, and it meant a lot to represent the school in the indoor conference.

I brought the men to their marks, and Sax jumped at the gun—anything to win. I called him back and penalized him three yards. He took it without a whimper. The next time, I got them off to a fair start. Three laps to go.

Chris shot out and took the lead, with Wallace at his shoulder. The rest bunched on the turn, and Sax brought up the rear. Sax let out on the back stretch and tried to take the lead, but as he was about to pass, Wallace swerved, apparently by accident, bumped Sax and sent him reeling to the outside of the track. Sax recovered, ran wide on the turn, and tried to take the lead again on the home stretch, but couldn't quite cut it down.

As they swung in toward the pole on the curve, Wallace again stepped wide, and, as Sax fell in behind Chris, Wallace fell back beside Sax, and they had him in as neat a little pocket as you ever saw. They ran in this position for a lap, Leighton purposely slowing down a pace so that all the stragglers could catch up with him.

As they started the last lap Sax became desperate and forgot himself, as I knew he would. He tried to fight his way out of the box, first shoving Wallace to one side, and then shouldering up beside Chris, but this was as far as he got.

No sooner had he come alongside, than Chris deliberately brought his elbow back and buried it in Sax's stomach. The race was over then, as far as Sax was concerned. He finished gamely, but only managed a poor fifth. Leighton won it, Wallace was second, and a mediocre lad by the name of Bush came in third.

Sax was having a pretty hard time getting his wind back after the wallop he'd received in the stomach. He was leaning against the wall of the gym with both hands over his mid-section as though it were giving him some trouble. Leighton started toward him with the evident intention of apologizing, but I grabbed him in time and told him that I'd do all the apologizing necessary.

I was watching Sax pretty close, because I wasn't quite sure what he was liable to do. I noticed a sort of puzzled expression come over his face when he started breathing regularly again, as though he was trying to figure what it was all about.

As soon as he saw me standing by myself, he came over and stood at my elbow. I didn't encourage him any, so pretty soon he spoke.

"Does—does that race mean that I don't make the trip, coach?"

He tried to keep his voice even, but it shook in spite of him. I didn't even turn my head.

"You knew beforehand that the first three men would be chosen for the team," I told him. "You finished fifth. Figure it out for yourself."

"But, coach!" he pleaded desperately, "he fouled me! Leighton fouled me! You saw it yourself! He—"

"He *what?*" I whirled fiercely and glared at him. "He *what,* did you say?"

"Why, he—oh!" I saw a peculiar light come into his eyes. They widened with the scared look of a man who sees something astounding for the first time, and realizes that it's been under his nose all the while. His face went scarlet and his gaze dropped to the track.

"Oh," he said, just "Oh," as he turned slowly and headed for the showers. At any rate, the kid was no fool, and I had a pretty good hunch that his first lesson had been learned.

The next week was one long nightmare, with Doc Brown playing the heavy lead. The old scoundrel finally managed to get across some of the nice pleasant things he'd been threatening for so long, for, on the Thursday before the meet I received an apologetic little note from the dean, saying that Wallace and my sprinting ace, had been reported by Doctor Brown to be flunking in his—Doctor Brown's—class in philosophy, and that he regretted the necessity of declaring them ineligible for athletic competition, until their work in his class showed a decided improvement. Now wasn't that nice? The old villain, I could have murdered him.

Of course you know what that did to my team. The loss of Wallace robbed me of some sure points in the quarter and knocked the spots out of my mile-relay team. The loss of my sprinter was the worst blow, however, because I had figured him as a sure first in the sprint and both the high and low hurdles. He was the most valuable man on the team, and without him in the line-up I figured my chances of winning the meet to be worth something slightly less than a cigar coupon.

I didn't mind the possibility of losing my job so much, there were plenty of jobs, and besides I was sure the student body would stand behind me to the last ditch, but it was the idea of the thing. It had resolved itself into a sort of show-down between school athletics and the old anti-athletic element in the faculty, and it sure looked as though they'd handed me a loaded cigar in our first major encounter. There was nothing to do, however, but patch the team up as best I could, and then pray for a few breaks.

Thursday evening I stopped at Sax's fraternity house. The boys told me he was upstairs in his room, so I went on up and found him humped over a table under a big droplight, figuring something on paper. He looked up guiltily when I came in, and tried to hide the paper.

"Writing to the girl?" I asked casually.

"Oh, hello, coach. Come on in. Have a chair. No," he answered my question, a trifle sheepishly, I thought. "To tell the truth I—I was doping out the meet Saturday night."

"How do we stack up?" I demanded.

"Why, not so good, coach, I'm afraid. We need another—another—" He stammered in confusion.

"Quarter-miler," I helped him out. Sax turned and started making lines on the paper. "How would you like to go?" I asked suddenly.

He almost fell out of his chair, as he whirled around to see if I was serious.

"How would I like to go!" he shouted. "How would I—" He

caught himself, settled back, swallowed a couple of times, and continued quietly, his voice husky. "I guess maybe you know how much I'd like to go, coach. I guess I'd like it more than anything else in the world, just now. I didn't think it meant so much till I found out I hadn't made the team. And I—I believe I've learned the other thing."

"I hope so, son," I said, as I got up to leave, "but you never can tell until you're in actual competition. You're a different person then. We all are under that strain. I'm hoping for the best, and gambling pretty heavy on you. We meet at the station tomorrow at noon. Good night."

I left him staring soberly at his dope sheet.

We arrived in Kansas City Friday afternoon. I generally like to give the boys a complete day of rest before a meet, and don't like to have them do any traveling on that day. I chased them to bed that night at ten o'clock, but sat up for a couple of hours longer myself, doping out the events as best I could, and trying to figure my crippled team for as many points as the law of averages and a barrel of luck would allow.

I was just about ready to turn in, and was about to pull down my shade, when a window suddenly lighted on a level with mine just across the court on which my room opened. I stared for a moment, just like anybody would, without any idea of being impolite, and my conscience bothered me even less when I noticed that the room belonged to Sax Demming. He had just switched on the light beside his bed and was in the act of climbing out. I thought maybe he might be sick or something, so I kept watching.

Somebody, however, had evidently rapped on the door. Sax opened it and stood staring sleepily at the man on the threshold, who proceeded to slide into the room in a slinky sort of way, which made me jump for my own light to turn it out, in order that I could see better.

The newcomer had a bundle under his arm. He came into the room, apologizing, apparently, for his late call, and then started to talk to Sax in an earnest sort of way, at the same time starting to unwrap the bundle. I was all attention now, and Sax seemed to have waked up enough to take an interest in what the stranger was saying.

The package finally revealed a pair of indoor track shoes. Sax's visitor was still talking to beat the band, explaining something about the shoes, which looked to me exactly like the kind we were already using. Sax took one of them in his hand, examined it, nodded his

*Warren Chappell*

*"I was doping out the meet Saturday night."*

head, and said something to the other fellow, who smiled in a relieved sort of way, as though he'd just finished a tough job. He talked a minute longer, grabbed Sax by the hand in a hasty shake, and slid out the door like he was on his way to rob a bank or assassinate a child.

I didn't like this lad's looks a bit, so I hurried to the door and hiked up the hall in the hope of waylaying him as he was waiting for the elevator. He evidently, however, was in too much of a hurry to wait and had already left by the stairs by the time I arrived. When I got back to my own room, Sax's light was out, so I went to bed and lay awake for another hour, wondering what the devil I was up against now. It looked worse than I was willing to admit, but I decided to let it rest until morning.

I got up about eight o'clock, feeling a little ragged, and joined the great army of cold-bath takers. There's nothing like a cold bath in the morning, unless, possibly, it's a clout over the head with a baseball bat. Their chief value, as I see it, is to shrivel you up like a withered peanut, and give you something to brag about.

I routed the boys out and got them down to breakfast. When they were all accounted for I went to Sax's room and found the door unlocked. I had no difficulty in finding the package, in which the shoes had been loosely wrapped, and I took one up to examine it.

As I had noticed the night before, they seemed to be identical to the ones I had chosen for the team, but, as I held the sole in the palm of my hand, and bent the rest to try the flexibility, I found that I was wrong. For, as I bent the shoe, I grunted with the pain of a sharp stab in my palm—spikes.

Yes, sir, spikes! Tiny little needle points, cleverly concealed in the little rubber pimples of the sole. Spikes which would allow the wearer to pass the test of stepping flat-footed on a piece of paper without leaving a mark, but would come into play the minute his foot was bent in running, and would grip the treacherous turns of the smooth track, giving him a tremendous advantage over his rivals.

Anything to win! I couldn't believe it, and dropped limply in a chair to reason with myself. But I had seen Sax accept them with my own eyes. I knew his failing under the excitement of competition, and just before a race, and yet—and yet—huh, I didn't know.

Then I recalled our conversation on the night I told him he would run. I recalled the pathetic light in his eyes when he learned I'd trust him in a race. And then I remembered what I'd said before I left. I had told the kid I'd gamble on him, and suddenly it came to me with convincing force that he was certainly worth gambling on. I could step in now, spoil everything, and prove nothing. On the other hand—

I arose and carefully replaced the shoes as I had found them. Five minutes later I was having breakfast with the squad.

I kept the whole team in bed most of the afternoon, and gave them a light meal around five o'clock. A couple of hours later, I bundled them into taxis and sent them to the Colosseum. I took the last cab from the hotel, and, just before leaving, I made a rush trip to Sax Demming's room. The shoes had disappeared.

The crowd started to come early, and before the first event was called the place was packed. One of the more affluent alumni repeated his yearly practice of hiring a brass band to entertain the assembled multitude, and to follow him about the streets in full blast after the meet was over. This was always his big night.

Firemen patrolled the aisles, enforcing the "no smoking" signs, which had been posted for the occasion. Not that there was any danger of fire, but because the coaches had got together and had originated this as an excuse to keep the building free from smoke, so the runners would have a fighting chance to get some halfway decent air in their lungs. The average spectator is pretty thoughtless after he's paid his admission.

The atmosphere of the dressing room was tense. I had every member of the team to a beautiful edge, and they all showed their excitement in different ways. Few of them would be recognized as the same individuals in everyday life. Some were talkative, others sullen, some were pale, some flushed, some forced grins, while others sat tight-lipped and rigid. They took their rubs in the order of their events and the room soon reeked with the pleasant odor of witch hazel, alcohol and wintergreen.

Sax sat over in a corner by himself, his eyes a trifle glassy with the strain. His hands trembled as he hung his clothes in the locker, and he would stop every now and then to steady himself with a long breath. I watched him narrowly, and guessed the terrific tension he was under.

He wrapped his insteps with black tire tape, and removed it several times before it was fixed to suit. He adjusted his pushers and worked on a pair of new shoes, which fitted nice and snug, like gloves. All the squad were wearing new shoes that night.

I spoke a last word to several of the boys, and went up to the track, which looked, at first glance, like a society function of some sort, rather than a track meet. All the officials were strutting about in evening clothes, which contrasted strangely with the scantily clad athletes, flashing up and down the straightaway, and jogging around the track, warming up for the first events.

I got a slight shock when I bumped into old Doc Brown, wandering around in a rusty old swallowtail, and sporting an official badge on one of his lapels. I'll bet it was the first track meet he'd ever attended, and how he'd ever managed to horn in as an official set me to thinking once more. I smelled a whole nest of mice, and my expression must have registered something of this sort, as I spoke to him.

"Well, doctor," I said, "you seem to have developed into a real track fan."

He glared at me out of his malevolent little eyes as though I'd accused him of stealing horses. He started to speak, changed his mind, and walked away. Nice pleasant chap. Personally, I believe he was a little cracked.

The meet started and the sprint heats thundered down the track, while the spectators yelled or held their breaths, according to their dispositions. I didn't score in the sprints nor in the hurdles, which followed next. My miler, however, came through with an unexpected win, and a youngster, whom I was merely running for the experience, nosed his way into third place, by some miracle or other.

The quarter mile came next, and my heart turned a flip-flop as Sax and Chris went to their marks. Chris drew the second lane from the pole, while Sax had a rotten break, and drew the next to last position on the outside.

The gun roared, and they all raced for the first turn, and the advantage of the pole. Naturally this resulted in a flying bunch of legs and elbows, with the almost inevitable result of a spill. The man in front of Sax slipped and tumbled, bringing Sax down with him. They both slid in a tangled mass, and brought up against the concrete railing of the boxes.

My cuss word was lost in the groan of the crowd, but I breathed again when I saw them both get up, apparently none the worse for wear. I hiked over to find Sax a little dazed, but otherwise all right. I saw Doc Brown heading in the same direction, but bumped the old boy aside and rushed Sax down to the dressing room.

It was on the tip of my tongue to satisfy my mind once for all, but the same peculiar feeling held me back. The battle, after all, wasn't mine. All I could do was help, and I figured the best way I could do that was to keep my mouth shut, and go ahead and gamble as I'd promised the boy I would. He felt pretty bad about the quarter, so I talked to him quietly a while, then stretched him out on a table and told him to wait till I called him for the relay.

In the meantime Chris had won the quarter, and things were looking rather promising. I scored some unexpected points in the pole vault, and also in the shot put, and, to make a long story short, I came down to the final event, the mile relay, just a single point behind the leaders, who, as luck would have it, were our choicest rivals in everything pertaining to athletics.

It so happened also that none of the other teams had a chance to win the meet by winning the relay so that we were the only two teams entered. Both teams, I felt, were rather well matched, although I knew I would feel the loss of Wallace, thanks to Doc Brown, mighty keenly. As things stood the result was a toss-up.

I was on my way to the dressing room to get the boys out to warm up, when I passed the refreshment stand. I had almost gone by, when my attention was attracted by a strangely familiar face, partially obscured by a hot-dog sandwich. I waited till the sandwich had been lowered, then leaped to the side of its owner, and grabbed his arm with such force that the hot dog hopped unnoticed to the floor. I dragged my prisoner to a corner and backed him into it.

"And now, my boy," I snarled in my most ferocious manner, "what were you doing in Sax Demming's room last night?"

The kid turned a pasty color, opened his mouth, but couldn't utter a sound. Finally he managed a couple of squeaks, which I took for a denial. I twisted his arm till he started to whimper.

"Don't lie to me, you little pup," I hissed, "out with it!"

"Oh, don't, coach, don't, please," he whined. "I'll tell you, honest! It was Doctor Brown—yes, it was! He made me do it; said he'd flunk me in his class. He'd do it too, and—and I've never flunked. All I did was to take the shoes and—and—"

"That'll do," I cut in. "What's your name, and where do you live?"

He told me and I let him go. He was thoroughly scared.

I got the relay team on the track and made them warm up well. The crowd was jumpy and nervous, for it was composed mostly of alumni and students of these two schools. Programs were crumpled and torn, serving the purpose of safety valves. A girl giggled hysterically every now and then.

I had decided to start Davis, the half-miler, first; Bush, my weakest man, second; Leighton third, and Demming anchor. All were drawn taut and quivering and I was in no better shape myself. My throat was dry as cotton, and the palms of my hands were wet and cold.

The starter called the teams to the starting post. Each man was to run three laps.

The gun roared, and the two figures shot from their marks, raced for the first turn and settled into their strides. Davis, slow on the start, swung in behind and stuck closely to the other's heels. They were well matched, and Davis, following my instructions, stayed close behind and swung even on the stretch.

Bush took the baton on a perfect touch-off, and gained just enough to put him in the lead. Then he proceeded to lose his head, and instead of coasting the turns and sprinting the straightaways, the darn fool tried to sprint the whole distance. He opened up five yards before the inevitable happened and he began to tie up. He couldn't stand the pace, and our rooters raged and pleaded as his man slowly cut him down, passed him and handed the other team a ten-yard lead.

Leighton took the stick on a well-timed touch-off, and set out after his man in a businesslike way that made my heart swell at the courage the lad possessed. He ran his race like the great veteran he was, conserving every ounce of strength, studying every turn, slowly closing the gap, and finally fighting to within two yards of the leader before he passed the baton to Sax. The crowd by this time was wild, but I could only clench my hands and pray.

Sax took out after his man with a careless fury that made me hold my breath as he leaned into the turn. But his shoes, by some miracle, held. He caught the leader as they came off the first turn, and they both raced shoulder to shoulder down the stretch. I gritted my teeth as they came to the second turn. They were both going too fast to take it well, and Sax was on the outside. Why didn't the idiot slow up? My heart dropped with a plop as I realized that he intended to fight for the pole with his arms—anything to win.

I would have turned away but I couldn't possibly shift my eyes. They were glued to the two speeding figures, and for this reason I perhaps saw what no one else would have noticed. For, a split second before they reached the turn, I saw Sax's head jerk back slightly, as though a thought had jammed itself forcibly into his brain. At the same instant his stride faltered and he swung wide, shunning his opponent as though he had the plague.

Sax's momentum had carried him into the concrete railing of the boxes. He warded himself off with his hand, and had just about floundered into his stride again when the crowd came to its feet with a great gasping groan. The other boy had leaned into the turn too far, had lost his feet, had tumbled to the floor. The baton shot out of his hand and rattled across the track.

And the groan of the crowd turned suddenly to a dead silence.

For Sax heard the groan, had turned his head, and finally stopped. With the race delivered to him, bound and tied by the hand of fate, he stopped, dead, recovered the baton of the fallen man, and handed it to him as he scrambled to his feet.

It was the most spectacular and cleanest piece of sportsmanship I had ever seen, but my own shout was lost in the tremendous din of the crowd. It was a great ovation to a great sportsman.

The race started again with the men in their original positions, side by side, but the other lad was too shaken by the fall to make much of a race out of it. They finished five yards apart, and the crowd closed in on the victor.

That was the reason I didn't get to Sax for several moments later. But when I'd finally wormed my way to the center of the circle, I found Doc Brown already there, together with several other officials. He was arguing.

"I insist that you examine this man's shoes," I heard him say.

My heart dropped like a chunk of lead, but bounced again like a rubber ball, as I noticed the expression on Sax's face. He was surprised at first, then grinned as he slipped off a shoe and handed it to Doc Brown.

The old boy bent it and prodded it a bit, and his face slowly took on an expression of blank surprise, followed suddenly by one of rage. He grunted something, handed the shoe back, but, as he turned to go I grabbed him, and whispered gently in his ear what I had already learned.

"You're a foxy old gent," I told him, "and crooked as they make 'em. You watched the team enough to figure Demming as the weak point, but your ignorance of that little thing called 'sportsmanship' has made an ass of you. Take my advice and resign."

A moment later I had dragged Sax off to one side.

"You see, coach," he explained, "I didn't want to tell you anything about it, because I was pretty much ashamed of the fact that they'd picked me for the goat. And besides I figured that, by pretending to accept them, I'd learn who was at the bottom of it. It sure worked out that way, didn't it?"

I patted him on the shoulder and sent him down to dress. As I turned, some one touched me on the arm. It was a lad from the Scroll and Quill.

"Congratulations on the meet, coach," he said. "Can you give us any dope yet on Saxon Demming?"

I regarded him fondly and patted him on the shoulder too.

"Take him, son, take him quick," I said. "You'll never get a better man."

# THE FIGHT

### By *THOMAS HUGHES*

*Illustrations by Hugh Thomson*

T OM was detained in school a few minutes after the rest, and on coming out into the quadrangle, the first thing he saw was a small ring of boys, applauding Williams, who was holding Arthur by the collar.

"There, you young sneak," said he, giving Arthur a cuff on the head with his other hand, "what made you say that—"

"Hullo!" said Tom, shouldering into the crowd, "you drop that, Williams; you shan't touch him."

"Who'll stop me?" said the Slogger, raising his hand again.

"I," said Tom; and suiting the action to the word, he struck the arm which held Arthur's arm so sharply, that the Slogger dropped it with a start, and turned the full current of his wrath on Tom.

"Will you fight?"

"Yes, of course."

"Huzza, there's going to be a fight between Slogger Williams and Tom Brown!" The news ran like wildfire about, and many boys who were on their way to tea at their several houses turned back, and sought the back of the chapel, where the fights come off.

"Just run and tell East to come and back me," said Tom to a small Schoolhouse boy, who was off like a rocket to Harrowell's, just stopping for a moment to poke his head into the Schoolhouse hall, where the lower boys were already at tea, and sing out, "Fight! Tom Brown and Slogger Williams."

Up start half the boys at once, leaving bread, eggs, butter, sprats, and all the rest to take care of themselves. The greater part of the remainder follow in a minute, after swallowing their tea, carrying their food in their hands to consume as they go. Three or four only remain, who steal the butter of the more impetuous, and make to themselves an unctuous feast.

In another minute East and Martin tear through the quadrangle, carrying a sponge, and arrive at the scene of action just as the combatants are beginning to strip.

Hugh Thomson

*"You shan't touch him."*

Tom felt he had got his work cut out for him, as he stripped off his jacket, waistcoat and braces. East tied his handkerchief round his waist, and rolled up his shirt-sleeves for him: "Now, old boy, don't open your mouth to say a word, or try to help yourself a bit—we'll do all that; you keep all your breath and strength for the Slogger." Martin meanwhile folded the clothes, and put them under the chapel rails; and now Tom, with East to handle him, and Martin to give him a knee, steps out on the turf, and is ready for all that may come: and here is the Slogger too, all stripped, and thirsting for the fray.

It doesn't look a fair match at first glance: Williams is nearly two inches taller, and probably a long year older than his opponent, and he is very strongly made about the arms and shoulders—"peels well," as the little knot of big fifth-form boys, the amateurs, say; who stand outside the ring of little boys, looking complacently on, but taking no active part in the proceedings. But down below he is not so good by any means; no spring from the loins, and feeblish, not to say shipwrecky about the knees. Tom, on the contrary, though not half so strong in the arms, is good all over, straight, hard, and springy, from neck to ankle, better perhaps in his legs than anywhere. Besides, you can see by the clear white of his eye and fresh bright look of his skin, that he is in tiptop training, able to do all he knows; while the Slogger looks rather sodden, as if he didn't take much exercise and ate too much tuck. The timekeeper is chosen, a large ring made, and the two stand up opposite one another for a moment, giving us time just to make our little observations.

"If Tom'll only condescend to fight with his head and heels," as East mutters to Martin, "we shall do."

But seemingly he won't, for there he goes in, making play with both hands. Hard all, is the word; the two stand to one another like men; rally follows rally in quick succession, each fighting as if he thought to finish the whole thing out of hand. "Can't last at this rate," say the knowing ones, while the partisans of each make the air ring with their shouts and counter-shouts, of encouragement, approval, and defiance.

"Take it easy, take it easy—keep away, let him come after you," implores East, as he wipes Tom's face after the first round with a wet sponge, while he sits back on Martin's knee, supported by the Madman's long arms, which tremble a little from excitement.

"Time's up," calls the timekeeper.

"There he goes again, hang it all!" growls East, as his man is at it again, as hard as ever. A very severe round follows, in which Tom gets out and out the worst of it, and is at last hit clean off his legs, and deposited on the grass by a right-hander from the Slogger.

Loud shouts rise from the boys of Slogger's house, and the School-house are silent and vicious, ready to pick quarrels anywhere.

"Two to one in half-crowns on the big un," says Rattle, one of the amateurs, a tall fellow, in thunder-and-lightning waistcoat, and puffy good-natured face.

"Done!" says Groove, another amateur of quieter look, taking out his notebook to enter it, for our friend Rattle sometimes forgets these little things.

Meantime East is freshing up Tom with the sponges for next round, and has set two other boys to rub his hands.

"Tom, old boy," whispers he, "this may be fun for you, but it's death to me. He'll hit all the fight out of you in another five minutes, and then I shall go and drown myself in the island ditch. Feint him—use your legs! draw him about! he'll lose his wind then in no time, and you can go into him. Hit at his body, too; we'll take care of his frontispiece by and by."

Tom felt the wisdom of the counsel, and saw already that he couldn't go in and finish the Slogger off at mere hammer and tongs, so changed his tactics completely in the third round. He now fights cautiously, getting away from and parrying the Slogger's lunging hits, instead of trying to counter, and leading his enemy a dance all round the ring after him. "He's funking; go in, Williams," "Catch him up," "Finish him off," scream the small boys of the Slogger party.

"Just what we want," thinks East, chuckling to himself, as he sees Williams, excited by these shouts, and thinking the game in his own hands, blowing himself in his exertions to get to close quarters again, while Tom is keeping away with perfect ease.

They quarter over the ground again and again, Tom always on the defensive.

The Slogger pulls up at last for a moment, fairly blown.

"Now then, Tom," sings out East, dancing with delight. Tom goes in in a twinkling, and hits two heavy body blows, and gets away again before the Slogger can catch his wind, which when he does he rushes with blind fury at Tom, and being skillfully parried and avoided, overreaches himself and falls on his face, amidst terrific cheers from the Schoolhouse boys.

"Double your two to one?" says Groove to Rattle, notebook in hand.

"Stop a bit," says that hero, looking uncomfortably at Williams, who is puffing away on his second's knee, winded enough, but little the worse in any other way.

After another round the Slogger, too, seems to see that he can't go in and win right off, and has met his match or thereabouts. So he, too, begins to use his head, and tries to make Tom lose his patience, and come in before his time. And so the fight sways on, now one, and now the other getting a trifling pull.

Tom's face begins to look very one-sided—there are little queer bumps on his forehead, and his mouth is bleeding; but East keeps the wet sponge going so scientifically, that he comes up looking as fresh and bright as ever. Williams is only slightly marked in the face, but by the nervous movement of his elbows you can see that Tom's body blows are telling. In fact, half the vice of the Slogger's hitting is neutralized, for he daren't lunge out freely for fear of exposing his sides. It is too interesting by this time for much shouting, and the whole ring is very quiet.

"All right, Tommy," whispers East; "hold on's the horse that's to win. We've got the last. Keep your head, old boy."

But where is Arthur all this time? Words cannot paint the poor little fellow's distress. He couldn't muster courage to come up to the ring, but wandered up and down from the great fives'-court to the corner of the chapel rails, now trying to make up his mind to throw himself between them, and try to stop them; then thinking of running in and telling his friend, Mary, who he knew would instantly report to the Doctor. The stories he had heard of men being killed in prize fights rose up horribly before him.

Once only, when the shouts of "Well done, Brown!" "Huzza for the Schoolhouse!" rose higher than ever, he ventured up to the ring, thinking the victory was won. Catching sight of Tom's face in the state I have described, all fear of consequences vanishing out of his mind, he rushed straight off to the matron's room, beseeching her to get the fight stopped, or he should die.

But it's time for us to get back to the close. What is this fierce tumult and confusion? The ring is broken, and high and angry words are being bandied about; "It's all fair"—"It isn't"—"No hugging!" the fight is stopped. The combatants, however, sit there quietly, tended by their seconds, while their adherents wrangle in the middle. East can't help shouting challenges to two or three of the other side, though he never leaves Tom for a moment, and plies the sponges as fast as ever.

The fact is, that at the end of the last round, Tom, seeing a good opening, had closed with his opponent, and after a moment's struggle, had thrown him heavily, by help of the fall he had learned from his village rival in the vale of White Horse. Williams hadn't the ghost of a chance with Tom at wrestling; and the conviction broke at once on the Slogger faction, that if this were allowed their man must be licked. There was a strong feeling in the School against catching hold and throwing, though it was generally ruled all fair within limits; so the ring was broken and the fight stopped.

The Schoolhouse are overruled—the fight is on again, but there is to be no throwing; and East in high wrath threatens to take his man away after next round (which he doesn't mean to do, by the way), when suddenly young Brooke comes through the small gate at the end of the chapel. The Schoolhouse faction rush to him. "Oh, hurrah! now we shall get fair play."

"Please, Brooke, come up, they won't let Tom Brown throw him."

"Throw whom?" says Brooke, coming up to the ring. "Oh! Williams, I see! Nonsense! of course he may throw him, if he catches him fairly above the waist."

Now, young Brooke, you're in the sixth, you know, and you ought to stop all fights. He looks hard at both boys. "Anything wrong?" says he to East, nodding at Tom.

"Not a bit."

"Not beat at all?"

"Bless you, no! Heaps of fight in him. Ain't there, Tom?" Tom looks at Brooke and grins.

"How's he?" nodding at Williams.

"So, so; rather done, I think, since his last fall. He won't stand above two more."

"Time's up!" The boys rise again and face one another. Brooke can't find it in his heart to stop them just yet, so the round goes on, the Slogger waiting for Tom, and reserving all his strength to hit him out should he come in for the wrestling dodge again, for he feels that that must be stopped, or his sponge will soon go up in the air.

And now another newcomer appears on the field, to wit, the underporter, with his long brush and great wooden receptacle for dust under his arm. He has been sweeping out the schools.

"You'd better stop, gentlemen," he says; "the Doctor knows that Brown's fighting—he'll be out in a minute."

"You go to Bath, Bill," is all that that excellent servitor gets by his advice. And being a man of his hands, and a staunch upholder of the Schoolhouse, can't help stopping to look on for a bit, and see Tom Brown, their pet craftsman, fight a round.

It is grim earnest now, and no mistake. Both boys feel this, and summon every power of head, hand, and eye to their aid. A piece of luck on either side, a foot slipping, a blow getting well home, or another fall, may decide it. Tom works slowly round for an opening; he has all the legs, and can choose his own time; the Slogger waits for the attack, and hopes to finish it by some heavy right-handed blow. As they quarter slowly over the ground, the evening sun comes out from behind a cloud and falls full on Williams' face. Tom darts in; the heavy right-hand is delivered, but only grazes his head. A short rally at close quarters, and they close; in another moment the Slogger is thrown again heavily for the third time.

"I'll give you three to two on the little one in half-crowns," said Groove to Rattle.

"No thank'ee," answers the other, diving his hands farther into his coat tails.

Just at this stage of the proceedings, the door of the turret which leads to the Doctor's library suddenly opens, and he steps into the close, and makes straight for the ring, in which Brown and the Slogger are both seated on their seconds' knees for the last time.

*It is grim earnest now.*

"The Doctor! the Doctor!" shouts some small boy who catches sight of him, and the ring melts away in a few seconds, the small boys tearing off, Tom collaring his jacket and waistcoat, and slipping through the little gate by the chapel, and round the corner to Harrowell's with his backers, as lively as need be; Williams and his backers making off not quite so fast across the close; Groove, Rattle, and the other bigger fellows trying to combine dignity and prudence in a comical manner, and walking off fast enough, they hope, not to be recognized, and not fast enough to look like running away.

Young Brooke alone remains on the ground by the time the Doctor gets there, and touches his hat, not without a slight inward qualm.

"Hah! Brooke. I am surprised to see you here. Don't you know that I expect the sixth to stop fighting?"

Brooke felt much more uncomfortable than he had expected, but he was rather a favorite with the Doctor for his openness and plainness of speech; so blurted out, as he walked by the Doctor's side, who had already turned back—

"Yes, sir, generally. But I thought you wished us to exercise a discretion in the matter, too—not to interfere too soon."

"But they have been fighting this half-hour and more," said the Doctor.

"Yes, sir; but neither was hurt. And they're the sort of boys who'll be all the better friends now, which they wouldn't have been if they had stopped any earlier—before it was so equal."

"Who was fighting with Brown?" said the Doctor.

"Williams, sir, of Thompson's. He is bigger than Brown, and had the best of it at first, but not when you came up, sir. There's a good deal of jealousy between our house and Thompson's, and there would have been more fights if this hadn't been let go on, or if either of them had had much the worst of it."

"Well, but Brooke," said the Doctor, "doesn't this look a little as if you exercised your discretion by only stopping a fight when the Schoolhouse boy is getting the worst of it?"

Brooke, it must be confessed, felt rather graveled.

"Now remember," added the Doctor, as he stopped at the turret-door, "this fight is not to go on—you'll see to that. And I expect you to stop all fights in future at once."

"Very well, sir," said young Brooke, touching his hat and not sorry to see the turret door close behind the Doctor's back.

# BILLY TOPSAIL AND THE DEVILFISH

### By *NORMAN DUNCAN*

#### *Illustration by Warren Chappell*

W HEN the Minister of Justice for the colony of Newfoundland went away from Ruddy Cove by the bay
steamer, he chanced to leave an American magazine at the home of
Billy Topsail's father, where he had passed the night. The magazine
contained an illustrated article on the gigantic species of cephalopods,
popularly known as devilfish.

Billy Topsail did not know what a cephalopod was; but he did
know a squid when he saw its picture, for Ruddy Cove is a fishing
harbor, and he had caught many a thousand for bait. So when he
found that to the lay mind a squid and a cephalopod were one and
the same, save in size, he read the long article from beginning to end,
doing the best he could with the strange, long words.

So interested was he that he read it again; and by that time he
had learned enough to surprise him, even to terrify him, notwithstanding the writer's assurance that the power and ferocity of the
creatures had generally been exaggerated.

He was a lad of sound common sense. He had never wholly
doubted the tales of desperate encounters with devilfish, told in the
harbor these many years; for the various descriptions of how the
long, slimy arms had curled about the punts had rung too true to be
quite disbelieved; but he had considered them somewhat less credible than certain wild yarns of shipwreck, and somewhat more
credible than the bedtime stories of mermaids which the grand-
mothers told the children of the place.

Here, however, in plain print, was described the capture of a
giant squid in a bay which lay beyond a point of land that Billy
could see from the window.

That afternoon Billy put out in his leaky old punt to "jig" squid for bait. He was so disgusted with the punt—so ashamed of the squat, weather-worn, rotten cast-off—that he wished heartily for a new one all the way to the grounds. The loss of the *Never Give Up* had brought him to humiliating depths.

But when he had once joined the little fleet of boats, he cheerfully threw his grapnel into Bobby Lot's punt and beckoned Bobby aboard. Then, as together they drew the writhing-armed, squirting little squids from the water, he told of the "big squids" which lurked in the deep water beyond the harbor; and all the time Bobby opened his eyes wider and wider.

"Is they just like squids?" Bobby asked.

"But bigger," answered Billy. "Their bodies is so big as hogsheads. Their arms is thirty-five feet long."

Bobby picked a squid from the heap in the bottom of the boat. It had instinctively turned from a reddish-brown to a livid green, the color of sea water; indeed, had it been in the water, its enemy would have had hard work to see it.

He handled it gingerly; but the ugly little creature managed somehow to twine its slender arms about his hand, and swiftly to take hold with a dozen cuplike suckers. The boy uttered an exclamation of disgust, and shook it off. Then he shuddered, laughed at himself, shuddered again. A moment later he chose a dead squid for examination.

"Leave us look at it close," said he. "Then we'll know what a real devilfish is like. Sure, I've been wantin' to know that for a long, long time."

They observed the long, cylindrical body, flabby and cold, with the broad, flaplike tail attached. The head was repulsively ugly—perhaps because of the eyes, which were disproportionately large, brilliant, and, in the live squid, ferocious.

A group of arms—two long, slender, tentacular arms, and eight shorter, thicker ones—projected from the region of the mouth, which, indeed, was set in the center of the ring they formed at the roots. They were equipped with innumerable little suckers, were flexible and active, and as long as the head, body and tail put together.

Closer examination revealed that there was a horny beak, like a parrot's, in the mouth, and that on the under side of the head was a curious tube-like structure.

"Oh, that's his squirter!" Billy explained. "When he wants to back up he points that forward, and squirts out water so hard as he can, and when he wants to go ahead he points it backward, and does the same thing. That's where his ink comes from, too, when he wants to make the water so dirty nobody can see him."

"What does he do with his beak?"

"When he gets his food in his arms he bites out pieces with his beak. He hasn't any teeth; but he's got something just as good—a tongue like a rasp."

"I wouldn't like to be cotched by a squid as big as a hogshead," Bobby remarked, timidly.

"Hut!" said Billy, grimly. "He'd make short work o' *you!* Why, b'y, they weighs half a ton apiece! I isn't much afraid, though," he added. "They're only squid. Afore I read about them in the book I used to think they was worse than they is—terrible ghostlike things. But they're no worse than squids, only bigger, and—"

"They're bad enough for *me,*" Bobby interrupted.

"And," Billy concluded, "they only comes up in the night or when they're sore wounded and dyin'."

"I'm not goin' out at night, if I can help it," said Bobby, with a canny shake of the head.

"If they was a big squid come up the harbor to your house," said Billy, after a pause, "and got close to the rock, he could put one o' they two long arms in your bedroom window, and—"

"'Tis in the attic!"

"Never mind that. He could put it in the window and feel around for your bed, and twist that arm around you, and—"

"I'd cut it off!"

"Anyhow, that's how long they is. And if he knowed you was there, and wanted you, he could get you. But I'm not so sure that he *would* want you. He couldn't see you, anyhow; and if he could, he'd rather have a good fat salmon."

Bobby shuddered as he looked at the tiny squid in his hand, and thought of the dreadful possibilities in one a thousand times as big.

"You leave them alone, and they'll leave you alone," Billy went on. "But if you once make them mad, they can dart their arms out like lightning. 'Tis time to get, then!"

"I'm goin' to keep an axe in my punt after this," said Bobby, "and if I sees an arm slippin' out of the water—"

"'Tis as big as your thigh!" cried Billy.

"Never mind. If I sees it I'll be able to cut it off."

"If I sees one," said Billy, "I'm goin' to cotch it. It said in the book that they was worth a lot to some people. And if I can sell mine I'm goin' to have a new punt."

But although Bobby Lot and Billy Topsail kept a sharp lookout for giant squids wherever they went, they were not rewarded. There was not so much as a sign of one. By and by, so bold did they become, they hunted for one in the twilight of summer days, even daring to pry into the deepest coves and holes in the Ruddy Cove rocks.

Notwithstanding the ridicule he had to meet, Bobby never ventured out in the punt without a sharp ax. He could not tell what time he would need it, he said; and thus he formed the habit of making sure that it was in its place before casting off from the wharf.

As autumn drew near they found other things to think of; the big squids passed out of mind altogether.

"Wonderful queer," Billy said, long afterwards, "how things happen when you isn't expectin' them!"

One day late in September—it was near evening of a gray day—Billy Topsail and Bobby Lot were returning in Bobby's punt from Birds' Nest Islands, whither they had gone to hunt a group of seals, reported to have taken up a temporary residence there. They had a mighty, muzzle-loading, flintlock gun; and they were so delighted with the noise it made that they had exhausted their scanty provision of powder and lead long before the seals were in sight.

They had taken the shortest way home. It lay past Chain Hole, a small, landlocked basin, very deep, with a narrow entrance, which was shallow at low tide. The entrance opened into a broad bay, and was called Chain Tickle.

"What's that in the tickle?" Billy exclaimed, as they were rowing past.

It was a black object, apparently floating quietly on the surface of the water. The boys gazed at it for a long time, but could make nothing of it. They were completely puzzled.

"'Tis a small bit o' wreck, I'm thinkin'," said Bobby. "Leave us row close and see."

"Maybe 'tis a capsized punt."

When they were within about thirty yards of the object they lay on their oars. For some unaccountable reason they did not care to venture nearer. Twilight was then fast approaching. The light was already beginning to fail.

"'Tis a wonderful queer thing!" Billy muttered, his curiosity getting the better of him. "Row ahead, Bobby. We'll go alongside."

"They's something movin' on it!" Bobby whispered, as he let his oars fall in the water. "Look! They's two queer, big, round spots on it—big as plates."

Billy thought he saw the whole object move. He watched it closely. It *did* stir! It was some living thing, then. But what? A whale?

A long, snakelike arm was lifted out of the water. It swayed this way and that, darted here and there, and fell back with a splash. The moving spots, now plainly gigantic eyes, glittered.

"'Tis the devilfish!" screamed Bobby.

Another arm was lifted up, then a third and a fourth and a fifth. The monster began to lash the water—faster and yet more furiously —until the tickle was heaving and frothy, and the whole neighborhood was in an uproar.

"Pull! Pull!" cried Bobby.

Billy, too, was in a panic. They turned the head of the punt and pulled with all their might. The water swirled in the wake of the boat. Perceiving, however, that the squid made no effort to follow, they got the better of their fright. Then they lay on their oars to watch the monster.

They wondered why it still lay in the tickle, why it so furiously lashed the water with its arms and great tail. It was Bobby who solved the mystery.

" 'Tis aground," said he.

That was evidently the situation. The squid had been caught in the shallow tickle when the tide, which ran swiftly at that point, was on the ebb. The boys took courage. Their curiosity still further emboldened them. So once more they turned the punt about and pulled cautiously toward the tickle.

There was less light than before, but still sufficient to disclose the baleful eyes and writhing arms of the squid when the boat was yet a safe distance away. One by one the arms fell back into the water, as if from exhaustion; slowly the beating of the tail subsided. After a time all sound and motion ceased. The boys waited for some further sign of life, but none came. The squid was still, as if dead.

"Sure, he's dead now," said Billy. "Leave us pull close up."

"Oh, no, b'y! He's but making believe."

But Billy thought otherwise. "I wants that squid," he said, in a dogged way, "and I'm goin' to have him. I'll sell him and get a new punt."

Bobby protested in vain. Nothing would content Billy Topsail but the possession of the big squid's body. Bobby pointed out that if the long powerful arms were once laid on the boat there would be no escape. He recalled to Billy the harbor story of the horrible death of Zachariah North, who, as report said, had been pursued, captured and pulled under water by a devilfish in Gander Bay.[1]

It was all to no purpose, however, for Billy obstinately declared that he would make sure of the squid before the tide turned. He admitted a slight risk, but he wanted a new punt, and he was willing to risk something to obtain it.

He proposed to put Bobby ashore, and approach the squid alone; but Bobby would not listen. Two hands might be needed in the boat, he said. What if the squid were alive, after all? What if it laid hold of the punt? In that event, two hands would surely be needed.

[1] Stories of this kind, of which there are many, are doubted by the authorities, who have found it impossible to authenticate a single instance of unprovoked attack.

"I'll go," he said. "But leave us pull slow. And if we sees so much as a wink of his eye we'll pull away."

They rowed nearer, with great caution. Billy was in the bow of the boat. It was he who had the ax. Bobby, seated amidships, faced the bow. It was he who did the rowing.

The squid was quiet. There was not a sign of life about it. Billy estimated the length of its body, from the beak to the point of the tail, as twenty feet, the circumference as "the size of a hogshead." Its tentacular arms, he determined, must be at least thirty-five feet long; and when the boat came within that distance he shuddered.

"Is you sure he's dead?" Bobby whispered, weakly.

"I don't know!" Billy answered, in a gasp. "I think so."

Bobby dropped the oars and stepped to the bow of the punt. The boat lost way and came to a stop within twenty feet of the squid. Still there was no sign of life.

The boys stared at the great, still body, lying quiet in the gathering dusk and haze. Neither seemed to feel the slight trembling of the boat that might have warned them. Not a word was spoken until Billy, in a whisper, directed Bobby to pull the boat a few feet nearer.

"But we're movin' already," he added, in a puzzled way.

The boat was very slowly approaching the squid. The motion was hardly perceptible, but it was real.

" 'Tis queer!" said Bobby.

He turned to take up the oars. What he saw lying over the port gunwale of the boat made him gasp, grip Billy's wrist and utter a scream of terror!

"We're cotched!"

The squid had fastened one of its tentacles to the punt. The other was poised above the stern, ready to fall and fix its suckers. The onward movement of the punt was explained.

Billy knew the danger, but he was not so terrified as to be incapable of action. He was about to spring to the stern to strike off the tentacle that already lay over the gunwale; but as he looked down to choose his step he saw that one of the eight powerful arms was slowly creeping over the starboard bow.

He struck at that arm with all his might, missed, wrenched the ax from the gunwale, and struck true. The mutilated arm was withdrawn. Billy leaped to the stern, vaguely conscious in passing that another arm was creeping from the water. He severed the first tentacle with one blow. When he turned to strike the second it had

*Warren Chappell*
*The monster began to lash the water.*

disappeared; so, too, had the second arm. The boat seemed to be free, but it was still within grasp.

In the meantime the squid had awakened to furious activity. It was lashing the water with arms and tail, angrily snapping its great beak and ejecting streams of black water from its siphon-tube. The water was violently agitated and covered with a black froth.

In this the creature manifested fear and distress. Had it not been aground it would have backed swiftly into the deep water of the basin. But, as if finding itself at bay, it lifted its uninjured tentacle high above the boat. Billy made ready to strike.

By this time Bobby had mastered his terror. While Billy stood with uplifted ax, his eyes fixed on the waving tentacle overhead, Billy heaved mightily on the oars. The boat slowly drew away from that highly dangerous neighborhood. In a moment it was beyond reach of the arms, but, still, apparently, within reach of the tentacle. The tentacle was withdrawn a short distance; then like a flash it shot toward the boat, writhing as it came.

Billy struck blindly—and struck nothing. The tentacle had fallen short. The boat was out of danger!

But still Billy Topsail was determined to have the body of the squid. Notwithstanding Bobby's pleading and protestation, he would not abandon his purpose. He was only the more grimly bent on achieving it. Bobby would not hear of again approaching nearer than the boat then floated, nor did Billy think it advisable. But it occurred to Bobby that they might land, and approach the squid from behind. If they could draw near enough, he said, they could cast the grapnel on the squid's back, and moor it to a tree ashore.

"Sure," he said, excitedly, "you can pick up a squid from behind, and it can't touch you with its arms! It won't be able to see us, and it won't be able to reach us."

So they landed. Billy carried the grapnel, which was attached to twelve fathoms of line. It had six prongs, and each prong was barbed.

A low cliff at the edge of the tickle favored the plan. The squid lay below, and some twenty feet out from the rock. It was merely a question of whether or not Billy was strong enough to throw the grapnel so far. They tied the end of the line to a stout shrub. Billy cast the grapnel, and it was a strong, true cast. The iron fell fair on the squid's back. It was a capture.

"That means a new punt for me," said Billy, quietly. "The tide'll not carry *that* devilfish away."

"And now," Bobby pleaded, "leave us make haste home, for 'tis growin' wonderful dark—and—and there might be another somewhere."

So that is how one of the largest specimens of *Architeuthis princeps*—enumerated in Prof. John Adam Wright's latest monograph on the cephalopods of North America as the "Chain Tickle specimen"—was captured. And that is how Billy Topsail fairly won a new punt; for when Doctor Marvey, the curator of the Public Museum at St. John's—who is deeply interested in the study of the giant squids—came to Ruddy Cove to make photographs and take measurements, in response to a message from Billy's father, he rewarded the lad.

# THE TWO-TWENTY LOW HURDLE RACE

From "The Human Comedy"

*By WILLIAM SAROYAN*

T HE boys' athletic coach of Ithaca High School stood in the office of the principal of Ithaca High School—a man whose last name was Ek, a circumstance duly reported by Mr. Robert Ripley in a daily newspaper cartoon entitled "Believe It or Not." Mr. Ek's first name was Oscar, and not worthy of notice.

"Miss Hicks," the principal of Ithaca High School said to the coach of Ithaca High School, "is the oldest and by far the best teacher we have ever had at this school. She was *my* teacher when I attended Ithaca High School and she was your teacher, too, Mr. Byfield. I'm afraid I wouldn't care to go over her head about punishing a couple of unruly boys."

"Hubert Ackley the Third is *not* an unruly boy," the coach said. "Homer Macauley—yes. Hubert Ackley—no. He is a perfect little gentleman."

"Yes," the principal said, "Hubert Ackley *does* come from a well-to-do family. But if Miss Hicks has asked him to stay in after school, then *in* it is. He *is* a perfect little gentleman, no doubt. His *father* was, I remember. Perfect—perfect. But Miss Hicks is the teacher of the ancient history class and she has never been known to punish anyone who has not deserved to be punished. Hubert Ackley will have to be satisfied to run the race some other time."

The matter was surely closed now, the principal felt. The coach turned and left the office. He did not go to the athletic field, however. He went to the ancient history classroom instead. There he found Homer and Hubert and Miss Hicks. He bowed to the old teacher and smiled.

"Miss Hicks," he said, "I have spoken to Mr. Ek about this

matter." The implication of his remark was that he had been given authorization to come and liberate Hubert Ackley III. Homer Macauley, however, leaped to his feet as it were *he* who was to be liberated.

"Not *you*," the coach said with a tone of contempt. He turned to the other boy and said, "Mr. Ackley."

"What do you mean?" the ancient-history teacher said.

"Mr. Ackley," the coach said, "is to get into his track suit immediately and run the two-twenty low hurdles. We're waiting for him."

"Oh, yeah?" Homer said. He was overflowing with righteous indignation. "Well," he said, "what about *me—Mr. Macauley?*" There was no reply from the coach, who walked out of the room followed by a somewhat troubled and confused young man—Hubert Ackley III.

"Did you see that, Miss Hicks?" Homer Macauley shouted. "Is that special privilege or not?"

The ancient-history teacher was so upset by what had happened that she could barely speak.

"Mr. Byfield," she whispered softly, "is fitted to teach athletics only to jackasses like himself." She paused to observe the unworthiness of her remark. "I'm sorry," she said. "But the man is not only ignorant, he is a liar!" It was delightful to see Miss Hicks with so much natural and uncontrollable bitterness. It made Homer feel that she was just about the best teacher ever.

"I never did like him," Homer said. "It sure is good to know that you don't like him either."

"I have taught ancient history at Ithaca High School thirty-five years," Miss Hicks said. "I have been the school mother of hundreds of Ithaca boys and girls. I taught your brother Marcus and your sister Bess, and if you have younger brothers or sisters at home I shall some day teach them, too."

"Just a brother, Miss Hicks," Homer said. "His name is Ulysses. How was Marcus in school?"

"Marcus and Bess," Miss Hicks said, "were both good—honest and civilized. Yes," she said, *"civilized,"* and she emphasized the word very carefully. "The behavior of ancient peoples had made them civilized from birth. Like yourself, Marcus sometimes spoke out of turn, but he was never a liar. Now these inferior human beings, these Byfields of the world who were never anything but fools—they think of me as an old woman. He came here and deliberately lied to me—just as he had lied to me time and again when he sat in this classroom as a boy. He has learned nothing except to toady shamelessly to those he feels are superior."

"Yeah?" Homer said, urging the ancient-history teacher to go on with her criticism.

"I have seen better men pushed around by his kind," she said. "The kind who go through life lying and cheating and crowding out men who are above such behavior. The two-twenty low hurdles! *Low* indeed!" The ancient-history teacher was terribly hurt. She blew her nose and wiped her eyes.

"Ah, don't feel bad, Miss Hicks," Homer said. "I'll stay in. You can punish me for talking out of turn. I guess I've got it coming, but from now on I'm going to try to be good. I never did know that teachers are human beings like anybody else—and *better,* too! It's all right, Miss Hicks. You can punish me."

"I didn't keep you in to punish you, Homer Macauley," the ancient-history teacher said. "I have always kept in only those who have meant the most to me—I have kept them in to be nearer them. I still do not believe I am mistaken about Hubert Ackley. It was Mr. Byfield who made him disobey me. I was going to send both of you to the field after a moment, anyway. You were not kept in for punishment, but for education. I watch the growth of spirit in the children who come to my class, and I am made happy by every fresh evidence of that growth. You apologized to Hubert Ackley, and even though it embarrassed him to do so, because your apology made him unworthy, he graciously accepted your apology. I kept you in after school because I wanted to talk to both of you— one of you from a good well-to-do family, the other from a good poor family. Getting along in this world will be even more difficult for him than for you. I wanted you to know one another a little better. It is very important. I wanted to talk to *both* of you."

"I guess I like Hubert," Homer said, "only he seems to think he is better than the other boys."

"Yes, I know," the ancient-history teacher said. "I know how you feel, but every man in the world *is* better than someone else, and not as good as someone *else*. Joe Terranova is brighter than Hubert, but Hubert is just as honest in his own way. In a democratic state every man is the equal of every other man up to the point of exertion, and after that every man is free to exert himself to do good or not, to grow nobly or foolishly, as he wishes. I am eager for my boys and girls to exert themselves to do good and to grow nobly. What my children *appear* to be on the surface is no matter to me. I am fooled neither by gracious manners nor by bad manners. I am interested in what is truly beneath each kind of manners. Whether one of my children is rich or poor, Catholic or Protestant or Jew, white or black or yellow, brilliant or slow, genius or simple-minded, is no matter to me, if there is humanity in him—if he has a heart— if he loves truth and honor—if he respects his inferiors and loves his superiors. If the children of my classroom are human, I do not want them to be alike in their *manner* of being human. If they are not corrupt, it does not matter to me how they differ from one another. I want each of my children to be himself. I don't want you, Homer, to be like somebody else just to please me or to make my work easier. I would soon be weary of a classroom full of perfect little ladies and gentlemen. I want my children to be *people*—each one separate—each one special—each one a pleasant and exciting variation of all the others. I wanted Hubert Ackley here to listen to this with you—to understand with you that if at the present you do not like him and he does not like you, that is perfectly natural. I wanted him to know that each of you will begin to be truly human when, in spite of your natural dislike of one another, you still respect one another. That is what it means to be civilized—that is what we are to learn from a study of ancient history." The teacher stopped now for a moment and looked at the boy who, for some reason that even he could not understand, was on the verge of tears.

"I'm glad I've spoken to you," she said, "rather than to anyone else I know. When you leave this school—long after you have forgotten *me*—I shall be watching for you in the world, and I shall never be startled by the good things I know you shall do." The ancient-history teacher blew her nose again and touched her handkerchief to her eyes. "Run along to the athletic field," she said. "Race against Hubert Ackley in the two-twenty low hurdles. If there isn't time to change to your track clothes, run as you are, even if everybody laughs at you. Before you go very far along in the world, you will hear laughter many times, and not the laughter of men alone, but the mocking laughter of things themselves seeking to embarrass and hold you back—but I know you will pay no attention to that laughter." The teacher sighed and said wearily, "Run along to the field, Homer Macauley. I shall be watching." The second son of the Macauley family of Santa Clara Avenue in Ithaca, California, turned and walked out of the room.

On the athletic field Hubert Ackley and the three boys who had already raced with him that day were taking their places in the lanes for the two-twenty low hurdle race. Homer reached the fifth lane just as the man with the pistol lifted his arm to start the race. Homer went to his mark with the others. He felt very good, but also very angry, and he believed that nothing in the world would be able to keep him from winning this race—the wrong kind of shoes, the wrong kind of clothes for running, no practice, or anything else. He would just naturally win the race.

Hubert Ackley, in the lane next to Homer's lane, turned to him and said, "*You* can't run this race—like *that*."

"No?" Homer said. "Wait and see."

Mr. Byfield, sitting in the grandstand, turned to the man next to him and said, "Who's that starting in the outside lane without track clothes?" Then he remembered who it was.

He decided to stop the race so that he could remove the fifth runner, but it was too late. The gun had been fired and the runners were running. Homer and Hubert took the first hurdle a little ahead of the others, each of them clearing nicely. Homer moved a little forward ahead of Hubert on the second hurdle and kept moving forward on the third, fourth, fifth, sixth, seventh and eighth hurdles. But close behind him was Hubert Ackley. The two boys exchanged words as they ran. On the first hurdle Hubert shouted, "Where did you learn to run like that?"

"Nowhere," Homer said. "I'm learning *now*."

On the second hurdle, Hubert said, "What's the hurry? You're going too fast."

"I'm going to win the race," Homer said.

On the third hurdle Ackley said, "Who said so?"

And on the fourth hurdle Homer said, "*I* said so."

On the fifth hurdle Hubert said, "Slow down. This is a long race. You'll get tired." And then suddenly he shouted, "Oh—oh, look out! Here comes Byfield!"

Homer reached the ninth hurdle exactly when the coach of Ithaca High School reached it, coming in the opposite direction. Nevertheless, Homer hurdled. He hurdled straight into the open arms of the athletic coach and the man and the boy fell to the ground. Hubert Ackley stopped running and turned to the other runners. "Stay where you are," he shouted. "Let him get up. He's running a good race, and he's had interference." Homer got to his feet quickly and went on running. The instant he started, the others started running also.

Everyone in the grandstand, even Helen Eliot, was amazed at what was happening in the race. Now the ancient-history teacher, Miss Hicks, was at the finish line of the race. She was cheering, but she was cheering for *each* of the boys.

"Come on, Homer!" she said. "Come on, Hubert! Hurry, Sam!—George!—Henry!"

At the next to the last hurdle Hubert Ackley caught up with Homer Macauley. "Sorry," he said, "I've got to do it."

"Go ahead," Homer said, "if you can."

Hubert Ackley ran a little in front of Homer and there was no longer far to go. Homer didn't clear the last hurdle, but he almost caught up with the front runner. The finish of the race was so close no one could tell whether Hubert Ackley won or whether Homer Macauley won. Sam, George and Henry came in soon after, and Miss Hicks, the ancient-history teacher, brought them all together.

"You ran beautifully," she said, "every one of you!"

"I'm sorry," Hubert Ackley said, "Miss Hicks. I should have stayed in, with Homer."

"It's all right now," Miss Hicks said, "and it was good of you to wait for Homer to get up when he was interfered with."

Furious and bitter and a little shocked by the fall he had taken, the coach of Ithaca High School came running toward the group which Miss Hicks had gathered around her.

"Macauley!" he shouted from a distance of fifteen yards. "For the remainder of this semester," he said, "for what you have just done, you are deprived of the privilege of taking part in any school sport activities."

The coach reached the group and stood glaring at Homer Macauley. The ancient-history teacher turned to him.

"Mr. Byfield," she said, "why are you punishing Homer Macauley?"

"Excuse me, Miss Hicks," the coach said. "I will make my decisions without any assistance from the ancient history department." He turned to Homer and said, "Do you understand?"

"Yes, sir," Homer said.

"Now go to my office and stay there until I tell you to go," Byfield said.

"Your office," Homer said. "But I've got to go—" He suddenly remembered that he had to be at work at four o'clock. "What time is it?" he said.

Hubert Ackley looked at his wrist watch. "It's a quarter to four," he said.

"Go to my office!" Byfield shouted.

"But you don't understand, Mr. Byfield," Homer said. "I've got some place to go. I'll be late."

Joe Terranova came into the group. "Why should he stay after school?" Joe said. "He didn't do anything wrong."

The coach had already suffered too much. "You keep your dirty little wop mouth shut!" he shouted at Joe. Then he pushed the boy, who went sprawling. But before he had touched the ground, Joe Terranova shouted: "w-o-p?"

Homer tackled Mr. Byfield as if they were on a football field, at the same time saying, "You can't call a friend of mine names."

By the time Homer and Byfield were on the ground again, Joe Terranova was on his feet. In a fury he leaped on Byfield so that the man sprawled all over the place. The principal of the school, Mr. Ek, came running, breathless and bewildered.

"Gentlemen!" he said. "Boys, boys!" He dragged Joe Terranova off the athletic coach, who did not get to his feet.

"Mr. Byfield," the principal of the school said, "what is the meaning of this unusual behavior?"

Speechless, Byfield pointed to Miss Hicks.

Miss Hicks stood above the man. "I've told you many times, Mr. Byfield, not to push people around," she said. "They don't like it." She turned to the principal of the school. "Mr. Byfield," she said, "owes Joe Terranova an apology."

"Is that so? Is that so, Mr. Byfield?" Mr. Ek said.

"Joe's people are from Italy," Miss Hicks said. "They are not, however, to be referred to as wops."

Joe Terranova said, "He doesn't need to apologize to me. If he calls me names, I'll bust him in the mouth. If he beats me up, I'll get my brothers."

"Joseph!" Miss Hicks said. "You must allow Mr. Byfield to apologize. He is not apologizing to you or to your people. He is apologizing to our own country. You must give him the privilege of once again trying to be an American."

"Yes, that's so," the principal of the school said. "This is America, and the only foreigners here are those who forget that this *is* America." He turned to the man who was still sprawled on the ground. "Mr. Byfield," he commanded.

The athletic coach of Ithaca High School got to his feet. To no one in particular he said, "I apologize," and hurried away.

Joe Terranova and Homer Macauley went off together. Joe walked well, but Homer limped. He had hurt his left leg when Byfield had tried to stop him.

Miss Hicks and Mr. Ek turned to the thirty or forty boys and girls gathered around. They were of many types and many nationalities.

"All right, now," Miss Hicks said. "Go along home to your families," and as the children were all a little bewildered, she added, "Brighten up, brighten up—don't be so upset. This is nothing."

"Yes," the principal of the school said, "brighten up. The War isn't going to last forever."

The children broke up into groups and walked away.

# HEAD OVER HEELS

*By B. J. CHUTE*

*Illustration by Tom Hall*

WOODY RIDGWAY dashed madly down the corridor of Macalester High School, rounded a corner with express-train speed, and crashed into another student who loomed up suddenly from the opposite direction.

Woody's carefully balanced pile of books teetered, tottered, and tumbled, sailing in all directions. He glared resentfully at the cause of their downfall, then said, "Oh, it's you," without enthusiasm, and got down on all fours to retrieve his scattered belongings.

"Sure, it's me." Speed Foster gazed down from his superior six-foot height with benign amusement. "Where were you going so fast? We'll have to get you for the track team." He then added "Ha, ha," to indicate that this was a rare and remarkable joke, and Woody looked up from his task with dark disapproval. Speed bent down and picked up a particularly heavy volume, turning it over in his hands. *"Socrates and His Influence,"* he read. "What do you want to read stuff like that for?"

"I'm giving a talk on Socrates to the Study Club," said Woody, getting to his feet with as much dignity as could be achieved behind a wavering pile of books.

This remark seemed to furnish Speed with a great deal of simple entertainment. "Study Club!" he snorted. "That bunch of cream puffs! You should join up with the Athletic Club and really do something worth while for once in your life."

"Phooey," said Woody, aware that this was a hopelessly inadequate retort but unable at the moment to think of anything better. "That bunch of muscle-bound mooses." He paused. "Or is it meese?"

"Muscle-bound!" Speed howled. "I like that! At least we don't stew around with our noses in books, and at least we get somewhere."

"Come up sometime and see my collection of trophies," said Woody, with quotes around his voice.

"Well, what's wrong with winning cups?" Speed demanded in an injured voice. "You're just jealous because you can't do it yourself. And, what's more, I'm going to be adding another one next week."

"Do tell," said Woody politely.

"I'm going to win the Ski Race."

"What ski race?"

"There you are," said Speed triumphantly. "That's typical. *What* ski race! Everyone in school knows about it, except you and that bunch of dodoes you call a Study Club. It's an obstacle race, shrimp—"

"Don't call me shrimp," said Woody, shifting Socrates to the other arm.

Speed ignored the request. "And every organization in school has entered someone—except, of course, the Great Study Club. There's two small silver cups being given for the Beginners and Intermediate races, and a big silver cup for the Experts. That's the one I'm going to win," he added comfortably. "And then I'm going to present it to the Athletic Club. What did your bunch of grinds ever do?"

"We could win cups, too, if we wanted to," said Woody hotly. "We just don't want to. Brains can beat brawn every time."

"Ha," said Speed. "Ha, ha."

Some lurking common sense in Woody warned him that this was the time to walk away and leave Speed in possession of the field, but the series of insults to his beloved Club was too much. "If one of us wanted to enter that silly race of yours," said Woody, jumping in with both feet and no overshoes, "we could win it in a walk."

A glint came into Speed's eye. "If you're so sure brains are superior to brawn," said Speed with a nasty chortle, "why don't you sign up?"

"I will," said Woody, without thinking.

"Splendid." The glint became brighter as Speed envisoned some good fun at Woody's expense. "Come along with me, and we'll get your name on the dotted line right now." He seized Woody's elbow, imperiling Socrates, and Woody pulled back.

His common sense was rearing its head again, after a brief vacation. "What's the hurry?" he said unhappily, suddenly aware of the dismal fact that he had never been on a ski in his life. "The race isn't for quite a while, is it?"

"A week from Friday," said Speed cheerily. "Come on. The office is right around the corner, and you can sign up there."

He dragged the protesting Woody along, and propped him up against the office counter with a pen in his hand. "You sign in whatever class you enter. Beginners for you, of course."

"Beginners nothing!" snapped Woody. "By the time I've put my mind to skiing, I'll be an expert. The whole Study Club will help me, what's more, and you can't beat that combination."

"You can't sign as an expert," Speed objected. "You've never raced before. You have to have raced at least once, even to be in the Intermediate Class."

"All right, then," said Woody superbly. "I'll sign up for all three classes. By the time I've run in the beginners I'll be eligible for the Intermediate, and as soon as I've run in that I'll be eligible for the Experts. What's wrong with that?"

"But the classes are run one right after another," Speed protested, aghast. "You can't do that."

"Why can't I?" said Woody. "I don't see anything against it in the rules." He signed his name with a flourish in all three classes, then gave Speed a sweet smile. "What's the trouble? Afraid I'll beat you?"

Satisfied with this retort, he picked up his books and waltzed merrily out of the office, but by the time he had walked ten feet he had an attack of realism and the smile left his face.

"Oh, golly!" Woody wailed, and ran madly down the hall in the direction of the Study Club's meeting room, bursting in upon his startled clubmates with the fearful news that he had entered the Skiing Race and that the honor of the Study Club was at stake.

Socrates was forgotten as the Club rallied round.

"You can't possibly back out now," the president, Bob Bryant, assured him. "But don't worry. We're behind you to a man. After all, anyone can learn to ski."

"You wouldn't like to take my place, would you?" Woody offered hopefully, but Bob shook his head.

"It's your Destiny," said Bob solemnly. "You have struck a great blow for the Club, and—as to learning to ski—that's perfectly simple. You can get books on the subject." He considered the problem for a moment. "I'll appoint a committee to study it up and teach you how to ski. Myself and—uh'm—Pat Marshall. The race is as good as won. It's merely a matter of applied intelligence.

At five-thirty the next morning, ignoring Woody's pitiful protests, Bob and Pat began to apply intelligence. They routed him out of his warm and cozy bed and herded him into a skiing outfit that reminded him irresistibly of an Arctic explorer.

"Where'd you get the money for this?" he demanded, trying to wedge his foot and three heavy socks into a skiing boot.

"We rented the outfit," Pat told him, "with money from the Club treasury."

Woody's gloom deepened. He was chairman of the Finance Committee. "I don't need all this stuff," he mourned.

"Your outfit," said Bob with gentle reproach, "is completely scientific. We added up everything all the skiing books said, divided by two, subtracted an ice axe which you probably won't need, and this is the result. Did you get the wax, Pat?"

"Wax!" Woody yelped. "What's wax for?"

"You put it on your skis to make you go faster."

"But I don't want to go faster. I don't want wax—I want glue. Are you sure you read the books right?"

"Relax," said Bob, with utter calmness.

It was cold out and the snow was powdery and fast, which pleased the committee but depressed Woody.

Bob produced a stack of books on skiing, and opened one with a judicial air. "Now," he said, "this is very simple. You're supposed to start on level ground, but, as you only have a week to learn and most of the race will be up and down hill, we'll omit that and start with a hill right away."

They permitted him to walk on foot to the top of the hill, then fastened him into his skis, pressed his poles into his hands, and stood back at a safe distance.

"Carry your poles behind you," said Bob, reading directions earnestly, "the body relaxed and the knees bent, with skis as close together as possible."

Woody heaved a deep sigh, peered nervously at the small hill, and gave himself a delicate shove. He progressed eighteen inches, wailed, and sat down backwards in the snow. Bob and Pat looked at each other in faint surprise, and then referred to their books.

"I don't think your knees were bent properly," Bob offered.

"And it says here that you should balance on the *balls* of the feet," Pat added helpfully.

"The balls of my feet," said Woody bitterly, "rolled right out from under me. Somebody help me up."

They pulled him to his feet and brushed off one or two layers of snow, murmuring words of comfort and encouragement.

"There now," said Bob, when he was finally reassembled. "Try it again. Remember to crouch, carry your poles back, bend your arms at the elbows, balance on the balls of your feet, keep the skis close together—"

"—plow the potato patch and put the cat out," Woody finished sardonically. "I know." He looked at the hill again, looked at his companions, and then insisted on shaking hands all around as a farewell gesture. "In case I don't see you again," he explained, then closed his eyes, set his teeth, and gave himself a shove.

"Why, that's colossal!" Pat applauded as Woody vanished over the brow of the hill, weaving unsteadily but miraculously upright. "In a week's time he'll be able to lick Speed with one foot tied behind his back and both hands—Oh, oh!"

A respectful hush fell on the watching committee, then Bob said, "I think his mistake was in trying to go round both sides of that tree at once. Maybe we'd better go and collect him."

They dashed halfway down the hill to where Woody and the tree had come to grips, and regarded their fallen comrade with solemn concern. Woody was flat on his back, his cap over one eye, his left ski pointing at the sky and the other wound affectionately around the tree trunk. He was saying something, and although the words were inaudible, the general impression seemed to be that he was vexed.

"Maybe we should unwrap him," said Bob. "You start with that ski there, Pat, and we'll work counter-clockwise."

Pat took hold of the nearest ski, and addressed Woody encouragingly. "That was fine as far as it went," he said brightly. "You had the crouch position splendidly."

The fallen warrior got the snow out of his mouth and his voice back. "Crouch," he echoed hollowly. "That was no crouch. That was complete collapse. Take me home."

They hauled him to his feet, moaning pathetically and trying to dig snow out from down his neck, and Bob told him that it had been a stirring performance and they were proud of him and that now he could go back and try it again.

"Again!" Woody screamed. "You mean, go down a hill like that again at two hundred miles an hour—"

"Schuss," said Bob.

"I will not shush," said Woody passionately. "I have a right to my opinions. I have certain inalienable constitutional rights, and I will *not* be shushed."

"I didn't say shush, I said schuss. It means going downhill straight at a great speed, and it's the mark of a fine skier."

In spite of his boner Woody looked gratified. "Fine skier, huh? That should show Speed a thing or two."

"Certainly," Bob and Pat agreed in chorus.

"Why in no time at all," said Bob, "you'll be doing stem turns and high jumps. It just shows the advantages of applying intelligence to a sport. Laugh at the Study Club, will he? Come on, Woody. We'll do that hill again."

"*We?*" said Woody feebly. "What a sense of humor *you've* got."

"And this time be careful of that tree."

"You tell that tree to be careful of me," said Woody with feeling.

"We'll teach you the turns," said Bob brightly, "and then you can go around trees, instead of through them. You'll need turns in the race, you know—it's nothing but obstacles."

"I know," said Woody, turning pale.

"Don't worry," Bob reassured him. "By that time you'll be able to do turns, standing on your head."

"That," said Woody, thinking about the tree episode, "is just what I'm afraid of."

The night before the skiing race, Woody crawled out of bed, at two A.M., pulled on his ski boots over his bare feet, fastened himself into his skiis, and proceeded to practice the kick turn in the middle of his room.

The first thing to go was the student lamp on his desk, and Woody, half through the turn, with one foot going south and the other going north, was unable to save a small table from following it. The resulting crash was impressive, and he would gladly have leaped back into bed, pulled the covers well up and pretended the whole thing had never happened, but, unfortunately, he suddenly realized that he had forgotten how to complete the turn.

Not wanting to spend the night in the middle of the floor with his feet being rugged individualists, he made a violent effort to raise his right ski, snarled the counterpane with the tip of it, and went over backwards with the evening's third—and best—crash.

This episode darkened his outlook considerably, and he arrived at the race that afternoon with serious misgivings but a powerful determination to show up Speed Foster.

The Study Club was out in full force to watch their representative surge on to victory, and as the contestants lined up they raised a mighty cheer. A moment later they were also obliged to raise their representative, as Woody skidded on an icy patch and sprawled full length.

Speed Foster, who was lounging around in a skillful way on his skis, laughed merrily. "Look what thinks it's going to win the Experts race," he remarked. "Applied intellect! That wasn't your intellect you applied to the snow, Woody. That was your nose." He then laughed heartily at his own joke and was echoed by his fellow members of the Athletic Club, who were delighted at the spectacle of one of the intellectual, fireside-hugging Study Clubbers competing with the great Foster.

The judge said, "Are you ready?" before Woody could think of a snappy retort, and a second later the whistle blew for the Beginners race.

It took Woody less than sixty seconds to realize what he had let himself in for. The course was nearly two miles long, over rough country, up hill and down, with a series of obstacles scattered at inconvenient intervals. Woody's natural and perfectly sound instinct was to go around these, but the officials had thought of that first and the course was circumscribed by red flags. If you went round a red flag you were disqualified and, appealing as the idea might be, there was still Speed Foster, who had to be shown up.

Beginners or not, the rest of the field immediately flew away down a small hill and vanished into the woods beyond. Woody got down the hill without falling, but managed to cross his skis at the bottom and did a graceful swan dive into a snowpile.

He sorted himself out, ignored the shouts of laughter from the Athletic Club, and, gritting his teeth, pushed his way into the woods.

After a while the woods began to seem very lonely, and Woody decided that his education had been neglected. Nothing in the skiing books had given instructions for getting out of a blackberry tangle. How to come down the side of a mountain, yes. They were very sound on mountains. How to jump six-foot crevasse, yes, indeed. It was all a matter of timing and balance and centrifugal force or something. But what did centrifugal force mean to a blackberry?

There was a fine ripping noise and Woody came loose, leaving a piece of a trouser leg as a memento.

The next item on the program was an open brook, about three feet across and running between high banks. Ten feet east there was a charming bridge, but the officials, with fiendish glee, had hung their flags on the west side of the bridge and the contestants had to figure out their own crossing.

Woody, however, thought this would be simple. And, up to a point, it was.

The point occurred when Woody had just succeeded in getting one ski on the opposite shore. That ski had gone over happily and willingly, without raising the slightest fuss. The remaining ski, however, was first coy and then obstinate and Woody, torn between loyalty to his left foot and a desire to keep up with his right one, tried to please both of them at once and fell neatly between, landing on his back in the brook.

The water babbled icily down his neck and Woody raised a howl that made the welkin ring, his skis wavering around above his head in strenuous complaint.

A voice said, "What are you doing down there?" and a face peered over the edge in kindly concern.

"A fellow racer!" thought Woody, relieved to find he wasn't the only one left so far behind.

"G-g-get me out of h-here," he pleaded. "This b-b-blighted b-brook's c-c-cold, and s-so'm I."

"I ought to be shoving on," said the skier, "but I can't leave you like that. The S.P.C.A. would be after me. Here." He stretched down a helping hand and pulled Woody to a sitting posture. "There. Think you can manage now? I'm ahead of the field, and I don't want to drop back."

"Ahead of the f-field?" said Woody. "You c-c-can't be. They're m-m-miles ahead of us."

"Why, that's ridicu——" The skier stopped suddenly and fixed Woody with a pitying look. "What race you entered in?"

"The B-b-beginners," said Woody, struggling to his feet and climbing to the opposite bank. "Wh-why?"

"Because I'm running in the Intermediate," the skier told him. "The Beginners race is over. See you later." He gave Woody another sympathetic look and took off, clearing the brook in an easy jump.

This came under the heading of a distinctly gloomy piece of news, especially as a moment later a great many more Intermediates dashed past, all of them clearing the brook and all of them glancing sideways at him in deepest sympathy.

Woody felt an impulse to sit down in the snow, take his skis off, walk home and find a nice warm fireside, some hot chocolate and some soft cushions. Then he thought of Speed Foster and stuck his chin out grimly. He wasn't going to have Speed able to say that a member of the Study Club couldn't even finish the course.

This thought put him in such a reckless mood that he went down quite a steep hill standing up, but the next hill presented more of a problem as it was dotted with trees and Woody and the stem turn were still strangers.

He solved the difficulty by falling down just before he hit each tree, and then getting up and going on to the next one, and he arrived at the bottom, looking like a snowman, only to find himself faced with a barbed-wire fence.

He propped one ski up resignedly against the top of the fence, seized it with both hands, and managed to push his leg over the fence by sheer will power. As usual, this was only half the job, and when he tried to retrieve the rest of himself he found that a lasting friendship had been established between the top strand of barbed wire and the seat of his pants.

"My fatal charm," Woody mourned. "The dear thing has become attached to me. Now what?"

He gave the ski on the larboard side a tentative wiggle, and the back of it skittered sideways and stuck in the bottom of the fence. Woody thought of his home and family and wished he had been a better boy.

"A split personality, that's what I am," said Woody.

And then he looked up and saw Speed Foster coming down the wooded hill.

Speed was cutting in and out of the trees in rapid, swinging arcs, and Woody, in spite of his position, was forced to admit that it was very pretty to watch.

Speed finished in the deep snow beside him in a long graceful telemark turn that sprayed snow all over Woody, and then leaned against a fence post and burst out laughing.

Woody remained silent.

"Brains over brawn!" Speed jeered, between spasms. "Look at the

Master Mind." He then did a particularly annoying thing. He put one hand on the nearest fence post and lightly vaulted the fence, doing it disdainfully as if it was so simple it was hardly worth the bother.

"Sorry I have to leave you," he said, "but I've got to get on and win that silver cup. See you next summer."

Woody, roused by fury, made a superhuman effort and pulled himself free from his numerous entanglements, sprawling in a heap at Speed's feet. This spectacle again reduced Speed to helpless laughter and Woody glared at him wrathfully, then gazed backwards as the rest of the Experts came into view.

Ahead of Speed and himself there stretched a long, precipitous hill—a hill much steeper than any of Woody's best nightmares. But Woody was not going to stand there waiting for the rest of the experts to arrive and join in the general amusement.

He stuck his poles into the snow, gave himself an energetic push, and vanished over the hill. Speed, suddenly roused, followed abruptly.

The landscape zipped past at express-train speed. Woody's feet accelerated and got ahead of the rest of him so that he sat down with a thump, unexpectedly landing in comfort on the backs of his skis.

Thus happily situated, he shot on down the hill like an escaping thunderbolt—with Speed flying after him, upright and more impressive but no faster. At the bottom of the hill stood a large crowd of cheering students, and Woody suddenly realized that this was the end of the course.

He shot over the finish line, a hair's breadth ahead of Speed, and knocked Bob down, explaining remorsefully, as they lay in a heap, that he had done his best but that life and one or two other small matters had been too much for him.

Speed, looking like a cat who has spent a profitable afternoon in the dairy, stepped up to the judge to receive the silver sup. And, as Speed stepped forward, the Study Club as one man stepped forward with him.

"We maintain," said Bob respectfully, getting to his feet and pushing the trophy back into the judge's hands with gentle firmness, "that our representative won the race."

Tom Hall

*The landscape zipped past at express-train speed.*

"What!" Speed yelped. "What you talking about?" He glanced sharply at Woody, but Woody looked completely dazed, and Speed turned back to Bob. "That's ridiculous."

"Not ridiculous at all," Bob told him kindly. "Did you ever hear of Socrates? Socrates had a very logical mind."

"What's Socrates got to do with this race?" the judge demanded.

"The cup belongs to Woody," Bob said calmly, and Pat and the other Study Clubbers nodded their heads righteously. "He came in first in the Experts class."

"First!" Speed howled. "He didn't even finish in the Beginners."

"But he raced with the Beginners," Bob pointed out, "so that made him eligible for the Intermediate. And when the Intermediates ran he was racing with them, too, so that made him eligible for the Experts. And in the Experts race he came in first—just ahead of you." Bob made a conclusive gesture. "So he won the Experts race, and he gets the cup. Isn't that right?" He appealed to the judge, who was looking confused.

"But—but—" said Speed.

Bob turned to him. "Woody came in ahead of you, didn't he?"

"Well, yes, but—"

"And he was properly signed up for the Experts class, wasn't he?"

"Well, yes, he was. But——"

"Then he won the race." Bob turned to the judge with a smile of happy triumph. "Any flaw in that argument?"

The judge gulped hard. "I can't see anything wrong with your line of reasoning," he admitted reluctantly.

"Reasoning," said Bob modestly, "is one of the things the Study Club does best. Then you agree that the cup belongs to Woody. You agree to that, too, don't you, Speed?"

The judge relinquished the gleaming trophy into Bob's hands, and Speed, seeing the coveted prize vanish from his grasp, gave a howl of pure anguish.

"Something wrong with our line of argument?" Bob inquired solicitously.

Speed gazed upon the cup with unutterable sorrow, then slowly shook his head. "No. No. I don't suppose there is."

Woody stepped forward. "Poor fellow," he said. "Poor, poor fellow. How sad it is not to be able to use your brain. And this is the guy who thought muscles were more important. Poor, poor chap."

"Shut up," said Speed, not grateful for this sympathy.

"Now if you were only trained in logic," Woody continued, "as we of the Study Club are, you'd see right away that there *is* a flaw in the argument, and you could claim the cup. But no. Just a vacuum from the neck up. It's pitiful."

'What flaw?" Speed demanded anxiously. "I can't see a flaw."

"No, of course you can't," said Woody. "My point exactly. Brains win over brawn every time. You'll have to admit that now, Speed."

"All right, all right," said Speed grimly. "I'll admit it."

"That's all I want to know," Woody told him. "We've proved our point. Here." He took the cup from Bob and placed it tenderly in Speed's hands. "Here you are, Speedikins. The flaw in the argument is that you can't win a race you never even started in, and I didn't start in the Experts class. I started in the Beginners."

Speed, his mouth open, stood and stared.

"Simple, isn't it?" said Woody sweetly. "Elementary, in fact. Brains over brawn, little man. You should try it sometime. But keep the cup," he added. "You're too easy to beat. It was not fair taking you on in a battle of wits, when you didn't have any weapons." With this crushing remark he turned to the Study Club and said, "Come on, fellows. I've got to get my bones onto a sofa." He turned and started off, rather stiffly.

"Hey," said Speed hoarsely.

Woody stopped and turned back.

"Heck," said Speed uncomfortably, "maybe I misjudged you. Look, Woody, how does a fellow get to join that Study Club of yours?"

A wide grin spread over Woody's features. "Confidentially, Speed," said Woody, "how does a fellow do turns on skis without falling on his nose? Socrates forgot to say."

# KNAPSACK OF SALVATION

## By WOLFGANG LANGEWIESCHE

### Illustration by Tom Hall

PARACHUTES are special stuff—in a class with sharks, snakes, poisons, drugs.

Miller and Johnson, Parachute Service, lived inconspicuously in the rear of Hangar 3 in a small workshop. When one wanted to practice tail spins or acrobatics, air law prescribed that 'chutes must be worn and one rented a 'chute from Miller and Johnson at a dollar an hour.

Miller and Johnson turned out to be two grizzled men in their fifties. There was nothing in their appearance to connect them with the circus, or with airmanship, for that matter; it was more like being measured for a new suit at the tailor's. We fixed the third day from then for the jump, weather permitting, and they went to work immediately selecting the 'chute and fitting the shoulder straps and leg straps and chest straps of the harness. The 'chute itself was not the usual seat-pack type, but was worn knapsackwise; that was to make it easier for the jumper to climb out of the ship deliberately without doing damage. Carried that way, it was heavy, and that was reassuring; it made you feel that at least you wouldn't have to jump off there defenseless.

"Now, when you pull the ripcord," began Miller, "don't be gentle about it."

"Give it all you've got," said Johnson. "Yank the thing right out."

"You bet I will," said I.

The ripcord was painted red; it looked much like the emergency brake in Continental railroad cars and, under the circumstances, that carried a pleasant suggestion.

When your inner man complains and wants to put his trust in something, there is nothing quite as suitable as a gadget. The gadget will presumably work, while the same thing cannot always be said of one's intelligence or of one's own nerve.

Then came the second 'chute. Air law says two 'chutes must be worn on "intentional jumps." The second one was only a small one, eighteen feet in diameter. If I should have to use it, Johnson said, it would bring me down "awful fast." It was worn on the stomach, buckled onto the harness of the first one. When it hung, it acted as a counterweight to the first one, and made you feel like a pack horse.

But all to the good; as far as I was concerned, the more gadgets, the better.

"Now when you take off——" said Miller (what an elegant circumlocution, I thought, for letting yourself fall from an airplane) "now when you take off, the main thing to remember is not to pull too soon. It is as much as your life is worth." And he explained how the 'chute might get fouled in the ship's tail and throw the ship out of control; the pilot, he said, was going to wear a 'chute himself, that being another legal requirement, and would jump. But I would get killed.

Miller said I was to take off in a shallow dive, away from the ship—"the way you dive into a swimming pool." That way, he said, I would fall face downward, and would pull the cord in that position, and the canopy would be free to string out nicely behind me. That was a new one. Wouldn't a parachute open in any position? Johnson said "yes," absolutely in any position, but smoothest that way. But he thought if I pulled in any other position, it would be just as well to keep my legs together and pulled up against the body in a crouching position, so the 'chute wouldn't get caught between them. Miller, started to emphasize again how important it was to wait and clear the tail of the ship. "Don't worry, though," said Johnson, "the pilot has done this job many times; he will kick the tail out of your way."

I asked how long I should count before pulling. Miller said not to count at all. "A man can count so very fast." He said it was better to use my own judgment and to wait until I had fallen clear.

"After all," said Johnson, "you are a pilot, you are used to the air; you won't be nervous."

"Not much!" I thought.

Johnson advised me to have my hand on the ripcoard before I even jumped. Miller had some parachute lore to cover that point. Some fellows got excited and couldn't find the ripcord, and went clutching for it all over themselves in a panic before they could find it. "Like this," said Johnson and started emitting gutteral sounds of horror and clutching at the air, with a facial expression that was most convincing. Both of them laughed heartily.

Johnson had a companion story of a case where a newspaper writer had tried a jump. He hadn't trusted himself to keep his wits about him, and so his rigger had tied a long string to the ripcord, and had gone up with him in the ship to do the pulling himself after the writer would have fallen deep enough—which was, said Miller, more or less the system of parachute that had been in use before 1919 and the invention of the self-pulled ripcord: a line connecting the jumper and the aircraft and jerking out the 'chute. But it had often failed to work. Instead, the man had got tangled up in the string, and jerked it out of the rigger's hand, and, being entangled, had then been unable to pull the cord himself; he had fallen straight down like a stone.

Between them they discussed an expedient sometimes used for breaking-in jumpers: tie one corner of a handkerchief around the ripcord, tie the other corner into a knot, and have the jumper hold the knot with his teeth. A man always knows where his mouth is, said Miller. But it sometimes happened, said Johnson, that the jumper in his excitement pulled out all his front teeth before he pulled out his ripcord.

"Now when you land," said Johnson, "just go limp. Never mind if it rolls you over a few times. Just go limp."

Miller said, "Now don't worry about the landing. If you come down on the field we will be under you anyway."

It had been decided that I should jump into an abandoned flying field, near the state fair grounds, five miles from the Metropolitan Airport.

"But, of course, it is hard to judge," said Johnson. This year they had bad luck—their last man had fallen into a canal, and the man before him had landed on the roof of the grandstand and had broken a leg.

The three days before the jump were like the last days of a school vacation when one's forward perspective in time used to be completely shut off. The third day was fine; there was no storm; there was no high wind. At five I went to the Airport.

Miller and Johnson were waiting. First of all there was a little thing to sign, all typed out for me. I, my heirs, executors, administrators, and assigns would make no fuss, whatever happened.

Then there was a long pause while we waited for their pilot. Miller sat on the workbench, and Johnson stood around, watching the sun come down. I looked over the ships in the hangar. I didn't feel like talking. If the thing worked, there would be lots of time to talk afterwards; if it didn't, talking would be pointless.

The pilot came, looked me over in passing, but said nothing. He grabbed a 'chute from the shelf, went out and started his engine. And they began to dress me up, goggles and 'chutes.

We filed out of the hangar, Miller ahead, Johnson behind me, not unlike a condemned man's walk to the chair.

At this moment, my whole past life flashed through my mind— it really did. This way: was there any evidence of mental disorder? There was the time when I wanted to quit school; there was the matter of the forgotten address; there was the fact that at parties I get moody and contrary; but all that wasn't convincing. Had it perhaps broken out suddenly? Rapidly, I ran through uncles and aunts; no insanity in the family.

I seemed to be sane.

"Just a moment," Johnson said, and took me aside. "Want to pay us now?" I couldn't get at my pocket past all the harness. We went in again. He unbuckled me, and we settled. He buckled me up again, and we went out. Miller and an old assistant started up the truck to drive to the fair grounds and be under me when I landed.

Johnson thought of another thing: "Now that ripcord, you better hold onto it; don't throw it away in your excitement. It costs five dollars."

I said, "I'll do my best." He said: "You pay for it if you don't."

I climbed into the ship and climbed out again on the wing, by way of rehearsal. What, I said to myself, if when we get upstairs all I do is shiver and finally shake my head and climb back into the ship and sit down. I could picture quite clearly their polite smiles as we came down again and they helped me out of the ship; certainly, they would say, you're quite right, it is really not worth the risk.

Was I sure that wouldn't happen? I was not.

I climbed in again.

He took off.

We rose across the familiar fields, swung around and climbed over the open country. A phrase went through my head: "I earnestly hope."

At a thousand feet, the silliness of the enterprise had faded: now in the air, it was simply an aeronautical job to be done, and to be done with the usual aeronautical attitude—judgment, deliberation, control. At two thousand feet, that attitude had taken full possession of me; so much so that now if anything had seemed wrong, I would no longer have minded even calling the whole thing off and returning to the airport, the way a good flier sometimes will.

But nothing did seem wrong.

At three thousand feet, we crossed over the state fair grounds, headed into the wind. The pilot poked me in the back and throttled back, to slacken the propeller blast and make it easier for me to climb out. I was glad I had rehearsed the job. It went smoothly, and I had attention to spare, for easing my two 'chutes past all sorts of hazards without having the ripcords catch and rip open.

He put on the power again, and I had to hold on tightly, for the wind was pushing me heavily from behind and threatened to throw me off.

I looked down; half a mile down . . .

I should like now to report hair-raising sensations. But actually I was cool—or perhaps the better word is dead. While I stood out there and looked down, my heart stopped pounding. It was the factor X again, coming in handy; I could feel no animalic fear of falling, because I could get no animal sense of the depth. Looking

Tom Hall

*I fell face downward, my left hand clawing at a cornfield,*
*my right holding the ripcord.*

back into the front cockpit, I could see the altimeter registering 2,500 feet; we had lost altitude while I had climbed out. But the position of a needle on a dial was evidence too thin and intellectual to give you a good scare. It was different when I looked at the pilot. He was tense and worried, thinking probably about the job ahead and the chance that something might miscarry and he might have to jump. I preferred not to watch him, for fear can be induced the sympathetic way from man to man.

He throttled back again and nodded. I felt no reluctance. I let go of my hold, took hold of the ripcord ring over my heart, and with one long step walked out into the farms below.

The fall was violent. I fell and fell. I fell face downward, my left hand clawing at a cornfield, right hand on my heart, holding the ripcord. I fell so hard that I couldn't even be afraid; I was all filled out by one feeling, a feeling which, translated into colloquial language, was: "Oh, boy; oh, boy, here I go!"

Falling is falling, from old habit, whether you do it in an optic vacuum or not. No factor X deadened that sensation. I held my breath, or rather my nerves did; they expected me presently to hit with terrific force, and to get hurt; because they had never known me to fall and then not hit and get hurt. I remember hearing myself gasp, which shows that I must have fallen quite deep below the airplane and its noise. I waited as long as I could. Then it seemed horribly urgent to find out whether or not the contraption would work.

Then I pulled the handle.

I gave it all I'd got. It came out with hardly any resistance, and went slack in my hand. I pulled it all the way out and stretched out my arm and held it far away from me, and grasped it hard; I must not lose it: point of aeronautical honor. Even while falling, I held it stretched out with my right, the way Marshal Bluecher holds his saber, in the pictures, riding an attack; even while falling, I thought that was funny. And I waited with some impatience to be caught up.

Nothing happened.

Then there was a vision of laundry fluttering on a line. That was the silk, stringing out behind me. A gentle force seemed to lift me by the shoulders and pull me upright, much as one might pick up a child who had fallen, and I had just time to think, "Is that all?"

Then the canopy opened. The harness grabbed me around the thighs, jerking my legs apart. A bolt of energy struck down on my head, traveled down along my spine, my legs, and my feet, just as a crack travels along a whip, until I thought my feet were going to snap off. Something jerked me upward with a huge lift—a fish would feel that way when he is hooked. And I remember hearing myself groan—against that peculiar stillness. Then the forces subsided, and I was afloat.

Of all the sensations of air-faring, that is the most dreamlike—floating under a parachute. It begins with a wave of triumphal emotion which is standard accompaniment of everyone's first parachute jump and is unlike any other experience—there is in it the sudden deliverance from danger, also release from perhaps the most concentrated bit of waiting there is, and also exultation of being high up in the air, flying for once in silence, for once almost without a machine.

I looked up at my 'chute; the simplest of all aircraft. It quivered, high above me, the merest handkerchief in size; it seemed incredible that so small a bit of silk should have so much holding power. In the stillness it gave out a thin sound, like a peanut whistle. That was the air, escaping through its center vent hole. It was a warning, though I didn't understand it; an indication of the speed with which I was actually coming down.

For the time being, I was well afloat with my magic carpet. The harness was holding up my weight so evenly that I was hardly conscious of it. It is like flying in dreams, flying simply because you are light. My feet were limp under me hanging into a cornfield. The view was the usual one from an airplane, the green plain, the distant horizon. But there was no wind; when I moved my hand, the air felt thin.

I experimented with steering the 'chute by pulling the lines so as to set the canopy askew; it let me slide off sidewise obediently enough. But it also set me to swinging, pendulum fashion, and I had to stabilize myself by throwing my weight about the way a child stops its own oscillations on a swing. When I looked down again, I found myself bearing down on the race course. There was the landing to think of now.

My descent had become more noticeable. I watched for a while, with an eye practiced by so many approaches, and it seemed to me that I was undershooting the intended.

The race track seemed the probable point of contact and within the race track, the corner where the stables were and the grandstand. If so, I should get hurt. Beyond it, there was the abandoned flying field. I grabbed the two forward ones of the lines and hung onto them. It helped a lot; the wind combined with the 'chute to carry me forward beautifully. I flew across the roof of the grandstand, across the race track itself, sliding along weightless, without footing, like a ghost.

But again the maneuver threw me into violent swinging. I worked hurriedly to stop it. The grass was beginning to dilate under me as if pulled up by a magnifying glass. Only one hazard was now still before me: the fence of the fair area. Beyond it was the clear field. There was little time left. The wind was drifting me toward the fence, but not fast enough. And I was too low now to do any more maneuvering. I had to take whatever was coming, and it began to look like a fifty-fifty shot. I could already distinguish the individual strands of barbed wire.

I was floating down steeply now, the sinking much more visible than the forward drift. I saw that I was going to light exactly on the fence, but in my innocence, I was not much worried. I decided I would simply step lightly on the top wire, kick myself off from it, and step down, still borne by the 'chute, still weightless, from the fence into the grass, on the airport side. As it was coming up against me, I stretched my right foot down to meet it; and I missed. The wind had carried me forward by about two feet or so, and I was across. Then the grass took a lunge. There was just time to go limp.

It came up through my legs and my whole body as if they had been unsubstantive as a ghost's, went right at my chin, and swatted the living daylights out of me. And that was only the begin-ning. For a long time thereafter, though I thought I was down, legs and arms kept falling all around me and kept me wondering where it all came from. Then bombardment subsided and it was quiet.

I looked up. The 'chute was standing upright in the grass, tug-ging at me with the force of a sail. I pulled in one of the lines and made it collapse and unbuckled my harness, working with a breathless haste for which there was no other reason than that my whole system was still timed for fast airwork. From the distance, people were running across the field, old Johnson doing his best to keep up with them. And the ship was coming in for a landing. I looked at my hand, and my ripcord was gone. Just before every-body arrived, I found it lying in the grass: a piece of wire rope, one yard long, attached to the ring. I also found a deep hollow scooped out of the soft ground, of the kind which in skiing is called a bath-tub. That was the place where I had hit. My shirt was torn, and my trouser legs were torn. My cheek was bleeding; despite the goggles, my spectacles were bent.

There was a great deal of excited talk. I had been lucky. The fence was nine feet high, with steep posts and very tight wires, not an ordinary farm fence at all, but more like a burglar-proof fac-tory fence. If I had landed on it, on this fence, with that force—I would have been cut in two. We stood around the 'chute. It lay there flat and dead on the grass. I felt as if I had landed some mon-ster fish.

# CHASED BY THE TRAIL

### By JACK LONDON

*Illustration by Warren Chappell*

WALT first blinked his eyes in the light of day in a trading post on the Yukon River. Masters, his father, was one of those world missionaries who are known as "pioneers," and who spend the years of their life in pushing outward the walls of civilization and in planting the wilderness. He had selected Alaska as his field of labor, and his wife had gone with him to that land of frost and cold.

Now, to be born to the moccasin and pack strap is indeed a hard way of entering the world, but far harder it is to lose one's mother while yet a child. This was Walt's misfortune when he was fourteen years old.

He had, at different times, done deeds which few boys get the chance to do, and he had learned to take some pride in himself and to be unafraid. With most people pride goeth before a fall; but not so with Walt. His was a healthy belief in his own strength and fitness, and knowing his limitations, he was neither overweening nor presumptuous. He had learned to meet reserves with the stoicism of the Indian. Shame, to him, lay not in the failure to accomplish, but in the failure to strive. So, when he attempted to cross the Yukon between two ice runs, and was chased by the trail, he was not cast down by his defeat.

The way of it was this. After passing the winter at his father's claim on Mazy May, he came down to an island in the Yukon and went into camp. This was late in the spring, just before the breaking of the ice in the river. It was quite warm, and the days were growing marvelously long. Only the night before, when he was talking with Chilkoot Jim, the daylight had not faded and sent him off to bed till after ten o'clock. Even Chilkoot Jim, an Indian boy who was about Walt's own age, was surprised at the rapidity with which summer was coming on. The snow had melted from all the southern hillsides and the level surfaces of the flats and islands; everywhere could be heard the trickling of water and the song of hidden rivulets; but somehow, under its three-foot ice-sheet, the Yukon delayed to heave its great length of three thousand miles and shake off the frosty fetters which bound it.

But it was evident that the time was fast approaching when it would again run free. Great fissures were splitting the ice in all directions, while the water was beginning to flood through them and over the top. On this morning a frightful rumbling brought the two boys hurriedly from their blankets. Standing on the bank, they soon discovered the cause. The Stewart River had broken loose and reared a great ice barrier, where it entered the Yukon, barely a mile above their island. While a great deal of the Stewart ice had been thus piled up, the remainder was now flowing under the Yukon ice, pounding and thumping at the solid surface above it as it passed onward toward the sea.

"Today um break um," Chilkoot Jim said, nodding his head "Sure!"

"And then maybe two days for the ice to pass by," Walt added, "and you and I'll be starting for Dawson. It's only seventy miles, and if the current runs five miles an hour and we paddle three, we ought to make it inside of ten hours. What do you think?"

"Sure!" Chilkoot Jim did not know much English, and this favorite word of his was made to do duty on all occasions.

After breakfast the boys got out the Peterborough canoe from its winter cache. It was an admirable sample of the boat-builder's skill, an imported article brought from the natural home of the canoe—Canada. It had been packed over the Chilkoot Pass, two years before, on a man's back and had then carried the first mail in six months into the Klondike. Walt, who happened to be in Dawson at the time, had bought it for three hundred dollars' worth of dust which he had mined on the Mazy May.

It had been a revelation, both to him and to Chilkoot Jim, for up to its advent they had been used to no other craft than the flimsy birch-bark canoes of the Indians and the rude poling-boats of the whites. Jim, in fact, spent many a happy half-hour in silent admiration of its perfect lines.

"Um good. Sure!" Jim lifted his gaze from the dainty craft, expressing his delight in the same terms for the thousandth time. But glancing over Walt's shoulder, he saw something on the river which startled him. "Look! See!" he cried.

A man had been racing a dog team across the slushy surface for the shore, and had been cut off by the rising flood. As Walt whirled round to see, the ice behind the man burst into violent commotion, splitting and smashing into fragments which bobbed up and down and turned turtle like so many corks.

A gush of water followed, burying the sled and washing the dogs from their feet. Tangled in their harness and securely fastened to the heavy sled, they must drown in a few minutes unless rescued by the man. Bravely his manhood answered.

Floundering about with the drowning animals, nearly hip-deep in the icy flood, he cut and slashed with his sheath-knife at the traces. One by one the dogs struck out for shore, the first reaching safety ere the last was released. Then the master, abandoning the sled, followed them. It was a struggle in which little help could be given, and Walt and Chilkoot Jim could only, at the last, grasp his hands and drag him, half-fainting, up the bank.

First he sat down till he had recovered his breath; next he knocked the water from his ears like a boy who has just been swimming; and after that he whistled his dogs together to see whether they had all escaped. These things done, he turned his attention to the lads.

"I'm Muso," he said, "Pete Muso, and I'm looking for Charley Drake. His partner is dying down at Dawson, and they want him to come at once, as soon as the river breaks. He's got a cabin on this island, hasn't he?"

"Yes," Walt answered, "but he's over on the other side of the river, with a couple of other men, getting out a raft of logs for a grubstake."

The stranger's disappointment was great. Exhausted by his weary journey, just escaped from sudden death, overcome by all he had undergone in carrying the message which was now useless, he looked dazed. The tears welled into his eyes, and his voice was choked with sobs as he repeated, aimlessly, "But his partner's dying. It's his partner, you know, and he wants to see him before he dies."

Walt and Jim knew that nothing could be done, and as aimlessly looked out on the hopeless river. No man could venture on it and live. On the other bank, and several miles upstream, a thin column of smoke wavered to the sky. Charley Drake was cooking his dinner there; seventy miles below, his partner lay dying; yet no word of it could be sent.

But even as they looked, a change came over the river. There was a muffled rending and tearing, and, as if by magic, the surface water disappeared, while the great ice sheet, reaching from shore to shore, and broken into all manner and sizes of cakes, floated silently up toward them. The ice which had been pounding along underneath had evidently grounded at some point lower down, and was now backing up the water like a mill-dam. This had broken the ice sheet from the land and lifted it on top of the rising water.

"Um break um very quick," Chilkoot Jim said.

"Then here goes!" Muso cried, at the same time beginning to strip his wet clothes.

The Indian boy laughed. "Mebbe you get um in middle, mebbe not. All the same, the trail um go downstream, and you go, too. Sure!" He glanced at Walt, that he might back him up in preventing this insane attempt.

"You're not going to try and make it across?" Walt queried.

Muso nodded his head, sat down, and proceeded to unlace his moccasins.

"But you mustn't!" Walt protested. "It's certain death. The river'll break before you get half-way, and then what good'll your message be?"

But the stranger doggedly went on undressing, muttering in an undertone, "I want Charley Drake! Don't you understand? It's his partner, dying."

"Um sick man. Bimeby—" The Indian boy put a finger to his forehead and whirled his hand in quick circles, thus indicating the approach of brain fever. "Um work too hard, and um think too much, all the time think about sick man at Dawson. Very quick um head go round—so." And he feigned the bodily dizziness which is caused by a disordered brain.

By this time, undressed as if for a swim, Muso rose to his feet and started for the bank. Walt stepped in front, barring the way. He shot a glance at his comrade. Jim nodded that he understood and would stand by.

"Get out of my way, boy!" Muso commanded, roughly, trying to thrust him aside.

But Walt closed in, and with the aid of Jim succeeded in tripping him upon his back. He struggled weakly for a few moments, but was too wearied by his long journey to cope successfully with the two boys whose muscles were healthy and trail-hardened.

"Pack um into camp, roll um in plenty blanket, and I fix um good," Jim advised.

This was quickly accomplished, and the sufferer made as comfortable as possible. After he had been attended to, and Jim had utilized the medical lore picked up in the camps of his own people, they fed the stranger's dogs and cooked dinner. They said very little to each other, but each boy was thinking hard, and when they went out into the sunshine a few minutes later, their minds were intent on the same project.

The river had now risen twenty feet, the ice rubbing softly against the top of the bank. All noise had ceased. Countless millions of tons of ice and water were silently waiting the supreme moment, when all bonds would be broken and the mad rush to the sea would begin. Suddenly, without the slightest apparent effort, everything began to move downstream. The jam had broken.

Slowly at first but faster and faster the frozen sea dashed past. The noise returned again, and the air trembled to a mighty churning and grinding. Huge blocks of ice were shot into the air by the pressure; others butted wildly into the bank; still others, swinging and pivoting, reached inshore and swept rows of pines away as easily as if they were so many matches.

In awe-stricken silence the boys watched the magnificent spectacle, and it was not until the ice had slackened its speed and fallen to its old level that Walt cried, "Look, Jim! Look at the trail going by!"

And in truth it was the trail going by—the trail upon which they had camped and traveled during all the preceding winter. Next winter they would journey with dogs and sleds over the same ground, but not on the same trail. That trail, the old trail, was passing away before their eyes.

Looking upstream, they saw open water. No more ice was coming down, although vast quantities of it still remained on the upper reaches, jammed somewhere amid the maze of islands which covered the Yukon's breast. As a matter of fact, there were several jams yet to break, one after another, and to send down as many ice runs. The next might come along in a few minutes; it might delay for hours. Perhaps there would be time to paddle across. Walt looked questioningly at his comrade.

"Sure!" Jim remarked, and without another word they carried the canoe down the bank. Each knew the danger of what they were about to attempt, but they wasted no speech over it. Wild life had taught them both that the need of things demanded effort and action, and that the tongue found its fit vocation at the camp fire when the day's work was done.

With dexterity born of long practice they launched the canoe, and were soon making it spring to each stroke of the paddles as they stemmed the muddy current. A steady procession of lagging ice-cakes, each thoroughly capable of crushing the Peterborough like an egg-shell, was drifting on the surface, and it required of the boys the utmost vigilance and skill to thread them safely.

Anxiously they watched the great bend above, down which at any moment might rush another ice run. And as anxiously they watched the ice stranded against the bank and towering a score of feet above them. Cake was poised upon cake and piled in precarious confusion, while the boys had to hug the shore closely to avoid the swifter current of mid-stream. Now and again great heaps of this ice tottered and fell into the river, rolling and rumbling like distant thunder, and lashing the water into fair-sized tidal waves.

Several times they were nearly swamped, but saved themselves by quick work with the paddles. And all the time Charley Drake's pillared camp smoke grew nearer and clearer. But it was still on the opposite shore, and they knew they must get higher up before they attempted to shoot across.

Entering the Stewart River, they paddled up a few hundred yards, shot across, and then continued up the right bank of the Yukon. Before long they came to the Bald-Face Bluffs—huge walls of rock which rose perpendicularly from the river. Here the current was swiftest inshore, forming the first serious obstacle encountered by the boys. Below the bluffs they rested from their exertions in a favorable eddy, and then, paddling their strongest, strove to dash past.

At first they gained, but in the swiftest place the current overpowered them. For a full sixty seconds they remained stationary, neither advancing nor receding, the grim cliff base within reach of their arms, their paddles dipping and lifting like clock-work, and the rough water dashing by in muddy haste. For a full sixty seconds, and then the canoe sheered in to the shore. To prevent instant destruction, they pressed their paddles against the rocks, sheered back into the stream, and were swept away. Regaining the eddy, they stopped for breath. A second time they attempted the passage; but just as they were almost past, a threatening ice cake whirled down upon them on the angry tide, and they were forced to flee before it.

"Um stiff, I think yes," Chilkoot Jim said, mopping the sweat from his face as they again rested in the eddy. "Next time um make um, sure."

"We've got to. That's all there is about it," Walt answered, his teeth set and lips tight-drawn, for Pete Muso had set a bad example, and he was almost ready to cry from exhaustion and failure. A third time they darted out of the head of the eddy, plunged into the swirling waters, and worked a snail-like course ahead. Often they stood still for the space of many strokes, but whatever they gained they held and they at last drew out into easier water far above. But every moment was precious. There was no telling when the Yukon would again become a scene of wild anarchy in which neither man nor any of his works could hope to endure. So they held steadily to their course till they had passed above Charley Drake's camp by a quarter of a mile. The river was fully a mile wide at this point, and they had to reckon on being carried down by the swift current in crossing it.

Walt turned his head from his place in the bow. Jim nodded. Without further parley they headed the canoe out from the shore, at an angle of forty-five degrees against the current. They were on the last stretch now; the goal was in fair sight. Indeed, as they looked up from the toil to mark their progress, they could see Charley Drake and his two comrades come down to the edge of the river to watch them.

*Warren Chappell*

*They whirled the Peterborough downstream.*

Five hundred yards; four hundred yards; the Peterborough cut the water like a blade of steel; the paddles were dipping, dipping, dipping in rapid rhythm—and then a warning shout from the bank sent a chill to their hearts. Round the great bend just above rolled a mighty wall of glistening white. Behind it, urging it on to lightning speed, were a million tons of long-pent water.

The right flank of the ice run, unable to get cleanly round the bend, collided with the opposite shore, and even as they looked they saw the ice mountains rear toward the sky, rise, collapse, and rise again in glittering convulsions. The advancing roar filled the air so that Walt could not make himself heard; but he paused long enough to wave his paddle significantly in the direction of Dawson. Perhaps Charley Drake, seeing, might understand.

With two swift strokes they whirled the Peterborough downstream. They must keep ahead of the rushing flood. It was impossible to make either bank at that moment. Every ounce of their strength went into the paddles, and the frail canoe fairly rose and leaped ahead at every stroke. They said nothing. Each knew and had faith in the other, and they were too wise to waste their breath. The shore-line—trees, islands and the Stewart River—flew by at a bewildering rate, but they barely looked at it.

Occasionally Chilkoot Jim stole a glance behind him at the pursuing trail, and marked the fact that they held their own. Once he shaped a sharper course toward the bank, but found the trail was overtaking them, and gave it up.

Gradually they worked in to land, their failing strength warning them that it was soon or never. And at last, when they did draw up to the bank, they were confronted by the inhospitable barrier of the stranded shore ice. Not a place could be found to land, and with safety virtually within arm's reach, they were forced to flee on down the stream. They passed a score of places, at each of which, had they had plenty of time, they could have clambered out; but behind pressed on the inexorable trail, and would not let them pause.

Half a mile of this work drew heavily upon their strength; and the trail came upon them nearer and nearer. Its sullen grind was in their ears, and its collisions against the bank made one continuous succession of terrifying crashes. Walt felt his heart thumping against his ribs and caught each breath in painful gasps. But worst of all was the constant demand upon his arms.

If he could only rest for the space of one stroke, he felt that the torture would be relieved; but no, it was dip and lift, dip and lift, till it seemed as if at each stroke he would surely die. But he knew that Chilkoot Jim was suffering likewise; that their lives depended each upon the other; and that it would be a blot upon his manhood should he fail or even miss a stroke.

They were very weary, but their faith was large, and if either felt afraid, it was not of the other, but of himself.

Flashing round a sharp point, they came upon their last chance for escape. An island lay close inshore, upon the nose of which the ice lay piled in a long slope. They drove the Peterborough half out of water upon a shelving cake and leaped out. Then, dragging the canoe along, slipping and tripping and falling, but always getting nearer the top, they made their last mad scramble.

As they cleared the crest and fell within the shelter of the pines, a tremendous crash announced the arrival of the trail. One huge cake, shoved to the top of the rim ice, balanced threateningly above them and then toppled forward.

With one jerk they flung themselves and the canoe from beneath, and again fell, breathless and panting for air. The thunder of the ice run came dimly to their ears; but they did not care. It held no interest for them whatsoever. All they wished was simply to lie there, just as they had fallen, and enjoy the inaction of repose.

Two hours later, when the river once more ran open, they carried the Peterborough down to the water. But just before they launched it, Charley Drake and a comrade paddled up in another canoe.

"Well, you boys hardly deserve to have good folks out looking for you, the way you've behaved," was his greeting. "What under the sun made you leave your tent and get chased by the trail? Eh? That's what I'd like to know."

It took but a minute to explain the real state of affairs, and but another to see Charley Drake hurrying along on his way to his sick partner at Dawson.

"Pretty close shave, that," Walt Masters said, as they prepared to get aboard and paddle back to camp.

"Sure!" Chilkoot Jim replied, rubbing his stiffened biceps in a meditative fashion.

# THE PROSPECTOR

By *HAMLIN GARLAND*

OLD POGOSA was seated in the shade of a farm wagon, not far from the trader's store at Washakie, eating a cracker and mumbling to herself, when a white man in miner's dress spoke to her in a kindly voice and offered her an orange. She studied him with a dim, shining, suspicious gaze, but took the orange. Eugene, the grandson of her niece, stood beside the stranger, and he, too, had an orange.

"Tell her," said the white man, "that I want to talk with her about old days; that I am a friend of her people, and that I knew Sitting Bull and Bear Robe. They were great chiefs."

As these words were interpreted to the old witch, her mouth softened a little and, raising her eyes, she studied her visitor intently. At last she said: "Ay, he was a great chief, Sitting Bull. My cousin. I came to visit Shoshoni many moons ago. Never returned to my own people."

To this the miner replied, "They say your husband, Iapi, was one of the sheep-eaters exiled to the mountains?"

Her eyes widened. Her gaze deepened. She clipped her forefinger in sign of agreement. "It was very cold up there in winter. We were often hungry, for the game had all been driven to the plain and we could not follow. Many of our children died. All died but one."

The stranger, whose name was Wetherell, responded with a sigh: "My heart is heavy when I hear of it. Because you are old and have not much food I give you this money." And he handed her a silver dollar and walked away.

The next day, led by Eugene, Wetherell and Kelley, his partner, approached the old Sioux, this time with a generous gift of beef.

"My brother, here, is paper-chief," he explained. "As a friend of the red people he wants to put in a book all the wrongs that the sheep-eaters suffered."

In this way the gold seekers proceeded to work upon Pogosa's withered heart. Her mind was clouded with age, but a spark of her old-time cunning still dwelt there, and as she came to understand that the white men were eager to hear the story of the lost mine she grew forgetful. Her tongue halted on details of the trail. Why should not her tale produce other sides of bacon, more oranges, and many yards of cloth? Her memory wabbled like her finger—now pointing west, now north. At one time the exiles found the gold in the cabin in a bag—like shining sand; at another it lay in the sand like shining soldiers' buttons, but always it was very beautiful to look upon, and always, she repeated, the white men fled. No one slew them. They went hurriedly, leaving all their tools.

"She knows," exulted Wetherell. "She knows, and she's the one living Indian who can direct us." To Eugene he exclaimed: "Say to her pretty soon she's going to be rich—mebbe go home to Cheyenne River. If she shows us the trail we will take her to her own people."

Like a decrepit eagle the crone pondered. Suddenly she spoke, and her speech was a hoarse chant. "You are good to me. The bones of my children lie up there. I will go once more before I die."

Kelley was quick to take advantage of sunset emotion. "Tell her we will be here before sunrise. Warn her not to talk to anyone." And to all this Eugene gave ready assent.

Wetherell slept very little that night, although their tent stood close beside the singing water of the Little Wind. They were several miles from the fort and in a lonely spot with only one or two Indian huts near, and yet he had the conviction that their plans and the very hour of their starting were known to other of the red people. At one moment he was sure they were all chuckling at the "foolish white men"; at another he shivered to think how easy it would be to ambush this crazy expedition in some of the deep, solitary defiles in those upper forests. "A regiment could be murdered and hidden in some of those savage glooms," said he to himself.

Kelley slept like a top, but woke at the first faint dawn, with the precision of an alarm clock. In ten minutes he had the horses in, and was throwing the saddles on. "Roll out, Andy," he shouted. "Here comes Eugene."

Wetherell lent himself to the work with suddenly developed enthusiasm, and in half an hour the little train of laden animals was in motion toward the hills. Pogosa was waiting, squatted on the ground at some distance from her tepee. Slipping from his horse, he helped her mount. She groaned a little as she did so, but gathered up the reins like one resuming a long-forgotten habit. For years she had not ventured to mount a horse, and her withered knees were of small service in maintaining her seat, but she made no complaint.

Slowly the little train crawled up the trail, which ran for the most part along the open side of the slope, in plain view from below. At sunrise they were so well up the slope that an observer from below would have had some trouble in making out the character of the cavalcade. At seven o'clock they entered the first patch of timber and were hidden from the plain.

On the steep places, where the old squaw was forced to cling to her saddle, groaning with pain, the kindly Wetherell walked beside her, easing her down the banks. In crossing the streams he helped her find the shallowest fording, and in other ways was singularly considerate. Kelley couldn't have done this, but he saw the value of it.

"It's a hard trip and we've got to make it as easy for the old bird as we can."

"She's human," retorted Wetherell, "and this ride is probably painful for her, mentally as well as physically."

"I s'pose it does stir her up some," responded Kelley. "She may balk any minute and refuse to go. We'd better camp early."

A little later Eugene called out, "She says set tepee here." And Kelley consented.

Again it was Wetherell who helped her from her saddle and spread his pack for her to rest upon. He also brought a blanket and covered her as tenderly as if she were his own grandmother. "She's pretty near all in," he said, in palliation of this action. He took a pleasure in seeing her revive under the influence of hot food.

When she began to talk, Eugene laughingly explained: "She stuck on you. She say you good man. Your heart big for old Injun woman."

Kelley chuckled. "Keep it up, Andy," he called through the tent. "I leave all that business to you."

Pogosa's face darkened. She understood the laugh. "Send him away," she commanded Eugene, all of which made Kelley grin.

The whole enterprise now began to take on poetry to Wetherell. The wilderness, so big, so desolate, so empty to him, was full of memories to this brown old witch. To her the rushing stream sang long-forgotten songs of war and the chase. She could hear in its clamor the voices of friends and lovers. This pathway, so dim and fluctuating, so indefinite to the white man, led straight into the heroic past for her. Perhaps she was treading it now, not for the meat and flannel which Kelley had promised her, but for the pleasure of reliving the past. She was young when her husband was banished. In these splendid solitudes her brave young hunter adventured day by day. Here beside one of these glorious streams her children were born in exile; here they suffered the snows of winter, the pests of summer; and here they had died one by one, till only she remained. Then, old and feeble, she had crawled back into the reservation, defiant of Washakie, seeking comfort as a blind dog returns to the fireside from which he has been cruelly spurned.

As she slept, the men spread a map on the ground, and for the hundredth time Wetherell measured the blank space lying between Bonneville Basin and Fremont's peak, marked "unexplored," and exclaimed:

"It's wonderful how a mountain country expands as you get into it. Don't look much on the map, but gee! a fellow could spend ten years looking for this mine, and then be no better off than when he started."

"Yes," responded Kelley, "it's certainly up to you to cherish the old lady."

In the morning Wetherell dressed hastily and crept into the little tent where Pogosa lay. "How are you, granny?" he asked. She only shook her head and groaned.

"She say her back broke," Eugene interpreted.

A brisk rubbing with a liniment which he had brought from his kit limbered the poor, abused loins, and at last Pogosa sat up. She suddenly caught Wetherell's hand and drew it to her withered breast.

"Good white man," she cried out.

"Tell her I'll make her eyes well, too," he commanded Eugene. "The medicine will hurt a little, but it will make her eyes stronger to see the trail."

Kelley could not suppress his amusement as he watched Wetherell's operations. "You'll spoil gran'ma," he remarked. "She'll be discontented with the agency doctor. I'm not discouragin' your massage operations, mind you, but I can't help thinking that she'll want clean towels, and an osteopath to stroke her back every morning, when she goes back to her tepee."

"If she only holds out long enough to help us to find the mine she can have a trained nurse, and waiting maid to friz her hair—if she wants it frizzed."

"You don't mean to let her in as a partner?"

"I certainly do! Isn't she enduring the agonies for us? I'm going to see that she is properly paid for it."

"A hunk of beef and plenty of blankets and flannels is all she can use; but first let's find the mine. We can quarrel over its division afterwards."

"I doubt if we get her a-horse today. She's pretty thoroughly battered up."

"We must move, Andy. Somebody may trail us up. I want to climb into the next basin before night. Let me talk to her."

She flatly refused to move for Kelley, and Eugene said: "She too sick. Legs sick, back sick, eyes sick. Go no farther."

Kelley turned to Wetherell. "It's your edge, Andy. She's balked on me."

Wetherell took another tack. He told her to rest. "By and by I'll come and rub your back again and fix your eyes. Tomorrow you will feel strong and well." To this she made no reply.

All the day Kelley kept his eyes on the back trail, expecting each moment to see some dusky trailer break from the cover. As night began to fall it was Wetherell who brought a brand and built a little fire near the door to Pogosa's tent so that the flame might cheer her, and she uttered a sigh of comfort as its yellow glare lighted her dark tepee walls. He brought her bacon, also, and hot bread and steaming coffee, not merely because she was useful as a guide, but also because she was old and helpless and had been lured out of her own home into this gray and icy world of cloud.

"Eddie," he said, as he returned to his partner, "we're on a wild-goose chase. The thing is preposterous. There isn't any mine—there can't be such a mine!"

"Why not? What's struck you now?"

"This country has been traversed for a century. It is 'sheeped' and cattle-grazed and forest-ranged—"

Kelley waved his hand out toward the bleak crags which loomed dimly from amid the slashing shrouds of rain. "Traversed! Man, nobody ever does anything more than ride from one park to another. The mine is not in a park. It's on some of these rocky-timbered ridges. A thousand sheepherders might ride these trails for a hundred years and never see a piece of pay quartz. It's a big country! Look at it now! What chance have we without Pogosa? Now here we are on our way, with a sour old wench who thinks more of a piece of bread than of a hunk of ore. It's up to you, Andy—you and your 'mash.'"

"Well, I've caught the mind-reading delusion. I begin to believe that I understand Pogosa's reasoning. She is now beginning to be eaten by remorse. She came into this expedition for the food and drink. She now repents and is about to confess that she knows nothing about the mine. She and Eugene have conspired against us and are 'doing' us—good."

"Nitsky! You're away off your base. The fact is, Pogosa is a Sioux. She cares nothing for the Shoshoni, and she wants to realize on this mine. She wants to go back to her people before she dies. She means business—don't you think she don't; and if her running-gear don't unmesh tonight or tomorrow she's going to make good—that's my hunch."

"I hope you're right, but I can't believe it."

"You don't need to. You keep her thinking you're the Sun god—that's your job."

It rained all that day, and when night settled down it grew unreasonably warm for that altitude, and down on the marshes the horses stood, patiently enduring the gnats and mosquitoes. They plagued Pogosa so cruelly that Wetherell took his own web of bobinet and made a protecting cage for her head and hands. Never before had she been shielded from the pests of outdoor life. She laughed as she heard the baffled buzzing outside her net, and, pointing her finger, addressed them mockingly. Wetherell took the same joy in this that a child takes in a kitten dressed as a doll. To Eugene he said:

"You tell her Injun plenty fool. He don't know enough to get gold and buy mosquito netting. If she is wise and shows me the mine she will never be bitten again. No flies. No mosquitoes. Plenty beef. Plenty butter and hot biscuits. Plenty sugar and coffee. White man's own horse carry her back to her people."

It took some time to make the old woman understand this, and then she replied briefly, but with vigor, and Eugene translated it thus: "White man all same big chief. Go find mine, *sure,* for you. No want other white man to have gold. All yours."

The morning broke tardily. The rain had ceased, but the gray mist still hid the peaks, and now and then the pines shook down a shower of drops upon the tent cloth as if impatient of the persistent gathering of moisture. Otherwise the forest was as still as if it were cut from bronze.

Kelley arose and, going outside, began kicking the embers together. "Wake up, Andy. It's a gray outlook we have," he announced, after a careful survey. "The worst sign is this warmth and stillness. We're in the heart of a storm, and the mosquitoes are hellish."

As Wetherell was creeping from the tent door one of the pines quivered and sent down a handful of drops, squarely soaking the back of his neck, and a huge mosquito stuck savagely to the end of his nose. He was not in the best of humor as he straightened up.

"I can stand cold and snow, or wet and cold, but this hot, sticky, dark weather irritates me. Let's climb high and see if we can't reach the frost line."

"We'll be frosty enough when this storm passes," Kelley said, comfortingly. Then in a note of astonishment and surprise, "Well, look at that!"

Wetherell looked where he pointed, and beheld Pogosa squatting before a meager fire at her tent door, her head carefully draped in her bobinet. He forgot his own lumps and bumps, and laughed. "So doth the white man's civilization creep upon and subdue the Amerind, destroying his robust contempt for the elements and making of him a Sybarite."

Eugene appeared, grinning ruefully. "Heap dam' moskeets. Drink my blood all night."

"I reckon you got gran'ma's share," said Kelley.

Pogosa met Wetherell's glance with an exultant smile and pointed at the net as if to say: "See, I am safe. The brutes cannot touch me."

"The old girl is on her taps this morning. She deserves a reward. Wait a jiffy. There"—and Kelley uncorked a flask and poured a wee drop of an amber-colored liquid into the cup of coffee which Wetherell was about to take to her—"say nothing and see what happens."

She ate a rousing breakfast and was especially pleased with the coffee. Kelley repeated the dose, and she, much invigorated, ordered Eugene to bring her pony to her. This tickled Kelley mightily.

"You see how it is! She's already the millionairess. Who ever heard of an Injun getting up a horse for an old squaw? Look at Eugene!"

Eugene was indeed in open rebellion, and Wetherell, not caring to have trouble with him, went down and brought up the pony himself. He also gave the old woman his slicker and insisted on her wearing it, whereat Eugene wondered again.

The rain was beginning as they took their way over the meadow, and Wetherell was near to being bogged the first crack out of the box. "Do we go up that cliff?" he asked.

Pogosa waved her forefinger back and forth as though tracing the doublings of the trail.

Kelley scanned the wall narrowly. "I don't quite see it," he remarked, openly, "but I reckon I can find it," and he spurred his horse to the front.

"No! No!" screamed Pogosa in a sudden fury, her voice shrill and nasal. Kelley stopped, and she motioned Wetherell to his place in the lead.

With a comical look in his eyes the trailer fell back. " 'Pears like I ain't good enough to precede her Majesty. Go ahead, Andy."

Wetherell, in doubt of his ability to scale that cliff, started forth. The old trail could be seen dimly, and also the recent tracks of three horses. They were not precisely fresh, but they gave some uneasiness.

"Who made 'em, Eugene, and when?" he asked.

"One man riding—white man," announced Eugene. "Two pack horse—very light pack—made—mebbe so—three days ago."

"The forest ranger from the other side, possibly."

Wetherell, by watching the hoofmarks, by studying the conformation of the cliff before him, and by glancing back now and again at Pogosa, contrived to find the way. Slowly and for several hours they climbed this vast dike. It was nearly eleven thousand feet above the sea here, and Kelley himself breathed with effort as he climbed.

"I begin to see why people don't use this trail much," he said, as they stopped to rest on one of the broad shelves. "I'm beginning to wonder how we're going to pack our ore to market over this road."

"It will take mighty rich ore to pay its own freight," responded Wetherell.

Pogosa seemed strangely excited. Her eyes were gleaming, her face working with emotion.

"See the old girl!" said Kelley. "We must be hot on the trail of the mine. It don't look like mineral formation, but gold is where you find it."

"Go on," signed Pogosa.

The way seemed interminable, and at times Wetherell despaired of getting his withered commander into the park which he was sure lay above this dike. At noon they halted long enough to make coffee. Kelley flavored it as before, and Pogosa was ready to go on an hour later.

As they rose above the dike and Bonneville's Peak came into view, a low humming sound startled the hunters. It came from Pogosa. With eyes lit by the reviving fires of memory, she was chanting a hoarse song. She seemed to have thrown off half the burden of her years. Her voice gradually rose till her weird improvisation put a shiver into Wetherell's heart. She had forgotten the present; and with hands resting on the pommel of her saddle, with dim eyes fixed upon the valley, was reliving the past.

"She singing old hunting song," Eugene explained. "Many years ago she sing it. This heap fine hunting-ground then. Elk, bighorn, bear. All fine things in summer. Winter nothing but bighorn. Sheep-eaters live here many summers. Pogos' young and happy then. Now she is old and lonesome. People all gone. Purty soon she die. So she say."

Even the unimaginative mind of Tall Ed Kelley thrilled to the tragic significance of this survivor of a dying race chanting her solitary song. Her memory was quickening under the touch of these cliffs and the sound of these streams. She was retracing the steps of her youth.

Kelley interpreted it differently. "She's close to it," he called. "It's here in this valley, in some of these ridges."

Resolutely, unhesitatingly, Pogosa rode down the first stream which ran to the north, making directly for a low hill on which could be discerned a low comb of deflected rocks of a dark color. At last, riding up the ledge, she slipped from her horse and, tottering forward, fell face downward on the grass beside an upturned giant slab of gray stone.

The men stared in wonder, searching the ground for evidence of mineral. None could be seen. Suddenly lifting her head, the crone began to sing again, uttering a heart-shaking wail which poured from her quivering lips like the cry of the forsaken. The sight of her withered hands strained together and the tears in her sunken cheeks went to the soul. The desolate rocks, the falling rain, the wild and monstrous cliffs, the encircling mountains, all lent irresistible power to her grief. She seemed the minstrel of her race mourning for a vanished world.

"Come away," Eugene urged with a delicacy which sprang from awe. *"Her husband buried there."*

Deeply touched to know that her grief was personal, and filled, too, with a kind of helpless amazement at this emotional outbreak, the gold seekers withdrew down the slope, followed by the riderless pony, leaving the old woman crouched close against the sepulcher of her dead, pouring forth the sobbing wail of her song.

"This looks like the end of our mine," said Kelley, gloomily. "I begin to think that the old witch led us up here just for the sake of visiting that grave."

"It looks that way," responded Wetherell, "but what can we do? You can't beat her, and we've done all we could to bribe her."

Eugene advised: "You wait. Bimeby she got done cryin'. To-morrow she got cold—want meat, coffee—plenty bad. Then we go get her."

They went into camp not far away in the edge of a thicket of scraggly wind-dwarfed pines, and put up their tents for the night.

"Wouldn't it put a cramp into you," began Kelley, as they stood beside their fire, "to think that this old relict has actually led us all the way up here in order to water the grave of a sweetheart who died forty years ago?"

"It shows how human she is."

"Human! She's superhuman. She's crazy, that's what she is."

"It is all very wonderful to me, but I'm worried about her. She mustn't stay out there in this rain. It's going to turn cold. See that streak in the west?"

As Wetherell left the camp fire and began to climb back toward the comb of rocks he felt not merely the sheer immensity of this granite basin, but the loneliness, its almost insupportable silence and emptiness. With the feeling of one who intrudes he called to the old woman. He stooped and put his arm about her. "Come," he said. "You will die here. Come to the fire."

She suffered him to lead her away, but her head hung on her breast, her arms were limp.

Back at the camp fire, after seeing that Pogosa had been properly taken care of, the men faced each other in gloomy silence.

"Right here we take our medicine, partner," remarked Kelley. "Here we put a dot and double the line. I'd like to break over that divide and see how it looks in there, but our lady friend seems indisposed, and we'll just toast our knees and think where we missed it."

"After all," said Wetherell, soothingly, "this morning may be merely incidental. Let us be patient. She may recover." And at dark he carried some hot drink over to her tepee, but found her sleeping, and decided not to awaken her.

Back at their fire, as the night deepened, the men lighted their pipes, and with blankets at their backs huddled close about it. An imperious voice broke from Pogosa's tent. Wetherell looked around at Eugene.

"Did you speak?" he asked.

Eugene protested. "No. Pogosa talk."

"It sounded like a chief's voice," Kelley began. "A vigorous voice."

Eugene, trembling like a scared puppy, crept close to Wetherell. His voice was a mere whisper. "That no Pogos'—that Injun spirit talking."

Kelley was amused. "A spirit, eh? What does this spirit Injun say?"

"Say, 'White man with red beard listen—come closer and listen'—"

"That's you, Andy. Draw close. Your side partner has something to say."

Wetherell, alarmed by this delirium of his patient, rose to his feet, and as he did so her harsh voice uttered a short phrase which stiffened Eugene with fright. He left his place and sidled after Wetherell.

"She say *me*, Eugene, come talk for you."

"Very true. You'll need him. This may be a dying confession," argued Kelley.

"You go ahead in tepee," Eugene urged. "Me sit outside. Pogos' medicine now. See 'um vision. Spirits talk to her."

As he peered in at the tepee door Wetherell perceived Pogosa dimly. She was sitting erect in her bed. Her eyes were wide, the pose of her head erect and vigorous. She appeared a span taller, and when she spoke her voice seemed to issue from a deep and powerful chest.

With Eugene as a scared interpreter, Pogosa said: "Here, now where we are encamped, a battle took place many winters ago, and some of the exiles were slain. One of these was Iapi, the husband of Pogosa. He it was who could not speak Shoshoni."

Impatiently Kelley asked, "Will she be able to show us the mine?"

"She will try, but she is old and her mind is misty. She say she is grateful to you, Red Beard, and will give the gold to you. She asks that you take her back to her own people after you find the mine."

"Is the mine far from here?" asked Wetherell, gently.

"No, but it is very hard to find."

"Can't you trace the trail on a piece of paper for me?" he inquired.

"No, Pogosa cannot make the road. She can only tell you. Send the other white man away."

"Vamoose!" Wetherell called with a note of triumph in his voice, and Tall Ed faded away.

With faltering voice Pogosa began the all-important part of her tale: "The mine is on the head of the Wind River. Not far, but the way is very hard. Pogosa will not be able to lead you. From where we are you cross the valley to the mountain. You turn to your right and descend to a small lake lying under a bank of snow. This bank is held up by a row of black rocks. Below this lake is a stream and a long hill of round stones, all mixed together. On the west side of this ridge, just above another small lake, you will find the mine."

"Can it be approached from below?"

"No, a great cañon and many cliffs are there—" Her voice ceased abruptly. As suddenly as if life had been instantly withdrawn, she fell back upon her bed, and Eugene, released from the grasp of her hand, fled to Kelley, leaving Wetherell alone with the mystery.

"She seems to have dropped into a sort of trance," he said to Kelley, as he came back to the camp fire.

"Have you faith enough to follow those directions?" asked his partner.

"I certainly have."

Kelley laughed. "She may have a different set of directions to-morrow night. What do you say, Eugene? Pogos' all same fraud?"

Eugene, cowering close to the fire, needed not speech to make evident his awe of the battlefield. "Injun spirits all round," he whispered. "Hear 'em? They cry to Pogos'."

He lifted a hand in warning.

"It's only the wind in the dead pines," said Kelley.

"Plenty Injun spirits. *They cry!*" persisted Eugene.

"There speaks the primitive man," remarked Wetherell. "Our ancestors in Ireland or Wales or Scotland all had the same awe and wonder of the dark—just as the negroes in the South believe that on certain nights the dead soldiers of Lee and Grant rise and march again."

Kelley yawned. "Let's turn in and give the witches full swing. It's certainly their kind of a night."

Eugene spoke up. "Me sleep in your tepee. Pogos' scare me plenty hard."

Ridicule could not affect him, and out of pity for his suffering Wetherell invited him to make down his bed in the doorway of his own little tent.

"I hope gran'ma won't have another fit in the middle of the night," said Kelley, sleepily. "If she does, you can interview her alone. I'm dead to the world till dawn."

Nothing happened after this save that an occasional nervous chill overcame Eugene and caused him to call out, "What's that?" in a suppressed tone. "You hear 'em voice?" he asked several times; to all of which Wetherell replied, "It is the wind. Lie down; it is only the wind."

Musing upon the singular business in the deep of the night, Wetherell concluded that Pogosa, in a moment of emotional exaltation, and foreseeing her inability to guide him in person, had taken this method of telling him truly where the mine lay.

A mutter of voices in Pogosa's tepee interrupted his thought. "She is delirious again," he thought, but the cold nipped, and he dreaded rising and dressing. As he hesitated he thought he could distinguish two voices.

Shaking Eugene, he whispered, "Listen, Eugene, tell me what is going on in Pogosa's tent."

The half-breed needed no awakening. "She speak Sioux. I no speak Sioux. Some Sioux man's talk with her. Mebbe so her husband."

Wetherell smiled and snuggled down in his bed. "All right, Eugene. If Iapi is there he will take care of her. Good night."

Morning broke gloriously clear, crisp, and frosty. The insects were inert. The air had lost its heat and murk. The sun struck upon the sides of the tepees with cheerful glow, and all was buoyant, normal, and bracing as the partners arose.

Hurrying to Pogosa's tepee, Wetherell peeped in. "I wonder if she remembers her performance?" he asked himself, but could not determine, since she refused to answer Eugene when he questioned her. She took the food which Wetherell gave her, but did not eat or drink. Slowly she rose and hobbled away over the frosty grass toward the grave of Iapi.

"That's a bad sign," observed Kelley. "What's she going to do now, Eugene?"

"She's goin' put meat by stone. Mebbe so Injun spirits come eat."

"Well, she'd better absorb some of the grub herself."

"I think it's a beautiful act," professed Wetherell, lifting his field glass to study her motions. "She's happy now. She and her dead sweetheart are together again."

"I know Iapi once," Eugene volunteered. "He big man, very strong. Good rider. One spring all people hungry. No game. Ponies weak. Iapi say go kill sheep. Washakie hear of killing sheep. Send warriors. Iapi here. Make battle. Kill mebbe so four, six Injun. Kill Iapi. Washakie sorry now. His spirit cry in trees last night."

"Better let Pogosa alone for the day. The sun is warming the rocks. She is no longer cold. We can leave our camp here and scout around on our own account, returning this afternoon."

They rode across the valley in the direction indicated by the Voice. It was a bewildering maze into which the prospector must descend in search of the gold which is marked in yellow letters on some maps of the state. Several times did Wetherell drop into the basins, searching in vain for the small lake and the black-walled bank of snow, but at last Eugene's eye detected faint indications of a trail.

"We've struck the right road this time," exulted Wetherell. "Here is the wall of black rocks." There was no snow, but he argued that, the season having been extraordinarily warm and wet, this landmark had temporarily disappeared.

"I am sure this is the lake and stream," declared Wetherell. "See where the snow has lain."

"How far down do you figure the mine was?"

"Some miles below, near a second lake. I'm afraid we can't make it this trip. It will be dark by the time we reach camp. We'll just mark the spot and come back tomorrow."

Kelley was for pushing on. "What matter if we don't get back?"

"I'm thinking of Pogosa—" He shrugged his shoulders. "There's grub and shelter handy. She can come down any time and feed."

"Yes, but I hate to think of her all alone. She may be worse."

"Send Eugene back. We don't need him now."

Wetherell was almost as eager to go on as Kelley, but could not banish the pathetic figure of Pogosa so easily. Now that all signs pointed to the actual mine, his blood was fired with passion for the gold.

"Eugene, go back and wait for us. See that Pogosa is comfortable. We'll return by dark."

The word "dark" sent a shiver through Eugene. He shook his head. "No. I'm afraid. Spirits come again."

"Come on," said Kelley. "You can't make him do that. If we hurry we can get down to the other lake and back by sunset. The squaw will take care of herself. She's used to being alone—besides, the spirits are with her."

With the hope that it was not far, Wetherell yielded and set off down the slope, following the bank of the stream. Soon the other lake could be seen not far below them, and, slipping, sliding amid a cascade of pebbles, the gold seekers, now glowing with certainty of success, plunged straight toward the pool. Two or three times this precipitous method of descent led them into blind alleys from which they were obliged to climb, but at last, just as the sun went behind the imperial peak, they came out upon the shore of the little tarn which lay shallowly over a perfectly flat floor of cream-colored sand.

"Here we are," called Kelley. "Now if your ghost proves a liar, Pogosa must answer for it. Here is the rocky ridge on the east—"

"And here is trail," called Eugene, pointing to a faint line leading straight into the pines.

Wetherell spurred his horse into this trail, and in less than five minutes came upon the mine. It was not a shining thing to look at, so he did not shout. It was merely a cavernous opening in a high ledge of dark rock. On one side stood the sunken and decaying walls of a small log hut. The roof had fallen in, and vines filled the interior. In front of the door and all about, lumps of reddish, rusty-looking rock were scattered. A big stone hollowed in the middle showed that it had been used as a mortar for crushing the ore. The tunnel itself was irregular in shape and almost high enough to admit a horse. It dipped slightly from the threshold.

Tall Ed spoke first, in a tone of suppressed excitement. "Well, let's see what she's like."

"I trust Pogosa. Up goes our poster," replied Wetherell.

"All right. You put up the sign while I examine this ore."

With his hatchet Wetherell set to work hewing a square face on a tree. He was putting the first tack in his placard when Kelley walked over toward him, and with exaggeratedly quiet voice said:

"Just look at that, will you?"

Wetherell took the lump of ore and thrilled to the sight. It needed no expert to discern the free gold which lay in thin scales and sparkling lumps all through the rock.

"I want to yell," said Kelley, and his voice trembled.

"Don't do it!" said Wetherell. "Let's hurry back to camp and move down here. I won't feel safe till we do."

"I don't leave this place tonight, Andy. You and Eugene go back to camp. I'll stay here and hold down the find."

Wetherell, tremulous with excitement and weak in the knees, remounted his horse and set off for camp. It was a long climb, and the latter part of it tedious by reason of the growing darkness and the weariness of the horses. Wetherell's pony would not lead and was fairly at the end of his powers, but at last they reached their camping-place.

Wetherell's first thought was of Pogosa. She was nowhere in sight and her tepee was empty.

"She on hill," declared Eugene. "Lying down on stone. Injun cry there three days."

"The poor old thing! She'll be famished and chilled to the bone. It's a shame, our leaving her alone this way. But that's the way of the man in love with gold. Greed destroys all that is tender and loyal in a man. I am going right up and bring her down. Eugene, you start a fire and put some coffee on to boil."

With a heart full of pity the repentant goldseeker hurried toward the cairn. The crumpled little figure, so tragic in its loneliness and helpless grief, was lying where he had left it. She did not stir at the sound of his footsteps, nor when he laid his hand softly on her shoulder.

"Come, Pogosa," he said, with gentle authority. "Come, coffee, fire waiting. We found the mine. You're rich. You shall go back to your people. Come!"

Something in the feel of her shoulder, in the unyielding rigidity of her pose, startled and stilled him. He shook her questioningly. She was stark as stone. Her body had been cold for many hours. Her spirit was with Iapi.

# TOM CHIST AND THE TREASURE CHEST

## By *HOWARD PYLE*

*Illustrations by the Author*

## I

TO tell about Tom Chist, and how he got his name, and how he came to be living at the little settlement of Henlopen, just inside the mouth of the Delaware Bay, the story must begin as far back as 1686, when a great storm swept the Atlantic coast from end to end. During the heaviest part of the hurricane a bark went ashore on the Hen-and-Chicken Shoals, just below Cape Henlopen and at the mouth of the Delaware Bay, and Tom Chist was the only soul of all those on board the ill-fated vessel who escaped alive.

This story must first be told, because it was on account of the strange and miraculous escape that happened to him at that time that he gained the name that was given to him.

Even as late as that time of the American colonies, the little scattered settlement at Henlopen, made up of English, with a few Dutch and Swedish people, was still only a spot upon the face of the great American wilderness that spread away, with swamp and forest, no man knew how far to the westward. That wilderness was not only full of wild beasts, but of Indian savages, who every fall would come in wandering tribes to spend the winter along the shores of the fresh-water lakes below Henlopen. There for four or five months they would live upon fish and clams and wild ducks and geese, chipping their arrowheads, and making their earthenware pots and pans under the lee of the sand hills and pine woods below the Capes.

Sometimes on Sundays, when the Rev. Hilary Jones would be preaching in the little log church back in the woods, these half-clad red savages would come in from the cold, and sit squatting in the back part of the church, listening stolidly to the words that had no meaning for them.

But about the wreck of the bark in 1686. Such a wreck as that which then went ashore on the Hen-and-Chicken Shoals was a godsend to the poor and needy settlers in the wilderness where so few good things ever came. For the vessel went to pieces during the night, and the next morning the beach was strewn with wreckage —boxes and barrels, chests and spars, timbers and planks, a plentiful and bountiful harvest to be gathered up by the settlers as they chose, with no one to forbid or prevent them.

The name of the bark, as found painted on some of the water barrels and sea chests, was the *Bristol Merchant,* and she no doubt hailed from England.

As was said, the only soul who escaped alive off the wreck was Tom Chist.

A settler, a fisherman named Matt Abrahamson, and his daughter Molly, found Tom. He was washed up on the beach among the wreckage, in a great wooden box which had been securely tied around with a rope and lashed between two spars—apparently for better protection in beating through the surf. Matt Abrahamson thought he had found something of more than usual value when he came upon this chest; but when he cut the cords and broke open the box with his broadax, he could not have been more astonished had he beheld a salamander instead of a baby of nine or ten months old lying half smothered in the blankets that covered the bottom of the chest.

Matt Abrahamson's daughter Molly had had a baby who had died a month or so before. So when she saw the little one lying there in the bottom of the chest, she cried out in a great loud voice that the Good Man had sent her another baby in place of her own.

The rain was driving before the hurricane storm in dim, slanting sheets, and so she wrapped up the baby in the man's coat she wore and ran off home without waiting to gather up any more of the wreckage.

It was Parson Jones who gave the foundling his name. When the news came to his ears of what Matt Abrahamson had found he went over to the fisherman's cabin to see the child. He examined the clothes in which the baby was dressed. They were of fine linen and handsomely stitched, and the reverend gentleman opined that the foundling's parents must have been of quality. A kerchief had been wrapped around the baby's neck and under its arms and tied behind, and in the corner, marked with very fine needlework, were the initials T. C.

"What d'ye call him, Molly?" said Parson Jones. He was standing, as he spoke, with his back to the fire, warming his palms before the blaze. The pocket of the greatcoat he wore bulged out with a big case bottle of spirits which he had gathered up out of the wreck that afternoon. "What d'ye call him, Molly?"

"I'll call him Tom, after my own baby."

"That goes very well with the initial on the kerchief," said Parson Jones. "But what other name d'ye give him? Let it be something to go with C."

"I don't know," said Molly.

"Why not call him 'Chist,' since he was born in a chist out of the sea? 'Tom Chist'—the name goes off like a flash in the pan." And so "Tom Chist" he was called and "Tom Chist" he was christened.

So much for the beginning of the history of Tom Chist. The story of Captain Kidd's treasure box does not begin until the late spring of 1699.

That was the year that the famous pirate captain, coming up from the West Indies, sailed his sloop into the Delaware Bay, where he lay for over a month waiting for news from his friends in New York.

For he had sent word to that town asking if the coast was clear for him to return home with the rich prize he had brought from the Indian seas and the coast of Africa, and meantime he lay there in the Delaware Bay waiting for a reply. Before he left he turned the whole of Tom Chist's life topsy-turvy with something that he brought ashore.

By that time Tom Chist had grown into a strong-limbed, thick-jointed boy of fourteen or fifteen years of age. It was a miserable dog's life he lived with old Matt Abrahamson, for the old fisherman was in his cups more than half the time, and when he was so there was hardly a day passed that he did not give Tom a curse or a buffet or, as like as not, an actual beating. One would have thought that such treatment would have broken the spirit of the poor little foundling, but it had just the opposite effect upon Tom Chist, who was one of your stubborn, sturdy, stiff-willed fellows who only grow harder and more tough the more they are ill-treated. It had been a long time now since he had made any outcry or complaint at the hard usage he suffered from old Matt. At such times he would shut his teeth and bear whatever came to him, until sometimes the half-drunken old man would be driven almost mad by his stubborn silence. Maybe he would stop in the midst of the beating he was administering, and grinding his teeth, would cry out: "Won't ye say naught? Won't ye say naught? Well, then, I'll see if I can't make ye say naught." When things had reached such a pass as this Molly would generally interfere to protect her foster son, and then she and Tom would together fight the old man until they had wrenched the stick or the strap out of his hand. Then old Matt would chase them out of doors and around and around the house for maybe half an hour, until his anger was cool, when he would go back again, and for a time the storm would be over.

Besides his foster mother, Tom Chist had a very good friend in Parson Jones, who used to come over every now and then to Abrahamson's hut upon the chance of getting a half dozen fish for breakfast. He always had a kind word or two for Tom, who during the winter evenings would go over to the good man's house to learn his letters, and to read and write and cipher a little, so that by now he was able to spell the words out of the Bible and the almanac, and knew enough to change tuppence into four ha'pennies. This is the sort of boy Tom Chist was and this is the sort of life he led.

In the late spring or early summer of 1699 Captain Kidd's sloop sailed into the mouth of the Delaware Bay and changed the whole fortune of his life.

And this is how you come to the story of Captain Kidd's treasure box.

## II

Old Matt Abrahamson kept the flat-bottomed boat in which he went fishing, some distance down the shore, and in the neighborhood of the old wreck that had been sunk on the Shoals. This was the usual fishing ground of the settlers, and here old Matt's boat generally lay drawn up on the sand.

There had been a thunderstorm that afternoon, and Tom had gone down the beach to bale out the boat in readiness for the morning's fishing.

It was full moonlight now, as he was returning, and the night sky was full of floating clouds. Now and then there was a dull flash to the westward, and once a muttering growl of thunder, promising another storm to come.

All that day the pirate sloop had been lying just off the shore back of the Capes, and now Tom Chist could see the sails glimmering pallidly in the moonlight, spread for drying after the storm. He was walking up the shore homeward when he became aware that at some distance ahead of him there was a ship's boat drawn up on the little narrow beach, and a group of men clustered about it. He hurried forward with a good deal of curiosity to see who had landed, but it was not until he had come close to them that he could distinguish who and what they were. Then he knew that it must be a party who had come off the pirate sloop. They had evidently just landed, and two men were lifting out a chest from the boat. One of them was a negro, naked to the waist, and the other was a white man in his shirt sleeves, wearing petticoat breeches, a Monterey cap upon his head, a red bandanna handkerchief around his neck, and gold earrings in his ears. He had a long, plaited queue hanging down his back, and a great sheath knife dangling from his side. Another man, evidently the captain of the party, stood at a little distance as they lifted the chest out of the boat. He had a cane in one hand and a lighted lantern in the other,

although the moon was shining as bright as day. He wore jack
boots and a handsome laced coat, and he had a long, drooping mus-
tache that curled down below his chin. He wore a fine, feathered
hat, and his long black hair hung down upon his shoulders.

All this Tom Chist could see in the moonlight that glinted and
twinkled upon the gilt buttons of his coat.

They were so busy lifting the chest from the boat that at first
they did not observe that Tom Chist had come up and was standing
there. It was the white man with the long, plaited queue and the
gold earrings that spoke to him. "Boy, what do you want here,
boy?" he said, in a rough, hoarse voice. "Where d'ye come from?"
And then dropping his end of the chest, and without giving Tom
time to answer, he pointed off down the beach, and said, "You'd
better be going about your own business, if you know what's good
for you; and don't you come back, or you'll find what you don't
want waiting for you."

Tom saw in a glance that the pirates were all looking at him,
and then, without saying a word, he turned and walked away. The
man who had spoken to him followed him threateningly for some
little distance, as though to see that he had gone away as he was
bidden to do. But presently he stopped, and Tom hurried on alone,
until the boat and the crew and all were dropped away behind and
lost in the moonlight night. Then he himself stopped also, turned,
and looked back whence he had come.

There had been something very strange in the appearance of the
men he had just seen, something very mysterious in their actions,
and he wondered what it all meant, and what they were going to
do. He stood for a little while thus looking and listening. He could
see nothing, and could hear only the sound of distant talking. What
were they doing on the lonely shore thus at night? Then, following
a sudden impulse, he turned and cut off across the sand hummocks,
skirting around inland, but keeping pretty close to the shore, his
object being to spy upon them, and to watch what they were about
from the back of the low sand hills that fronted the beach.

He had gone along some distance in his circuitous return when
he became aware of the sound of voices that seemed to be drawing

closer to him as he came toward the speakers. He stopped and stood listening, and instantly, as he stopped, the voices stopped also. He crouched there silently in the bright, glimmering moonlight, surrounded by the silent stretches of sand, and the stillness seemed to press upon him like a heavy hand. Then suddenly the sound of a man's voice began again, and as Tom listened he could hear someone slowly counting. "Ninety-one," the voice began, "ninety-two, ninety-three, ninety-four, ninety-five, ninety-six, ninety-seven, ninety-eight, ninety-nine, one hundred, one hundred and one"—the slow, monotonous count coming nearer and nearer; "one hundred and two, one hundred and three, one hundred and four," and so on in its monotonous reckoning.

Suddenly he saw three heads appear above the sandhill, so close to him that he crouched down quickly with a keen thrill, close beside the hummock near which he stood. His first fear was that they might have seen him in the moonlight; but they had not, and his heart rose again as the counting voice went steadily on. "One hundred and twenty," it was saying—"and twenty-one, and twenty-two, and twenty-three, and twenty-four," and then he who was counting came out from behind the little sandy rise into the white and open level of shimmering brightness.

It was the man with the cane whom Tom had seen some time before—the captain of the party who had landed. He carried his cane under his arm now, and was holding his lantern close to something that he held in his hand, and upon which he looked narrowly as he walked with a slow and measured tread in a perfectly straight line across the sand, counting each step as he took it. "And twenty-five, and twenty-six, and twenty-seven, and twenty-eight, and twenty-nine, and thirty."

Behind him walked two other figures; one was the half-naked negro, the other man with the plaited queue and the earrings, whom Tom had seen lifting the chest out of the boat. Now they were carrying the heavy box between them, laboring through the sand with shuffling tread as they bore it onward. As he who was counting pronounced the word "thirty," the two men set the chest down on the sand with a grunt, the white man panting and blowing and wiping his sleeve across his forehead. And immediately he who counted took out a slip of paper and marked something down upon it. They stood there for a long time, during which Tom lay behind the sand hummock watching them, and for a while the silence was uninterrupted. In the perfect stillness Tom could hear the washing of the little waves beating upon the distant beach, and once the far-away sound of a laugh from one of those who stood by the ship's boat.

One, two, three minutes passed, and then the men picked up the chest and started on again; and then again the other man began his counting. "Thirty and one, and thirty and two, and thirty and three, and thirty and four"—he walked straight across the level open, still looking intently at that which he held in his hand—"and thirty and five, and thirty and six, and thirty and seven," and so on, until the three figures disappeared in the little hollow between the two sandhills on the opposite side of the open, and still Tom could hear the sound of the counting voice in the distance.

Just as they disappeared behind the hill there was a sudden faint flash of light; and by and by, as Tom lay still listening to the counting, he heard, after a long interval, a far-away muffled rumble of distant thunder. He waited for a while, and then arose and stepped to the top of the sand hummock behind which he had been lying. He looked all about him, but there was no one else to be seen. Then he stepped down from the hummock and followed in the direction which the pirate captain and the two men carrying the chest had gone. He crept along cautiously, stopping now and then to make sure that he still heard the counting voice, and when it ceased he lay down upon the sand and waited until it began again.

Presently, so following the pirates, he saw the three figures again in the distance, and, skirting around back of a hill of sand covered with coarse sedge grass, he came to where he overlooked a little open level space gleaming white in the moonlight.

The three had been crossing the level of sand, and were now not more than twenty-five paces from him. They had again set down the chest, upon which the white man with the long queue and the gold earrings had seated himself to rest, the negro standing close beside him. The moon shone as bright as day and full upon his face. It was looking directly at Tom Chist, every line as keen cut with white lights and black shadows as though it had been carved in ivory and jet. He sat perfectly motionless, and Tom drew back with a start, almost thinking he had been discovered. He lay silent, his heart beating heavily in his throat; but there was no alarm, and presently he heard the counting begin again, and when he looked once more he saw they were going away straight across the little open. A soft, sliding hillock of sand lay directly in front of them. They did not turn aside, but went straight over it, the leader helping himself up the sandy slope with his cane, still counting and still keeping his eyes fixed upon that which he held in his hand. Then they disappeared again behind the white crest on the other side.

So Tom followed them cautiously until they had gone almost half a mile inland. When next he saw them clearly it was from a little sandy rise which looked down like the crest of a bowl upon the floor of sand below. Upon this smooth, white floor the moon beat with almost dazzling brightness.

The white man who had helped to carry the chest was now kneeling, busied at some work, though what it was Tom at first could not see. He was whittling the point of a stick into a long wooden peg, and when, by and by, he had finished what he was about, he arose and stepped to where he who seemed to be the captain had stuck his cane upright into the ground as though to mark some particular spot. He drew the cane out of the sand, thrusting the stick down in its stead. Then he drove the long peg down with a wooden mallet which the negro handed to him. The sharp rapping of the mallet upon the top of the peg sounded loud in the perfect stillness, and Tom lay watching and wondering what it all meant. The man, with quick-repeated blows, drove the peg farther and farther down into the sand until it showed only two or three inches above the surface. As he finished his work there was another faint flash of light, and by and by another smothered rumble of thunder, and Tom, as he looked out toward the westward, saw the silver rim of the round and sharply outlined thundercloud rising slowly up into the sky and pushing the other and broken drifting clouds before it.

The two white men were now stooping over the peg, the negro man watching them. Then presently the man with the cane started straight away from the peg, carrying the end of a measuring line with him, the other end of which the man with the plaited queue held against the top of the peg. When the pirate captain had reached the end of the measuring line he marked a cross upon the sand, and then again they measured out another stretch of space.

So they measured a distance five times over, and then, from where Tom lay, he could see the man with the queue drive another peg just at the foot of a sloping rise of sand that swept up beyond into a tall white dune marked sharp and clear against the night sky behind.

As soon as the man with the plaited queue had driven the second peg into the ground they began measuring again, and so, still measuring, disappeared in another direction which took them in behind the sand dune where Tom no longer could see what they were doing.

The negro still sat by the chest where the two had left him, and so bright was the moonlight that from where he lay Tom could see the glint of it twinkling in the whites of his eyeballs.

Presently from behind the hill there came, for the third time, the sharp rapping sound of the mallet driving still another peg, and then after a while the two pirates emerged from behind the sloping whiteness into the space of moonlight again.

They came direct to where the chest lay, and the white man and the black man lifting it once more, they walked away across the level of open sand, and so on behind the edge of the hill and out of Tom's sight.

## III

Tom Chist could no longer see what the pirates were doing, neither did he dare to cross over the open space of sand that now lay between them and him. He lay there speculating as to what they were about, and meantime the storm cloud was rising higher and higher above the horizon, with louder and louder mutterings of thunder following each dull flash from out the cloudy, cavernous depths. In the silence he could hear an occasional click as of some iron implement, and he opined that the pirates were burying the chest, though just where they were at work he could neither see nor tell.

*Howard Pyle*

*Tom opined that the pirates were burying the chest.*

Still he lay there watching and listening, and by and by a puff of warm air blew across the sand, and a thumping tumble of louder thunder leaped from out the belly of the storm cloud, which every minute was coming nearer and nearer. Still Tom Chist lay watching.

Suddenly, almost unexpectedly, the three figures reappeared from behind the sandhill, the pirate captain leading the way, and the negro and white man following close behind him. They had gone about halfway across the white, sandy level between the hill and the hummock behind which Tom Chist lay, when the white man stopped and bent over as though to tie his shoe.

This brought the negro a few steps in front of his companion.

That which then followed happened so suddenly, so unexpectedly, so swiftly, that Tom Chist had hardly time to realize what it all meant before it was over. As the negro passed him the white man arose suddenly and silently erect, and Tom Chist saw the white moonlight glint upon the blade of a great dirk knife which he now held in his hand. He took one, two silent, catlike steps behind the unsuspecting negro. Then there was a sweeping flash of the blade

in the pallid light, and a blow, the thump of which Tom could
distinctly hear even from where he lay, stretched out upon the sand.

Howard Pyle

*The pirate captain looked impassively on.*

There was an instant echoing yell from the black man, who ran
stumbling forward, who stopped, who regained his footing, and
then stood for an instant as though rooted to the spot.

Tom had distinctly seen the knife enter his back, and even thought that he had seen the glint of the point as it came out from the breast.

Meantime the pirate captain had stopped, and now stood with his hand resting upon his cane looking impassively on.

Then the black man started to run. The white man stood for a while glaring after him; then he, too, started after his victim upon the run. The black man was not very far from Tom when he staggered and fell. He tried to rise, then fell forward again, and lay at length. At that instant the first edge of the cloud cut across the moon, and there was a sudden darkness; but in the silence Tom heard the sound of another blow and a groan, and then presently a voice calling to the pirate captain that it was all over.

He saw the dim form of the captain crossing the level sand, and then, as the moon sailed out from behind the cloud, he saw the white man standing over a black figure that lay motionless upon the sand.

Howard Pyle

*Tom Chist scrambled up and ran away.*

Then Tom Chist scrambled up and ran away, plunging down into the hollow of sand that lay in the shadows below. Over the next rise he ran, and down again into the next black hollow, and so on over the sliding, shifting ground, panting and gasping. It seemed to him that he could hear footsteps following, and in the terror that possessed him he almost expected every instant to feel the cold knife blade slide between his own ribs in such a thrust from behind as he had seen given to the poor black man.

So he ran on like one in a nightmare. His feet grew heavy like lead, he panted and gasped, his breath came hot and dry in his throat. But still he ran and ran until at last he found himself in front of old Matt Abrahamson's cabin, gasping, panting, and sobbing for breath, his knees relaxed and his thighs trembling with weakness.

As he opened the door and dashed into the darkened cabin (for both Matt and Molly were long ago asleep in bed) there was a flash of light, and even as he slammed to the door behind him there was an instant peal of thunder, heavy as though a great weight had been dropped upon the roof of the sky, so that the doors and windows of the cabin rattled.

## IV

Then Tom Chist crept to bed, trembling, shuddering, bathed in sweat, his heart beating like a trip hammer, and his brain dizzy from that long, terror-inspired race through the soft sand in which he had striven to outstrip he knew not what pursuing horror.

For a long, long time he lay awake, trembling and chattering with nervous chills, and when he did fall asleep it was only to drop into monstrous dreams in which he once again saw ever enacted, with various grotesque variations, the tragic drama which his waking eyes had beheld the night before.

Then came the dawning of the broad, wet daylight, and before the rising of the sun Tom was up and out of doors to find the young day dripping with the rain of overnight.

His first act was to climb the nearest sand hill and to gaze out toward the offing where the pirate ship had been the day before.

It was no longer there.

Soon afterwards Matt Abrahamson came out of the cabin and he called to Tom to go get a bite to eat, for it was time for them to be away fishing.

All that morning the recollection of the night before hung over Tom Chist like a great cloud of boding trouble. It filled the confined area of the little boat and spread over the entire wide spaces of sky and sea that surrounded them. Not for a moment was it lifted. Even when he was hauling in his wet and dripping line with a struggling fish at the end of it a recurrent memory of what he had seen would suddenly come upon him, and he would groan in spirit at the recollection. He looked at Matt Abrahamson's leathery face, at his lantern jaws cavernously and stolidly chewing at a tobacco leaf, and it seemed monstrous to him that the old man should be so unconscious of the black cloud that wrapped them all about.

When the boat reached the shore again he leaped scrambling to the beach, and as soon as his dinner was eaten he hurried away to find the Dominie Jones.

He ran all the way from Abrahamson's hut to the parson's house, hardly stopping once, and when he knocked at the door he was panting and sobbing for breath.

The good man was sitting on the back-kitchen doorstep smoking his long pipe of tobacco out into the sunlight, while his wife within was rattling about among the pans and dishes in preparation of their supper, of which a strong, porky smell already filled the air.

Then Tom Chist told his story, panting, hurrying, tumbling one word over another in his haste, and Parson Jones listened, breaking every now and then into an ejaculation of wonder. The light in his pipe went out and the bowl turned cold.

"And I don't see why they should have killed the poor black man," said Tom, as he finished his narrative.

"Why, that is very easy enough to understand," said the good reverend man. " 'Twas a treasure box they buried!"

In his agitation Mr. Jones had risen from his seat and was now stumping up and down, puffing at his empty tobacco pipe as though it were still alight.

"A treasure box!" cried out Tom.

"Aye, a treasure box! And that was why they killed the poor black man. He was the only one, d'ye see, besides they two who knew the place where 'twas hid, and now that they've killed him out of the way, there's nobody but themselves knows. The villains— Tut, tut, look at that now!" In his excitement the dominie had snapped the stem of his tobacco pipe in two.

"Why, then," said Tom, "if that is so, 'tis indeed a wicked, bloody treasure, and fit to bring a curse upon anybody who finds it!"

"'Tis more like to bring a curse upon the soul who buried it," said Parson Jones, "and it may be a blessing to him who finds it. But tell me, Tom, do you think you could find the place again where 'twas hid?"

"I can't tell that," said Tom, "'twas all in among the sand humps, d'ye see, and it was at night into the bargain. Maybe we could find the marks of their feet in the sand," he added.

"'Tis not likely," said the reverend gentleman, "for the storm last night would have washed all that away."

"I could find the place," said Tom, "where the boat was drawn up on the beach."

"Why, then, that's something to start from, Tom," said his friend. "If we can find that, then maybe we can find whither they went from there."

"If I was certain it was a treasure box," cried out Tom Chist, "I would rake over every foot of sand betwixt here and Henlopen to find it."

"'Twould be like hunting for a pin in a haystack," said the Rev. Hilary Jones.

As Tom walked away home, it seemed as though a ton's weight of gloom had been rolled away from his soul. The next day he and Parson Jones were to go treasure-hunting together; it seemed to Tom as though he could hardly wait for the time to come.

## V

The next afternoon Parson Jones and Tom Chist started off together upon the expedition that made Tom's fortune forever. Tom carried a spade over his shoulder and the reverend gentleman walked along beside him with his cane. As they jogged along up the beach they talked about the only thing they could—the treasure box. "And how big did you say 'twas?" quoth the good gentleman.

"About so long," said Tom Chist, measuring off upon the spade, "and about so wide, and this deep."

"And what if it should be full of money, Tom?" said the reverend gentleman, swinging his cane around and around in wide circles in the excitement of the thought, as he strode along briskly. "Suppose it should be full of money, what then?"

"By Moses!" said Tom Chist, hurrying to keep up with his friend, "I'd buy a ship for myself, I would, and I'd trade to Injy and to Chiny to my own boot, I would. Suppose the chist was all full of money, sir, and suppose we should find it; would there be enough in it, d'ye suppose, to buy a ship?"

"To be sure there would be enough, Tom; enough and to spare, and a good big lump over."

"And if I find it 'tis mine to keep, is it, and no mistake?"

"Why, to be sure it would be yours!" cried out the parson, in a loud voice. "To be sure it would be yours!" He knew nothing of the law, but the doubt of the question began at once to ferment in his brain, and he strode along in silence for a while. "Whose else would it be but yours if you find it?" he burst out. "Can you tell me that?"

"If ever I have a ship of my own," said Tom Chist, "and if ever I sail to Injy in her, I'll fetch ye back the best chist of tea, sir, that ever was fetched from Cochin Chiny." Parson Jones burst out laughing. "Thankee, Tom," he said; "and I'll thankee again when I get my chist of tea. But tell me, Tom, didst thou ever hear of the farmer girl who counted her chickens before they were hatched?"

It was thus they talked as they hurried along up the beach together, and so came to a place at last where Tom stopped short and stood looking about him. "'Twas just here," he said, "I saw the boat last night. I know 'twas here, for I mind me of that bit of wreck yonder, and that there was a tall stake drove in the sand just where yon stake stands."

Parson Jones put on his barnacles and went over to the stake toward which Tom pointed. As soon as he had looked at it carefully he called out: "Why, Tom, this hath been just drove down into the sand. 'Tis a brand-new stake of wood, and the pirates must have set it here themselves as a mark, just as they drove the pegs you spoke about down into the sand."

Tom came over and looked at the stake. It was a stout piece of oak nearly two inches thick; it had been shaped with some care, and the top of it had been painted red. He shook the stake and tried to move it, but it had been driven or planted so deeply into the sand that he could not stir it. "Aye, sir," he said, "it must have been set here for a mark, for I'm sure 'twas not here yesterday or the day before." He stood looking about him to see if there were other signs of the pirates' presence. At some little distance there was the corner of something white sticking up out of the sand. He could see that it was a scrap of paper, and he pointed to it, calling out:

"Yonder is a piece of paper, sir. I wonder if they left that behind them?"

It was a miraculous chance that placed that paper there. There was only an inch of it showing, and if it had not been for Tom's sharp eyes, it would certainly have been overlooked and passed by. The next windstorm would have covered it up, and all that afterwards happened never would have occurred.

"Look, sir," he said, as he struck the sand from it, "it hath writing on it."

"Let me see it," said Parson Jones. He adjusted the spectacles a little more firmly astride of his nose as he took the paper in his hand and began conning it. "What's all this?" he said; "a whole lot of figures and nothing else." And then he read aloud, " 'Mark— S. S. W. S. by S.' What d'ye suppose that means, Tom?"

"I don't know, sir," said Tom. "But maybe we can understand it better if you read on."

" 'Tis all a great lot of figures," said Parson Jones, "without a grain of meaning in them so far as I can see, unless they be sailing directions." And then he began reading again: " 'Mark—S. S. W. by S. 40, 72, 91, 130, 151, 177, 202, 232, 256, 271'—d'ye see, it must be sailing directions—'299, 335, 362, 386, 415, 446, 469, 491, 522, 544, 571, 598'— what a lot of them there be—'626, 652, 676, 695, 724, 851, 876, 905, 940, 967. Peg. S. E. by E. 269 foot. Peg. S. S. W. by S. 427 foot. Peg. Dig to the west of this six foot.' "

"What's that about a peg?" exclaimed Tom. "What's that about a peg? And then there's something about digging, too!" It was as though a sudden light began shining into his brain. He felt himself growing quickly very excited. "Read that over again, sir," he cried. "Why, sir, you remember I told you they drove a peg into the sand. And don't they say to dig close to it? Read it over again, sir—read it over again!"

"Peg?" said the good gentleman. "To be sure it was about a peg. Let's look again. Yes, here it is. 'Peg S. E. by E. 269 foot.'"

"Aye!" cried out Tom Chist again, in great excitement. "Don't you remember what I told you, sir, 269 foot? Sure that must be what I saw 'em measuring with the line."

Parson Jones had now caught the flame of excitement that was blazing up so strongly in Tom's breast. He felt as though some wonderful thing was about to happen to them. "To be sure, to be sure!" he called out, in a great big voice. "And then they measured out 427 foot, south-southwest by south, and they then drove another peg, and then they buried the box six foot to the west of it. Why, Tom—why, Tom Chist! if we've read this aright, thy fortune is made."

Tom Chist stood staring straight at the old gentleman's excited face, and seeing nothing but it in all the bright infinity of sunshine. Were they, indeed, about to find the treasure chest? He felt the sun very hot upon his shoulders, and he heard the harsh, insistent jarring of a tern that hovered and circled with forked tail and sharp white wings in the sunlight just above their heads; but all the time he stood staring into the good old gentleman's face.

It was Parson Jones who first spoke. "But what do all these figures mean?" And Tom observed how the paper shook and rustled in the tremor of excitement that shook his hand. He raised the paper to the focus of his spectacles and began to read again. "'Mark 40, 722, 91—'"

"Mark?" cried out Tom, almost screaming. "Why, that must mean the stake yonder; that must be the mark." And he pointed to the oaken stick with its red tip blazing against the white shimmer of sand behind it.

"And the 40 and 72 and 91," cried the old gentleman, in a voice

equally shrill—"why, that must mean the number of steps the pirate was counting when you heard him."

"To be sure that's what they mean!" cried Tom Chist. "That is it, and it can be nothing else. Oh, come, sir—come, sir; let us make haste and find it!"

"Stay! stay!" said the good gentleman, holding up his hand; and again Tom Chist noticed how it trembled and shook. His voice was steady enough, though very hoarse, but his hand shook and trembled as though with a palsy. "Stay! stay! First of all, we must follow these measurements. And 'tis a marvelous thing," he croaked, after a little pause, "how this paper ever came to be here."

"Maybe it was blown here by the storm," suggested Tom Chist.

"Like enough; like enough," said Parson Jones. "Like enough, after the wretches had buried the chest and killed the poor black man, they were so buffeted and bowsed about by the storm that it was shook out of the man's pocket, and thus blew away from him without his knowing aught of it."

"But let us find the box!" cried Tom Chist, flaming with his excitement.

"Aye, aye," said the good man; "only stay a little, my boy, until we make sure what we're about. I've got my pocket compass here, but we must have something to measure off the feet when we have found the peg. You run across to Tom Brooke's house and fetch that measuring rod he used to lay out his new byre. While you're gone I'll pace off the distance marked on the paper with my pocket compass here."

## VI

Tom Chist was gone for almost an hour, though he ran nearly all the way and back, upborne as on the wings of the wind. When he returned, panting, Parson Jones was nowhere to be seen, but Tom saw his footsteps leading away inland, and he followed the scuffling marks in the smooth surface across the sand humps and down into the hollows, and by and by found the good gentleman in a spot he at once knew as soon as he laid his eyes upon it.

It was the open space where the pirates had driven their first peg, and where Tom Chist had afterwards seen them kill the poor black man. Tom Chist gazed around as though expecting to see some sign of the tragedy, but the space was as smooth and as undisturbed as a floor, excepting where, midway across it, Parson Jones, who was now stooping over something on the ground, had trampled it all around about.

When Tom Chist saw him he was still bending over, scraping away from something he had found.

It was the first peg!

Inside of half an hour they had found the second and third pegs, and Tom Chist stripped off his coat, and began digging like mad down into the sand, Parson Jones standing over him watching him. The sun was sloping well toward the west when the blade of Tom Chist's spade struck upon something hard.

If it had been his own heart that he had hit in the sand his breast could hardly have thrilled more sharply.

It was the treasure box!

Parson Jones himself leaped down into the hole, and began scraping away the sand with his hands as though he had gone crazy. At last, with some difficulty, they tugged and hauled the chest up out of the sand to the surface, where it lay covered all over with the grit that clung to it. It was securely locked and fastened with a padlock, and it took a good many blows with the blade of the spade to burst the bolt. Parson Jones himself lifted the lid. Tom Chist leaned forward and gazed down into the open box. He would not have been surprised to have seen it filled full of yellow gold and bright jewels. It was filled half full of books and papers, and half full of canvas bags tied safely and securely around and around with cords of string.

Parson Jones lifted out one of the bags, and it jingled as he did so. It was full of money.

He cut the string, and with trembling, shaking hands handed the bag to Tom, who, in an ecstacy of wonder and dizzy with delight, poured out, with swimming sight, upon the coat spread on the ground a cataract of shining silver money that rang and twinkled and jingled as it fell in a shining heap upon the coarse cloth.

Parson Jones held up both hands into the air, and Tom stared at what he saw, wondering whether it was all so, and whether he was really awake. It seemed to him as though he was in a dream.

There were two-and-twenty bags in all in the chest: ten of them full of silver money, eight of them full of gold money, three of them full of gold dust, and one small bag with jewels wrapped up in wad cotton and paper.

" 'Tis enough," cried out Parson Jones, "to make us both rich men as long as we live."

The burning summer sun, though sloping in the sky, beat down upon them as hot as fire; but neither of them noticed it. Neither did they notice hunger nor thirst nor fatigue, but sat there as though in a trance, with the bags of money scattered on the sand around them, a great pile of money heaped upon the coat, and the open chest beside them. It was an hour of sundown before Parson Jones had begun fairly to examine the books and papers in the chest.

Of the three books, two were evidently log books of the pirates who had been lying off the mouth of Delaware Bay all this time. The other book was written in Spanish, and was evidently the log book of some captured prize.

It was then, sitting there upon the sand, the good old gentleman reading in his high, cracking voice, that they first learned from the bloody records in those two books who it was who had been lying inside the cape all this time, and that it was the famous Captain Kidd. Every now and then the reverend gentleman would stop to exclaim, "Oh, the bloody wretch!" or, "Oh, the desperate, cruel villains!" and then would go on reading again a scrap here and a scrap there. And all the while Tom Chist sat and listened, every now and then reaching out furtively and touching the heap of money still lying upon the coat.

One might be inclined to wonder why Captain Kidd had kept those bloody records. He had probably laid them away because they so incriminated many of the great people of the colony of New York that, with the books in evidence, it would have been impossible to bring the pirate to justice without dragging a dozen or more fine gentlemen into the dock along with him. If he could have kept them in his own possession they would doubtless have been a great weapon of defense to protect him from the gallows. Indeed, when Captain Kidd was finally brought to conviction and hung, he was not accused of his piracies, but of striking a mutinous seaman upon the head with a bucket and accidentally killing him. The authorities did not dare to try him for piracy. He was really hung because he was a pirate, and we know that it was the log books that Tom Chist brought to New York that did the business for him; he was accused and convicted of manslaughter for killing of his own ship carpenter with a bucket.

So Parson Jones, sitting there in the slanting light, read through these terrible records of piracy, and Tom, with the pile of gold and silver money beside him, sat and listened to him.

What a spectacle, if anyone had come upon them! But they were alone, with the vast arch of sky empty above them and the wide white stretch of sand a desert around them. The sun sank lower and lower, until there was only time to glance through the other papers in the chest.

They were nearly all goldsmiths' bills of exchange drawn in favor of certain of the most prominent merchants of New York. Parson Jones, as he read over the names, knew of nearly all the gentlemen by hearsay. Aye, here was this gentleman; he thought that name would be among 'em. What? Here is Mr. So-and-so. Well, if all they say is true, the villain has robbed one of his own best friends. "I wonder," he said, "why the wretch should have hidden these papers so carefully away with the other treasures, for they could do him no good?" Then, answering his own question: "Like enough because these will give him a hold over the gentlemen to whom they are drawn so that he can make a good bargain for his own neck before he gives the bills back to their owners. I tell you what it is, Tom," he continued, "it is yourself shall go to New York and bargain for the return of these papers. 'Twill be as good as another fortune to you."

The majority of the bills were drawn in favor of one Richard

Chillingsworth, Esquire. "And he is," said Parson Jones, "one of the richest men in the province of New York. You shall go to him with the news of what we have found."

"When shall I go?" said Tom Chist.

"You shall go upon the very first boat we can catch," said the parson. He had turned, still holding the bills in his hand, and was now fingering over the pile of money that yet lay tumbled out upon the coat. "I wonder, Tom," said he, "if you could spare me a score or so of these doubloons?"

"You shall have fifty score, if you choose," said Tom, bursting with gratitude and with generosity in his newly found treasure.

"You are as fine a lad as ever I saw, Tom," said the parson, "and I'll thank you to the last day of my life."

Tom scooped up a double handful of silver money. "Take it, sir," he said, "and you may have as much more as you want of it."

He poured it into the dish that the good man made of his hands, and the parson made a motion as though to empty it into his pocket. Then he stopped, as though a sudden doubt had occurred to him. "I don't know that 'tis fit for me to take this pirate money, after all," he said. "But you are welcome to it," said Tom.

Still the parson hesitated. "Nay," he burst out, "I'll not take it; 'tis blood money." And as he spoke he chucked the whole double handful into the now empty chest, then arose and dusted the sand from his breeches. Then, with a great deal of bustling energy, he helped to tie the bags again and put them all back into the chest.

They reburied the chest in the place whence they had taken it, and then the parson folded the precious paper of directions, placed it carefully in his wallet, and his wallet in his pocket. "Tom," he said, for the twentieth time, "your fortune has been made this day."

And Tom Chist, as he rattled in his breeches pocket the half dozen doubloons he had kept out of his treasure, felt that what his friend had said was true.

As the two went back homeward across the level space of sand Tom Chist suddenly stopped stock-still and stood looking about him. "'Twas just here," he said, digging his heel down into the sand, "that they killed the poor black man."

"And here he lies buried for all time," said Parson Jones; and as he spoke he dug his cane down into the sand. Tom Chist shuddered. He would not have been surprised if the ferrule of the cane had struck something soft beneath that level surface. But it did not, nor was any sign of that tragedy ever seen again. For, whether the pirates had carried away what they had done and buried it elsewhere, or whether the storm in blowing the sand had completely leveled off and hidden all sign of that tragedy where it was enacted, certain it is that it never came to sight again—at least so far as Tom Chist and the Rev. Hilary Jones ever knew.

## VII

This is the story of the treasure box. All that remains now is to conclude the story of Tom Chist, and to tell of what came of him in the end.

He did not go back again to live with old Matt Abrahamson. Parson Jones had now taken charge of him and his fortunes, and Tom did not have to go back to the fisherman's hut.

Old Abrahamson talked a great deal about it, and would come in his cups and harangue good Parson Jones, making a vast protestation of what he would do to Tom—if he ever caught him— for running away. But Tom on all these occasions kept carefully out of his way, and nothing came of the old man's threatenings.

Tom used to go over to see his foster mother now and then, but always when the old man was from home. And Molly Abrahamson used to warn him to keep out of her father's way. "He's in as vile a humor as ever I see, Tom," she said; "he sits sulking all day long, and 'tis my belief he'd kill ye if he caught ye."

Of course Tom said nothing, even to her, about the treasure, and he and the reverend gentleman kept the knowledge thereof to themselves. About three weeks later Parson Jones managed to get him shipped aboard of a vessel bound for New York town, and a few days later Tom Chist landed at that place. He had never been in such a town before, and he could not sufficiently wonder and marvel at the number of brick houses, at the multitude of people coming and going along the fine, hard, earthen sidewalk, at the shops and the stores where goods hung in the windows, and, most of all, the fortifications and the battery at the point, at the rows of threatening cannon, and at the scarlet-coated sentries pacing up and down the ramparts. All this was very wonderful, and so were the clustered boats riding at anchor in the harbor. It was like a new world, so different it was from the sandhills and the sedgy levels of Henlopen.

Tom Chist took up his lodgings at a coffeehouse near to the town hall, and thence he sent by the postboy a letter written by Parson Jones to Master Chillingsworth. In a little while the boy returned with a message, asking Tom to come up to Mr. Chillingsworth's house that afternoon at two o'clock.

Tom went thither with a great deal of trepidation, and his heart fell away altogether when he found it a fine, grand brick house, three stories high, and with wrought-iron letters across the front.

The counting house was in the same building; but Tom, because of Mr. Jones's letter, was conducted directly into the parlor, where the great rich man was awaiting his coming. He was sitting in a leather-covered armchair, smoking a pipe of tobacco, and with a bottle of fine old Madeira close to his elbow.

Tom had not had a chance to buy a new suit of clothes yet, and so he cut no very fine figure in the rough dress he had brought with him from Henlopen. Nor did Mr. Chillingsworth seem to think very highly of his appearance, for he sat looking sideways at Tom as he smoked.

"Well, my lad," he said, "and what is this great thing you have to tell me that is so mightily wonderful? I got what's-his-name—Mr. Jones's—letter, and now I am ready to hear what you have to say."

But if he thought but little of his visitor's appearance at first, he soon changed his sentiments toward him, for Tom had not spoken twenty words when Mr. Chillingsworth's whole aspect changed. He straightened himself up in his seat, laid aside his pipe, pushed away his glass of Madeira, and bade Tom take a chair.

He listened without a word as Tom Chist told of the buried treasure, of how he had seen the poor negro murdered, and of how he and Parson Jones had recovered the chest again. Only once did Mr.

Chillingsworth interrupt the narrative. "And to think," he cried, "that the villain this very day walks about New York town as though he were an honest man, ruffling it with the best of us! But if we can only get hold of these log books you speak of. Go on; tell me more of this."

When Tom Chist's narrative was ended, Mr. Chillingsworth's bearing was as different as daylight is from dark. He asked a thousand questions, all in the most polite and gracious tone imaginable, and not only urged a glass of his fine old Madeira upon Tom, but asked him to stay for supper. There was nobody to be there, he said, but his wife and daughter.

Tom, all in a panic at the very thought of the two ladies, sturdily refused to stay even for the dish of tea Mr. Chillingsworth offered him.

He did not know that he was destined to stay there as long as he should live.

"And now," said Mr. Chillingsworth, "tell me about yourself."

"I have nothing to tell, Your Honor," said Tom, "except that I was washed up out of the sea."

"Washed up out of the sea!" exclaimed Mr. Chillingsworth. "Why, how was that? Come, begin at the beginning, and tell me all."

Thereupon Tom Chist did as he was bidden, beginning at the very beginning and telling everything just as Molly Abrahamson had often told it to him. As he continued, Mr. Chillingsworth's interest changed into an appearance of stronger and stronger excitement. Suddenly he jumped up out of his chair and began to walk up and down the room.

"Stop! stop!" he cried out at last, in the midst of something Tom was saying. "Stop! stop! Tell me; do you know the name of the vessel that was wrecked, and from which you were washed ashore?"

"I've heard it said," said Tom Chist, "'twas the *Bristol Merchant.*"

"I knew it! I knew it!" exclaimed the great man, in a loud voice, flinging his hands up into the air. "I felt it was so the moment you began the story. But tell me this, was there nothing found with you with a mark or a name upon it?"

"There was a kerchief," said Tom, "marked with a T and a C."

"Theodosia Chillingsworth!" cried out the merchant. "I knew it! I knew it! Heavens! To think of anything so wonderful happening as this! Boy! boy! dost thou know who thou art? Thou art my own brother's son. His name was Oliver Chillingsworth, and he was my partner in business and thou art his son." Then he ran out into the entryway, shouting and calling for his wife and daughter to come.

So Tom Chist—or Thomas Chillingsworth, as he now was to be called—did stay to supper, after all.

This is the story, and I hope you may like it. For Tom Chist became rich and great, as was to be supposed, and he married his pretty cousin Theodosia (who had been named for his own mother, drowned in the *Bristol Merchant*).

He did not forget his friends, but had Parson Jones brought to New York to live.

As to Molly and Matt Abrahamson, they both enjoyed a pension of ten pounds a year for as long as they lived; for now that all was well with him, Tom bore no grudge against the old fisherman for all the drubbings he had suffered.

The treasure box was brought on to New York, and if Tom Chist did not get all the money there was in it (as Parson Jones had opined he would) he got at least a good big lump of it.

And it is my belief that those log books did more to get Captain Kidd arrested in Boston town and hanged in London than anything else that was brought up against him.

# DICK TURPIN

## By *CHARLES J. FINGER*

### I

DICK TURPIN was a highwayman and many a man and many a coach did he stop on the road, and his name was known at widely separated places, at Harrogate as well as Epping, at Bath and at Epsom quite as well as at Tunbridge Wells. Indeed, he never failed to announce his name to those he robbed, and many counted it as a noteworthy thing to have been stopped by him. Tales were told of how, dressed in the height of fashion, he had rented great wainscotted rooms in Soho and entertained, not the gentry to be sure, but tough spirits of his own kidney. And once, according to tradition, he surprised Mr. Pope of Twickenham as he walked in the fields, but found nothing on the man except a bundle of papers which the poet seemed to be trying to hide, so after looking through them, the highwayman tossed the bundle into a hedge. Seeing the little man run to his papers, Turpin, full of suspicion, took them again suspecting some hidden treasure that he had possibly over-looked, but there was nothing but scrawling writing. So the thief counted it gain when he returned the papers and was handed a gold chain which had been overlooked, knowing nothing of the treasure that lay hidden in the Essay on Man. For all that, the highwayman was twitted shortly afterwards by the witty and charming Mrs. Bellenden when he stopped her coach on Hownslow Heath. When he called on her to deliver her jewels to him she flung her rings in his face, calling him a dull boor who did not know real treasure from silly gold, she having in mind the Twickenham affair. But what she meant, he did not at all understand.

In the year 1739, Dick Turpin, the Thaxted butcher's son, whose real name was Tom Palmer, had an encounter that yielded nothing but disappointment, though there hung on it an adventure the tale of which all England loves to this day. The Briton does not readily relinquish his heroes of popular mythology, and romance hangs to the tale of Turpin, true or false, as it hangs to the tale of King Alfred and the cakes, or the tale of Guy Fawkes and his gunpowder barrel, or to the tale of Sweeny Todd, the Demon Barber of number 186 Fleet Street, who is said to have robbed unwary customers and converted them into meat pies. So here is the tale of Turpin, and on part of it at least, the finger of certitude may be placed.

One day, Turpin, a fellow splendid enough with his silver-mounted horse trappings and pistols and sword: his coat of scarlet and his satin waistcoat: and last, but most important, his bonny mare Black Bess, rode down from Chingford way. He saw, and noted a drover taking cattle Londonward. Now, his knowledge of his former trade told him that animals in such condition would bring a good, round price, whereupon he laid his plans carefully and renewed a somewhat sagging acquaintance with the ostler at the Cow and Tub Inn. After a while, he learned from the ostler that, on a certain Wednesday, the cattle man would leave London bound for his home in Fyfield.

The way to the village of Fyfield led through Epping Forest, and, having checked up the ostler's information by private observation, not only seeing the drover prepare for the journey at the Inn, but also watching him as he passed through Hackney, Turpin loosed his rein and cantered easily to the River Ching, a little willow-bordered stream, and there waited in patience to the end that he might levy tribute on the returning farmer. But the cattle man was far longer in getting to that place than the highwayman's calculations had led him to expect; indeed, the western sky was red and gold before he appeared. At length he came in sight, a broad-faced, jolly-looking, corpulent fellow on a slow nag, riding unsuspiciously across the patch of heathy open land which Dick commanded from his hiding-place. Seeing that all was ripe for action, the highwayman leaped to saddle and went into the road with a dash, drawing rein sharply so that Black Bess blocked the road and halted the red-faced drover. Then out came Dick's sword with a flourish and the point of it was at the farmer's chest.

"Stand and deliver!" cried Turpin.

The farmer's horse stopped mechanically, and, the reins being loosed, it fell to cropping the herbage between the cart ruts as if being halted on the king's highway was an ordinary occurrence and an everyday matter. As for the man, he turned his large blue eyes on the dashing highway robber, and, in the patient tone of one who is resigned to all things, said:

"Standing I already am, but I have nothing to deliver."

"None of your nonsense," exclaimed Turpin, a little staggered with the bull-necked affirmation. "In London you sold cattle and sold them well. Where is the money?"

The red-faced man gave a little laugh, then said: "Would that I knew. True I sold well, but—"

"No excuses," interrupted Turpin impatiently. "Out with your purse and quickly."

He was brisk, and acted in a competent and businesslike manner, making a little thrust with his blade in the air, but the drover remained unexcited.

"I have no love for your weapon," observed the farmer with vast gravity. "Why not put it aside, lad? The truth is that my purse, and all that was in it was taken by one of your trade less than an hour ago, and on this side of Buckhurst Hill, and mighty vexed the fellow seemed to be at the sorry showing I made. Only a couple of shillings had I, though he searched me well, believing I lied when I said that I had no more."

"What!" roared Dick. "Two shillings?"

The man nodded his head by way of reply and there was something in his solid calmness which led the highwayman to believe that he spoke the truth. "If you lie—" he blustered, then dropped the point of his sword.

The farmer who had been turning things over in his mind, laughed a little softly. "So also said the other fellow who stopped me," he said. "He made me take off my boots and he went through my pockets, but nothing did he find. Two shillings I had when I left London, with which I intended to pay my fare tonight at Epping Inn, but now that, too, is gone. Luckily they know me there for an honest man, and money or no money, I may stay there for the night. To be sure, the fellow at Buckhurst Hill wished me well at parting, but little good are his wishes when he leaves me penniless."

The straightforward heartiness of the man woke a kind of delight in human fellowship in Dick Turpin, so he returned his sword to its scabbard, saying that he would ride a little way with him for company's sake.

"But what of the money that you had for the cattle you sold?" he asked, and the farmer laughed softly as he tugged at his rein to lift his nag's head, and, seeing that there was no more to fear from the highwayman, thumped the ribs of his animal with his heels.

"Little of the money that a man earns does he keep," grumbled the farmer. "To be sure, I sold my cattle at a good price, as you say, but many were the hands stretched out to take it before I could put it in my purse. Like hawks after young chicks are men after money in the city. There was the man who owns the land that I till, and to his agent went nine-tenths of what I had. There was a lawyer, too, with papers, and him I had to fee. Much more there was."

A silence fell then as they rode together, and when the farmer again spoke there was a good-humored smile on his face and he looked at Turpin out of the tail of his eyes. "If all the men that you stop on the road are in like sorry case, then is your business as bad as mine, I think."

The highwayman made no reply, but merely rubbed his ear with vexation, so the farmer went on in his dull, monotonous way, with many windings and loopings, to tell of this and of that and of the other. So it came about that Turpin heard much of London, and of how his companion had visited Hallam's Booth where he had seen and heard the affecting tragedy of The Trial and Ancient History of Fair Rosamund, "the which," he said, "I am sure would wring tears from a heart of stone. For seeing the sweet wench so sad, I had a mind to run to her side." Then there was a long tale of how he had gone with a lawyer's clerk to Marylebone Gardens and there heard martial music, and also saw a Punch and Judy show at which he "laughed until the tears ran," though while he watched, some light-fingered fellow had taken his watch.

So they rode and talked until the moon came up, when, becoming aware of a clatter of horse hoofs in the distance, Dick bade his farmer farewell and turned his mare's head to plunge into the nearest cover, which chanced to be a grove of tall oaks.

Turpin discarded all concealment a few minutes later when he saw that the coming rider was alone and riding fast. When the horseman was a dozen yards away, he guided Black Bess into the middle of the road and turned, as though going in the same direction as the coming rider. The horseman coming alongside, he drew his pistol, leaned over and caught at the other's bridle, shouting as he did so, "Stand! Your money or your life!"

"Neither!" roared the other as he pushed his steed in such way as to shoulder Black Bess, and, at a glance, Dick Turpin recognized his friend and fellow highwayman, Tom King.

"Business must be bad indeed," said King, "when you stop a man who has but two shillings which he took from a farmer," and at that Dick stared at him dolefully.

"Bad indeed," he made reply. "Five men and a coach have I stopped since Monday, and not enough to pay an ostler. It seems to me that there is no more money in the world."

The pair stood with nothing to say, then dismounted and sat under a tree, while the horses, with reins hanging loose, softly munched the grass. Falling to talk presently there were comparisons and the relating of experiences, with much bewailing because of the sad days on which they had fallen. Presently Tom King advanced a theory that where men were few, as in the country, money must perforce be scanty. Wealth, he said, was to be had only by bold doings in the towns where were roaring crowds and bustling multitudes. Then, like the farmer, Tom King told tales of what he had seen, of gay throngs at Vauxhall Gardens where men and women played for high stakes, of taverns merry with the sound of French horns, and of many glimmering lights in pleasure gardens where people sat at tables eating and drinking and singing until the early hours of the morning.

In a limited way Dick Turpin had imagination, and, while his knowledge of London was confined to the smaller streets and alleys in the neighborhood of Drury Lane for the most part, yet, when he heard the tales told by Tom King, he began to picture himself moving in a fashionable throng, passing as an honest citizen, and, by some deed of derring do, winning a fortune in a single swoop. His idea of what might actually be done was hazy in the extreme, but there was the certainty that he had fallen on evil days and so anything promised more than his present way of life.

## II

A few days later, Tom King and Dick Turpin sat in the bow window of an alehouse overlooking the river Thames, idly watching the boats as they discharged crowds of brilliantly dressed men and women bound for Vauxhall Gardens. For Turpin it was a wonderful sight to see a great barge, adorned with flags and streamers, its band of music and chattering and laughing pleasure lovers.

Seated near them was a rustily dressed fellow of nervous ways who drank glass after glass of wine, and on whom Turpin looked with a kind of awe. The man seemed to know the names and conditions of every great personage, and made a running commentary upon the figures as they passed. "That," said he, "is Walpole, who dropped five thousand the other night at cards, and with him is Lord Chesterfield. No. Not the big man with the red face: that's Fielding. The other, I mean, with the beetled brow. Walpole rode two horses to death hastening to tell the King that his father was dead. The drunken man behind him, he with the lady, is Lord Granby. A merry rascal that. He has doubtless come from Jenny Whim's tavern in Chelsea." There was much more of it, and Turpin was all ear. Particularly was he eager to know more of Walpole the rider.

"I have a mare," he said, "that I will ride against your Walpole." But the rusty man laughed at that.

"I knew him at Eton," said the rustily dressed man. "A Norfolk family and proud, every one of them with an eye for a horse and a hand for a playing card."

At the garden gate Dick stared in heavy wonder at the line of coaches and the silken ladies who descended from them, and, once in the garden, his delight was unbounded. The sound of the great organ playing something that set the people to clapping their hands, the great paintings here and there, the strange mechanical toys with painted landscapes and little coaches that moved along miniature roads, the tiny river with toy boats and splashing cascade and water mill, the figures of wood which walked and sat and disappeared into caves; all these things charmed the simple highwayman to the point of loud admiration, and it amazed him that amidst all, young gallants walked, taking no more heed of the things about them than he would take of the furze bushes on Hampstead Heath. Then, too, there were the parading masks, the wine parties, the wax-lighted summer houses and the glitter and the sparkle and the fine dresses. Dick Turpin was like a child in a great toy shop, and well-nigh distracted with it all.

So the two knights of the road, who were dressed as bravely as any there, wandered up and down the winding paths, taking no hand in the festivities, with Tom King, more sophisticated than his friend, keeping a sharp lookout for possible business. After much walking they came, quite unexpectedly, upon a quiet corner where was a summer house of latticed work all grown about with climbing plants. Within, a little party of four sat at cards around a table lit with a dozen wax candles set in glass bowls. There, too, sat the tall man with deepset eyes and a Roman nose, whom their rusty friend of the riverside inn had named as Henry Fielding; but he was watching the players, apparently a friend. In contrast with the players with their gold bedizened clothes, he was plainly dressed in a snuff-colored brown suit, but his occasional bursts of loud, boisterous laughter made him seem the gayest one there.

The sight of so much gold coin, heaped on the table, arrested the attention of the highwaymen, and Tom King checked his companion and drew him aside to the cover of a laurel bush in the rear of the summer house. Then there were whispered plans, tentative plans, impossible plans. Could one dash in and destroy the lights while the other seized the gold? Could the party be successfully challenged as are the inmates of a coach on the heath? There was an interminable list of mights, and coulds, and ifs, and meanwhile, most tantaliz-

ingly, a few feet away, the gold clinked and the laughter of the careless players rang out. Now and then there were little disputes and
one or other of the players would appeal to the man named Fielding.

Now, many things might have happened, but nothing then
planned by the highwaymen did, for, by chance, one of a band of
masked merrymakers came running, pursued in sport by another,
and the runners stumbled on the hiding place of Tom King and
Dick Turpin. Had the two plotters remained where they were even
then, all might have gone well, but, ever alert against discovery, they
leaped to their feet and ran. As luck had it, at the same moment the
heavily built man named Fielding chanced to step out of the summer
house and Tom King ran into his arms. Now, King was slight and
active, but the big man was strong and suspicious too. Perceiving a
couple of men running from cover with what seemed to be two in
pursuit of them, he acted promptly and laid hold of the highwayman, calling meanwhile to those within to bring lights. But Tom
King was hardy, keen and bright, and struggled vigorously.

"If ye be an honest man, keep still until we have seen your face,"
roared Fielding as he took a firm grip of King's collar. "But if you
are one of those thieving rogues who infest this place and London,
then—"

The sentence was left unfinished, for Tom King gave a furious
wrench and freed himself, leaving the collar of his fine coat in the
big man's hands.

Things became confused then and the card players shouted an
alarm, while the maskers gathered near by. Tom King, running
with all possible speed, caught up with his companion, and the two
of them made for a little group of trees some hundred yards away.
The obscurity of the gardens aided them wonderfully, and it was
much darker there. Beyond was an open space, lighted and dotted
with people, who, having heard the outcry, stood staring and listening. The hunted men saw the rusty-looking man of the riverside
inn, too, and he seemed to be going from group to group, and, from
each group there went up a cry of "Thieves are about!" That, indeed, was no new cry there. Night after night there had been
trouble, and frequently footpads were caught, so that thief hunting

had almost become one of the expected sports. Just now people were more on the *qui vive,* for it had been rumored that highwaymen accustomed to haunt the roads north of London were in town, and rewards were out. Indeed, the hue and cry for Tom Palmer, *alias* Dick Turpin, had been over the town since the Dover coach was robbed, nearly six months before.

Not long did the highwaymen stay in the clump of trees, for half-a-dozen young fellows, eager for something new and exciting, advanced that way, and the two men made a dash for a row of bushes. They were at once seen and a great halloo went up, some giving cry like huntsmen. Having gained the hedge, King and Turpin made their way along it to a place where they thought it joined the boundary fence, only to find their cover stop short close to the edge of an ornamental pond.

Again they were seen and the air seemed to be at once full of noise, and lanterns glittered everywhere. To make matters worse, there came to their ears the sound of a trumpet, for Valentine Snow, musician and public favorite, had gotten wind of the man hunt and was making merry with a fanfare. At one moment the coast seemed clear and they were about to make another dash, for their pursuers had no plan and hunted in groups and little bands, but other shadows, moving furtively, appeared and they caught the flash of swords. So they crouched low and were like men caught in a torrent where everywhere was danger.

The sound of the trumpet caused the majority of the pursuers to gather in the quadrangle surrounding the orchestra, and, regaining their feet, the highwaymen could see, by the light of a thousand lamps, the steadily gathering crowd of men and women, the latter, with their great headdresses of feathers and flowers, making a great ado in the summoning of their escorts. Here and there men were standing on seats and others on supper tables addressing little knots of people, and it became clear than plans were being laid for systematic pursuit.

No time was lost then, and, making a swift dash, the highwaymen ran in the direction of what they thought was the Thames. Soon they came to a hedge fence where was an opening, crowded through, and, after a little indecision, turned sharply to the left, ran crouchingly under the cover of the vegetation, sped across a vacant piece of land that was almost a swamp, hit upon a gap in a board wall and discovered, on the other side, a quiet and dark street. Two minutes later they were at the riverside and by merest chance came upon a boat boy who had a leaky wherry. They persuaded him to take them and, after much rowing, for the tide was against them, were landed at Salisbury Stairs. So, by back ways and alleys they reached the corner of Drury Lane and Coal Street where, a few doors away, stood Old Matthew's Inn. The house was dark and the window shutters were up, but the highwaymen, after knocking in a peculiar manner and giving, after challenge from within, a pass word, were admitted. They found themselves in a room full of hopeful striplings, of pickpockets, housebreakers and dice players and were immediately surrounded, heroes for the moment.

The innkeeper, Old Matthew, a fat and red-faced rascal, was none too pleased to see them, and his face fell as he heard their tale. Nothing in his manner invited them. Indeed, he was politely hostile. "It is dangerous, I tell you," he said emphatically. "I tell you, as I told that young fool, Jack Sheppard, when he got out of Newgate and came here, that London is no place to hide in when Bow Street and Newgate get wind of you." There was the shaking of a fat and warning forefinger and much head-nodding. He pondered awhile, then added: "Fifteen year it is since I told Jack that same thing, and I remember it as if it was yesterday. And there is the hue and cry out, and now Captain Hawk is wanted, too. It's dangerous, I say, dangerous. Not that I'm a man at any time to turn my back on a lad in trouble. Mind you that." He paused again and seemed to be searching his mind for some powerful argument, some suitable flower of speech, then, sitting on the head of a beer barrel he said dolefully, "The skies is very dark. The skies is very dark, I tell you, lads."

For a time there was a hubbub of talk, some advising this, some that, but soon Tom King called for wine and threw a gold coin on the table. Then he commanded attention by hammering on the table. "Here's a luck to us all—drink, everybody."

That created a pleasant diversion and the dark clouds conjured by Old Matthew were soon forgotten.

## III

All the next day Dick Turpin and Tom King lay in a rear room littered with empty barrels, household goods, smoked hams, discarded clothes, and all manner of depressing things. It was clear that there was to be no venturing abroad until the noise of the Vauxhall affair had quieted, for, without sufficient justification, as far as evidence was concerned, it was said that Dick Turpin was one of the men found in the gardens.

The day waxing late, both men grew impatient, nor were they any too trustful of their acquaintances in the face of the reward offered for their apprehension. The old innkeeper, they knew, would shelter them as long as he could with safety to himself, for he knew on which side his bread was buttered and many a guinea had he gained by the sale of watches and rings that the highwaymen had given him to dispose of. So toward evening, the grandson of Matthew, a shock-headed lad, was sent to the stables near Smithfield where their horses lay, and the two men made themselves ready for flight.

A little before eight that evening the horses arrived, both in the best of condition, Black Bess shapely and shining and snorting loudly, bravely set off with her handsome trappings. The eyes of Dick Turpin grew bright and shining when he saw his pet, and at once he began to tell Old Matthew the tale he had heard about Walpole who had ridden two horses to death. "My mare," he said, "would wear out twenty."

The two highwaymen were drinking a farewell glass with Old Matthew, when there came to their ears the clatter of hoofs in the street. At the same moment a short, red-bearded man thrust his head in at the door and shouted that police officers were coming, then promptly disappeared. Cautiously the two robbers peered through the window, craning their necks to get a side glance, and caught sight of a little band riding that way. Behind the horsemen were many curious townsmen, at least a score, all keenly agog to know what was afoot. But the foremost rider had not reached the door before Tom King and Dick Turpin were again in the rear room, Old Matthew with them, the tapster being left to attend to matters in the tap room.

From their hiding place the three heard the confusion of noise and voices, and it was a little time before the words of one of the crowd came to them clearly.

"Without loss of time," he commanded, "let us know where this Dick Turpin is hidden. We are told that your master knows."

Then there was noise again and much calling for drink. The three in the dark back room were very quiet, and the old innkeeper took down a picture that hung on the wall, so disclosing a peephole that revealed the barroom. As he did so he signaled to the two to be silent.

"A tough crowd," he said, hoarsely, speaking in the hollow of his hand. "And Lord, what a time! I am here at a most damnable risk to myself, for that they will search the house is not to be doubted."

"Some other way out there must be," suggested Turpin. "A cellar? A back door? The roof?"

"There is only one way out—the front way," was Matthew's answer.

"We might make a dash for it," said King.

"A pretty suggestion indeed," said Matthew. "Be trapped, you would, and this house battered about my ears. I remember all too well what was done to Jonathan Wild's house. But wait a while. Belike I can talk them over." With that, he went out into the tap room, and, at his appearance, the confusion grew wilder.

"Let us end the matter, Tom," said Turpin. "It is not likely that the old man can keep them long with all his wine and wit."

"But how?" asked King, very thoughtful and serious. "A bold dash? I am willing."

"There is the roof, and from one roof there is way to another. A risk, yes. But I would risk much for Black Bess."

The sound of many moving feet made them hasten, for it seemed evident that the excitement had spread and others from the street had entered. Like a trumpet blast they heard the voice of the officer in charge crying out that notwithstanding all that the innkeeper said, the house would have to undergo a thorough search.

Lighting a candle then, which they carefully shaded, the two men sought the stairway, which was shielded by a door. This they bolted on the inside, and mounted the stairs to find themselves in a long, low room over the bar. It was a bedroom, and the window of it gave on the street. Opening the casement they looked down and saw that it was a drop of some fourteen feet to the cobblestones below, no great matter for light and active men. By the yellow light that shot through the window and open door of the inn they saw their horses on the other side of the street, tethered by their reins to an empty and horseless cart. The horses of the police officers were grouped about the door below, stamping and snorting, and through the night came the swell of the voices.

As they looked, surveying the situation, they saw down the street, turning the corner from Long Acre, four mounted men, and it became clear that action must not be delayed. Further, there was plainly a change below, for doors were opening and slamming, and, at the foot of the stairway, men were thundering on the bolted door. Dick crawled out of the casement, hung a moment to the window ledge, then dropped into the street, his companion following close on his heels.

In spite of his sorry trade, Turpin was tall and straight and lean as a harrier, hardy, keen and bright, and no athlete could have crossed the street, released his horse, and leaped into the saddle quicker than he did. Black Bess gave a snort, and, without signal, broke into a canter. Dick supposed that his companion was equally lucky, but, turning as he rode to look at the horsemen coming from Long Acre, he was astonished to see that somehow Tom King's horse had slipped on the cobblestones and that the rider was on the ground, on hands and knees. Like a shot there leaped from the inn door a couple of the officers. One of them darted at Tom King, and the horse, startled, broke away and cantered toward the four horsemen. For a moment Dick Turpin meditated a rescue. He had, indeed, drawn his sword with the intention of charging at the officers.

Seeing the riders thus, the bystanders fled precipitately, urging one another and looking over their shoulders as they ran. Highwaymen trapped had a reputation for recklessness.

Yet there seemed still a chance that Tom King might win to freedom, for he was wrestling with a man in uniform and was clearly the superior in agility. But another came running from the inn with sword upraised at a moment when King had gained his feet.

"Shoot, Dick, shoot!" called King, and the words were no sooner said than Turpin fired at the officer with the upraised sword. Perhaps in the uncertain light his aim was false and perhaps his mare swerved. Which it was Dick Turpin never knew and his heart fell when he saw his friend fall before the luckless shot. The rest was blotted out, for at the noise of the shot the houses vomited forth people and the little troop of horsemen dashed forward.

"Stand, Dick Turpin! You are prisoner!" roared an officer.

But the knight of the road was taking no chances. Pressing Black Bess with his knees and loosing her rein he bent low, fearing shots. Then the shrill sound of a whistle broke on his ears and pistols cracked. The canter became a swift gallop then, nor did he feel a measure of safety until Black Bess had the soft turf of Lamb's Conduit Fields under her hoofs, and, his pursuers nowhere in sight, he was riding up the almost imperceptible rise that led to Highgate.

## IV

You must figure him something of a dandy in a way, his mare, his cherished treasure, a creature of beauty and grace, his figure gay with buckskin breeches and spurred jack boots, his waistcoat of white satin and his coat of scarlet cloth, as he rides in the moonlight. To him a night ride meant nothing, for he knew the country well, and for years his way had led to quiet places where inns were far apart and roads not too well frequented, but well shadowed with tall elms.

At Highgate he turned, taking the road that led eastward, and so came to the village of Tottenham. Descending the road on the north of that settlement, a collection of not more than two dozen houses all darkened, he became aware of the clatter of hoofs behind him, and, turning, saw a little band of horsemen riding at full speed. At once he was filled with black forebodings, for he had supposed that his pursuers were thrown off the trail. Still there could be no mistake, for, as the horsemen came through Tottenham High Street, he heard the cry of "Stop, thief! Stop, thief!" At that he became convinced of his danger. The officers, he saw, must have split into parties, some taking one road, some another, and he had but lost time in his detour. Yet, with foolish daring, he gave a shout which the pursuers answered with a defiant yell, and a shot was fired at random. Then Dick Turpin shook his rein, and Black Bess broke into a rapid canter.

He laughed a little then, for the joy of the chase was in him and the steady beat of the mare's hoofs made him happy in spite of sorrow at his friend's death. Then, too, after the turmoil of the town, the gentle rustling of the leaves as the soft night air played with them was like music to his ears. About the men on his trail he troubled little, feeling that he could shake them off whenever he chose. Besides, Epping Forest was not far away. For the present, let Black Bess show her paces and tire those who followed.

A couple of miles farther he heard the sound of approaching men as he was descending a gentle slope. It was plain that travelers were on the road and coming toward him, but, also, his pursuers were on his heels and on either side of the road were tall hawthorn bushes through which it was impossible to press. Deciding quickly, he lightly pressed his mare, full of determination to meet matters boldly. Luckily for him there was a turn in the road so that he was not seen by those approaching until he was almost upon them. So it came about that he encountered them just as they were fording Palmer's Creek. No pause. No hesitation. At them he charged, calling on them to make way as he galloped, and this they did without objecting word or hampering hand. Indeed, the considerable splashing made by his mare as she dashed into the water aided him, for the riders, all unprepared for fight and on their way from Enfield to London, were careful of their clothes and at vast trouble to guard themselves from the leaping water drops. So they merely shielded themselves as best they could, complaining loudly at the unseemly haste and discourtesy of the wild night rider, and little thinking him to be a hunted man.

By all that, Dick Turpin was the gainer, doubly so because when the Enfield men met the officers there was a halting to talk, the pursuers wanting to know whether the highwayman seemed to be making for Epping Forest and why so many had not stopped the fugitive.

Meantime, Dick Turpin had gained the clean, white town of Edmonton where stood the Cat and Bagpipes, an inn and alehouse well known to him. Ten miles he had ridden already and his mare was as fresh as when she stood in Drury Lane, nor was rider any the worse for the travel. The sight of the inn gladdened him. In the moonlight it seemed to invite, with its red-curtained windows, its plank seat outside the door, its creaking swinging sign, the horse trough and tall elms, so that for a moment he regretted the chase.

At the sound of the approaching rider the ostler came from the stable and instantly recognized Dick. Many a gold coin he had received from Turpin and many an evening they had sat and talked of horseflesh. In the lad, Turpin noticed a new eagerness.

"There is no passage, Dick," said the lad. "That is, I am told to wake the house should you pass. So speed, Dick, speed, and good luck be with you."

"But why this haste?" asked Dick. "Tonight I ride to Chingford, and there are those behind me who must be thrown off the scent."

Hearing that, the ostler became doubly insistent.

"Not to Chingford," he said. "Captain Hawk is in danger. He stopped the mail coach and things went wrong, and now has gone to St. Albans."

He was interrupted from further explanation by the sound of the shrill whistle of the pursuing officers, at which noise the dogs of the neighborhood started barking. Hearing the lad's words, Dick Turpin did some complicated thinking. The road to Epping closed, Hawk's house in the hands of the officers, the man himself all but captive, and Tom King dead: things were in parlous condition.

Plainly, Turpin could not stay about London, and to go by the way of St. Albans would mean the capture of Hawk. He pondered awhile. Then, suddenly, there shot through his memory what the man had said about Walpole, whose name, it seemed, had become famous because he rode two horses to death to carry news to a king. He, Dick Turpin, could do better than the Norfolk squire. Then came the decision.

"Listen," he said. "Tell the men who follow that I ride to York. If they care to follow, they will find me at the Black Prince Inn."

"But, captain, that is madness," insisted the ostler. "Four days the coach takes."

"Let that be so," answered the highwayman, warming to his boast-ful decision. "Let this rider Walpole learn that not a horse in all England can do what Black Bess does. See that you let them know."

His voice was hoarse with excitement, and by the light of the lantern the ostler saw his eyes shining as he leaned to stroke his mare's neck.

"Then go, and good luck," said he. "But there is no time to lose, for here they come."

What with the clatter of hoofs, the noise of the whistle and the barking of dogs, the villagers were awake and heads were thrust from windows, for Edmonton was not accustomed to strange noises when it was near ten of the night. Turpin arranged himself in the saddle and swallowed a pot of ale with noisy appreciation, but, in spite of the ostler's urging, did not move until the officers were within earshot.

Then, standing in his stirrups, he made one of his dramatic flourishes, calling out to the men that Black Bess would show all England what could be done and that he would prove this Norfolk Walpole a very trifler. "And if any of you care to follow," he shouted, "see to it that you get new horseflesh, for though the beasts you ride have gone a mere ten miles, they will not carry you to Waltham Cross." There was a wave of his hand and he was gone.

One man, bolder than his fellows, rode after Dick Turpin a little way, and while the highwayman knew, yet he made no sign that he did, believing that the man's purpose was to note whether he turned off on the road that led to Chingford. He allowed the fellow to follow, seeing to it that he stayed well in the rear, for Turpin had no mind to put Black Bess in danger of a chance shot. Coming to a low stone wall hard by a great oak, he reined in his mare and stood until the officer was well within sound of his voice.

"You are a plucky fellow and hold your life lightly. But hear me. It is idle for you to follow except you have a horse as clean limbed as mine, for she will carry me to York. I'll show your Norfolk squires what an Essex horse can do! Talk of your Walpole who rode two horses to death!" Dick spat in disgust, for that Walpole's eminence was altogether due to the fact that he had accomplished a feat of horsemanship was fixed in his mind. Little he knew of statesmanship and diplomatic ability.

"Four days' coach ride to York," warned the man.

"Be it so," said Dick. "Black Bess shall do it tonight."

The man listened and thought a while. Then he said: "Dick Turpin, I knew you when you were a lad, and I am not the sort to see you run your head into a noose. Our officer is Skellum, and he has a warrant by which he may have fresh horses wheresoever he finds them, and it is not likely that your mare can outride twenty."

"That you shall see," boasted Dick.

"But it is madness and I mean you nothing but good," insisted the man. "Slip away to Suffolk and get in a farmer's smock until the smoke has blown away."

"For that, thanks," replied the highwayman. "But tell your fellows that I ride to York, and so farewell."

"One thing more," said the man. "If you are so set on your ride, remember that this side of Warmington, on Alconbury Hill, there is an inn and the ostler is Jack Holt, a good man and true. You may trust him and he will help a man at a pinch."

There was no more then, for the officer had stayed too long already for his own good, and he turned to rejoin his fellows. So away, then, went Dick Turpin and Black Bess, hoofs rattling merrily on the good road, the lift and swing of the mare filling the man with a joyful sense that he and the beast were one. Ten miles, twelve miles, London behind him and a long road and a quiet night ahead!

In the man there was a glory in the strength of his mare, a vast pride in her speed, and he was swept with a whirlwind of fierce joy as he thought that what Black Bess did that night would be told and sung all over the countryside. So they sped under the thin moon, cautiously over marsh lands, fast where the turf was clean and soft. Thatched cottages and dark farmhouses swept past, haystacks and windmills leaped from shadow worlds into stolidity, little streams and ponds and dark waters where frogs croaked came and went. But it was joy to ride, for the air was clean and the wind good to feel on cheek and lip, and the smell of the countryside was better than wine. It was good to ride when man and beast were as one and the rest of the world was sleeping, except for the blundering few that followed far behind.—If only this Walpole of Norfolk were there to see!

Up hill and down dale, past great estates and gray churches, through villages and hamlets, fording creeks and clattering over bridges! Through sleeping Langford they passed swiftly, pausing to rest a brief while beyond, and at the foot of the hill where crouched the village of Sandy. Carefully Dick rubbed his mare down, bathing her and using his satin waistcoat by way of brush, then on again, leaving the road to cut across the fields and so avoid a turn, coming again into the highway near St. Neots. Across the road was a turnpike gate and the keeper of it fast asleep. No matter. A touch of the spur and Black Bess rose to it, going over and landing light, as the night-capped turnpike man came to his door, shouting for his toll. Straight, then, to Huntingdon and through the High Street. Ninety-nine miles done and the mare going strong at the end of six hours' ride. The hoarse crowing of the cocks on the outskirts of town sounded like trumpetings of victory to the rider, and when, hard by the market place he saw a watchman with lantern and stout stick, he had to draw reign sufficiently long to tell that fellow that he had ridden from London, and York town would be his journey's end. "See to it," he shouted, as he trotted off again, "that news gets to that fellow Walpole that at three in the morning I was in Huntingdon."

From Huntingdon to Alconbury Hill no great speed was made,

and Dick nursed his mare carefully, though with no doubt as to the final outcome. Halting a while in a wood of oak trees whose wealth of light spring green seemed touched to silver, the highwayman chanced to see, away on the hilltop, two yellow lights, and then suddenly remembered the name of Jack Holt, ostler at the Inn of the Golden Goose. Thereupon he mentally blessed the police officer and made his way through Little Stukeley, walking and leading the mare.

Arrived at the inn he saw that every one there was still abed, though the leaping color and light of a fire in the waiting room gave him the hope that the man he sought was afoot somewhere, alert and active.

When Jack Holt did appear, which was as soon as he heard the horse, he was all for saddling and bridling a fresh horse speedily, thinking the rider to be some belated wayfarer in haste, well supplied with money, for it was rare indeed that riders came at that time of night or early morning. When he heard how matters stood and that Dick had ridden from London, the fellow could not do too much, be the rider a highwayman or one on a king's errand. His grandfather, he said, had befriended Captain Hind, the Gentleman Knight of the Road, and he himself had once seen Claude Duval, so he came honestly, he suspected, by his admiration for Dick Turpin of whom he had heard. Meanwhile, he was not idle. With warm water from the kitchen he bathed Black Bess, and no mother could have been more gentle. As he worked, when he was not talking in his broad, north-country accent, he kept up a low hissing, though when he detected a little swelling above a hoof, he dropped into a kind of low moaning. Yet the while he was quick and nimble. But it was a rare miracle that he worked, for, in a very short while, the mare was whinnying softly and nosing the hay, comfortable in a stall and covered with a blanket. So, all things about the mare being made orderly, the good Jack Holt did what might be done for the rider, bringing him food and drink, the which was sorely enough needed. That being done, he made a clean bed of straw near the stall in which Black Bess rested and bade Dick rest a while, telling him that with the early morning must come travelers. As for Dick, being so weary, he was soon like a man dead, nor did he know that he slept until he felt a light hand on his face.

"Now you must slip out quietly," said Holt. "The officers are coming from London and you have slept a little short of an hour. But I will show you a way by following which you may gain time."

Dick was on his feet at once and a moment later had the mare saddled and the reins over the crook of his arm. Then Jack Holt led him to the rear of the stable which, as he then saw, was perched on the crest of a hill, the front of it facing the inn, the rear giving sharply on a place so steep as almost to be precipitous. It was a tall bluff rather than a hillside, a bluff dropping so straight that it seemed as though a goat would hardly find foothold. At the bottom of it, looking like a mass of bushes, lay Walton Woods, and faintly, by the gray light, could be seen a white, winding road.

"Lead your mare down there," said Holt, "and if she is as sure-footed as she seems to be, and if you do not grow giddy, you will save at least three miles. The officers must change horses and doubtless also eat. And if I can I will send them by way of Peterborough while you take the road to Warmington. So good luck to you."

There was no more then, for, guided by Holt, Dick led the mare out by way of four stone steps, and the stable door was closed on man and mare. It was none too soon, for through the deadly still of the early morning came the ring of horses' hoofs nearer and nearer. Straining his ears, the highwayman could sometimes hear the clang of scabbards on iron stirrups.

A long time seemed to pass in dread and in watchfulness as horse and man descended the dangerous hill. A slip at any time would have brought confusion or death upon them, a loose stone might mean an early end. Soon, Dick had to throw the reins over the mare's neck, leaving her to pick her own way, for with his jack boots and spurs he was in far sorrier straits than the beast. But Black Bess went, delicate as a cat, now daintily stepping, now sliding on her haunches, and she was on level ground before her master, who, toward the last, somehow lost his footing and went rolling, saving himself by clutching at bushes.

At Warmington the world began to wake. Farmers' lads and

early milkmaids looked up from their work to see the strange rider, and there were hubbubs in chicken yards and the barking of dogs as they passed. There was more noise in the market place and much shouting, for the strange-looking rider was something new to the early men who had come with their pigs and sheep and cattle for market day. Those in the street who saw, rushed into the inn and to houses to tell others, and so there was confusion. Trying to avoid the market place in which there were too many, though the morning was yet so young, Dick turned down a side street, people flocking fast on his heels in astonishment. Then he saw that he had made a mistake, for the street was narrow and at the lower end of it was a man with a low market cart to which was harnessed a donkey and the fractious beast had backed in such manner that the cart stood across the street, blocking the way from house to house. Through the gap of houses Dick saw beyond the clean white country road with trees on either side, an arcade of green. At the barrier went the highwayman and fire flew from the stones as Bess leaped. Over cart and donkey she flew, the little man, who was hot and hatless, waving his arms furiously. So, clear of the town at a leap, as it were, they passed into the open again and along a ridge, on either side of which was wide, free country, plowed land and grass land and fields bordered with high elms bearing countless rooks' nests.

Straight over the low, flat-topped hill to Fineshade Abbey went horse and rider and already in the valley faint wisps of mist began to rise. Past the abbey lands they went, over the boulder-strewn watercourse and up on to the ridge, the rough top of which was softened by ferns and moss, leaving the winding road again to cut across an untilled piece of heather land, into a stretch of timbered country and so to Stamford, where Dick dismounted for a short while and Black Bess nibbled the grass, all fragrant and cool because of the dewfall.

An unpleasant surprise awaited him, for when he remounted, it became clear that the gallant mare was tiring. But still she kept on bravely, though the lilt and the spring were gone out of her stride. The plunge into the cold water when they crossed the Trent, for they forded at a pebbly place and the water was deeper than it looked, left the mare plainly weaker. Still, with the caressing warmth of the sun, she pulled together wonderfully and there were miles when she went at a rapid trot. No Tartar stallion could have bested her, no Arab desert horse shown more endurance.

Up hill and down dale, then, and along a hard, rough road shut in by low hedges, they went, and Black Bess grew heavy-hoofed; but at Thorne, some early morning rider came from a side lane mounted on a stout cob and there was a change. Up went the ears of Bess and there was a new energy in her and her hoofs beat with a steady thud again as she strove to overtake her fellow. In her veins was new life, in her sinews new strength, and she snorted in a movement of exaltation as she went for a while side by side with her rival, then passed him. At the milestone that read

### YORK
### 15 M.

weariness and exhaustion seemed to come upon the mare suddenly. One moment she was moving, pluckily, heavily, then of a sudden, she was down in a heap. There was one struggle to regain her feet and that was all. Close by, a brook ran through the meadow and Dick Turpin staggered to the water, bringing back some in his hat, but he saw that it was useless and that there was no hope. One moment he stared stupidly, then he was rent with a whirlwind of passion that ended in sobs. Thief and robber, caring for nothing that most men hold dear, yet there was in him an unsuspected love for his mare, a fullness of soul until then unknown. He lifted her head, looked into her glazing eyes, lovingly patted her neck, spoke to her; then he drew away and stood in the road gazing at the strange black heap that was once arched neck and rounded flank and glossy mane. Something had gone out of the world for him. The sweetness of the new day, the murmur of the wind in the grass, the song of the lark in the air—all these he was conscious of only as things in a dream world. The only real thing seemed to be there in the yellow dust of the road.

Presently he set off toward York, walking mechanically, a travel-stained figure with bent head. But not far did he go. He turned and retraced his steps, walking slowly until he reached the strange heap that was once Black Bess. Then he sat by her side on a stone and there those who pursued found him.

· · · · ·

There is, on the desk before me as I write, an old woodcut of the execution of Dick Turpin at York Castle, and the date of the event is given as April 10th, 1739. With the artist, it was probably necessary to bear in mind the habit of hero worship. At any rate, as the crowd is pictured standing about the gallows tree, there is but one prepossessing face. Dick Turpin alone is handsome and debonaire as he stands on the fatal ladder in his finery, attired in fine laced coat and highly polished jack boots, a flower at his breast. The hangman is plainly a villain and ugly to excess. The sheriff who stands on the overcrowded execution platform has the face of a demon, and the attendant minister of the gospel, who is pictured as a bishop arrayed in full canonicals, has about him an air of cynical levity. As for the military—apparently the British army in the days of King George the Second was composed of Calibans.

According to the popular account, Dick Turpin's manner of going to his death was marked by dramatic distinction. His passing was a remarkable achievement. Though "under the influence of a drug," yet at the last moment there came from him "a burst of scornful laughter at the irony of fate," and, "at the moment when the sea of faces and the other varied objects around faded from before Dick's eyes, yet there was no quailing in that last glance." And the woodcut shows that plainly. The highwayman's features are stern but pleasant, his manner noble and easy, his bearing frank and unashamed. The law, as typified in the sheriff, is obviously vindictive and brutal. With fine spiritual insight, according to the popular mythology, the highwayman would not allow death to be meted out to him at the hands of a common hangman, and "no sooner had the hangman spoke the word, than, with a sudden bound, the Prince of Highwaymen threw himself off the ladder. . . . And so, bold and defiant to the last, the gallant Dick Turpin met his fate."

# THE RED-HEADED LEAGUE

## By A. CONAN DOYLE

*Illustration by Frederick Dorr Steele*

I HAD CALLED upon my friend, Mr. Sherlock Holmes, one day in the autumn of last year, and found him in deep conversation with a very stout, florid-faced, elderly gentleman, with fiery red hair. With an apology for my intrusion, I was about to withdraw, when Holmes pulled me abruptly into the room and closed the door behind me.

"You could not possibly have come at a better time, my dear Watson," he said, cordially.

"I was afraid that you were engaged."

"So I am. Very much so."

"Then I can wait in the next room."

"Not at all. This gentleman, Mr. Wilson, has been my partner and helper in many of my most successful cases, and I have no doubt that he will be of the utmost use to me in yours also."

The stout gentleman half rose from his chair and gave a bob of greeting, with a quick, little, questioning glance from his small, fat-encircled eyes.

"Try the settee," said Holmes, relapsing into his armchair and putting his finger tips together, as was his custom when in judicial moods. "I know, my dear Watson, that you share my love of all that is bizarre and outside the conventions and humdrum routine of everyday life. You have shown your relish for it by the enthusiasm which has prompted you to chronicle, and, if you will excuse my saying so, somewhat to embellish so many of my own little adventures."

"Your cases have indeed been of the greatest interest to me," I observed.

"You will remember that I remarked the other day, just before we went into the very simple problem presented by Miss Mary

Sutherland, that for strange effects and extraordinary combinations we must go to life itself, which is always far more daring than any effort of the imagination."

"A proposition which I took the liberty of doubting."

"You did, doctor, but none the less you must come round to my view, for otherwise I shall keep on piling fact upon fact on you, until your reason breaks down under them and acknowledges me to be right. Now, Mr. Jabez Wilson here has been good enough to call upon me this morning, and to begin a narrative which promises to be one of the most singular which I have listened to for some time. You have heard me remark that the strangest and most unique things are very often connected not with the larger but with the smaller crimes, and occasionally, indeed, where there is room for doubt whether any positive crime has been committed. As far as I have heard, it is impossible for me to say whether the present case is an instance of crime or not, but the course of events is certainly among the most singular that I have ever listened to. Perhaps, Mr. Wilson, you would have the great kindness to recommence your narrative. I ask you, not merely because my friend Dr. Watson has not heard the opening part, but also because the peculiar nature of the story makes me anxious to have every possible detail from your lips. As a rule, when I have heard some slight indication of the course of events, I am able to guide myself by the thousands of other similar cases which occur to my memory. In the present instance I am forced to admit that the facts are, to the best of my belief, unique."

The portly client puffed out his chest with an appearance of some little pride, and pulled a dirty and wrinkled newspaper from the inside pocket of his greatcoat. As he glanced down the advertisement column, with his head thrust forward, and the paper flattened out upon his knee, I took a good look at the man, and endeavored, after the fashion of my companion, to read the indications which might be presented by his dress or appearance.

I did not gain very much, however, by my inspection. Our visitor bore every mark of being an average commonplace British trades- man, obese, pompous, and slow. He wore rather baggy gray shepherd's check trousers, a not overclean black frock coat, unbuttoned in the front, and a drab waistcoat with a heavy brassy Albert chain, and a square pierced bit of metal dangling down as an ornament. A frayed top hat and a faded brown overcoat with a wrinkled velvet collar lay upon a chair beside him. Altogether, look as I would, there was nothing remarkable about the man save his blazing red head, and the expression of extreme chagrin and discontent upon his features.

Sherlock Holmes's quick eye took in my occupation, and he shook his head with a smile as he noticed my questioning glances. "Beyond the obvious facts that he has at some time done manual labor, that he takes snuff, that he is a Freemason, that he has been in China, and that he has done a considerable amount of writing lately, I can deduce nothing else."

Mr. Jabez Wilson started up in his chair, with his forefinger upon the paper, but his eyes upon my companion.

"How, in the name of good fortune, did you know all that, Mr. Holmes?" he asked. "How did you know, for example, that I did manual labor? It's as true as gospel, for I began as a ship's carpenter."

"Your hands, my dear sir. Your right hand is quite a size larger than your left. You have worked with it, and the muscles are more developed."

"Well, the snuff, then, and the Freemasonry?"

"I won't insult your intelligence by telling you how I read that, especially as, rather against the strict rules of your order, you use an arc-and-compass breastpin."

"Ah, of course, I forgot that. But the writing?"

"What else can be indicated by that right cuff so very shiny for five inches, and the left one with the smooth patch near the elbow where you rest it upon the desk."

"Well, but China?"

"The fish that you have tattooed immediately above your right wrist could only have been done in China. I have made a small study of tattoo marks, and have even contributed to the literature of the subject. That trick of staining the fishes' scales of a delicate pink is quite peculiar to China. When, in addition, I see a Chinese coin hanging from your watch-chain, the matter becomes even more simple."

Mr. Jabez Wilson laughed heavily. "Well, I never!" said he. "I thought at first that you had done something clever, but I see that there was nothing in it, after all."

"I begin to think, Watson," said Holmes, "that I make a mistake in explaining. 'Omne ignotum pro magnifico,' you know, and my poor little reputation, such as it is, will suffer shipwreck if I am so candid. Can you not find the advertisement, Mr. Wilson?"

"Yes, I have got it now," he answered, with his thick, red finger planted half-way down the column. "Here it is. This is what began it all. You just read it for yourself, sir."

I took the paper from him, and read as follows:

> "To the Red-headed League: On account of the bequest of the late Ezekiah Hopkins, of Lebanon, Pa., U. S. A., there is now another vacancy open which entitles a member of the League to a salary of £4 a week for purely nominal services. All red-headed men who are sound in body and mind, and above the age of twenty-one years, are eligible. Apply in person on Monday, at eleven o'clock, to Duncan Ross, at the offices of the League, 7 Pope's Court, Fleet Street."

"What on earth does this mean?" I ejaculated, after I had twice read over the extraordinary announcement.

Holmes chuckled, and wriggled in his chair, as was his habit when in high spirits. "It is a little off the beaten track, isn't it?" said he. "And now, Mr. Wilson, off you go at scratch, and tell us all about yourself, your household, and the effect which this advertisement had upon your fortunes. You will first make a note, doctor, of the paper and the date."

"It is *The Morning Chronicle,* of April 27, 1890. Just two months ago."

"Very good. Now, Mr. Wilson?"

"Well, it is just as I have been telling you, Mr. Sherlock Holmes," said Jabez Wilson, mopping his forehead; "I have a small pawn-broker's business at Coburg Square, near the city. It's not a very large affair, and of late years it has not done more than just give me a living. I used to be able to keep two assistants, but now I only keep one; and I would have a job to pay him, but that he is willing to come for half wages, so as to learn the business."

"What is the name of this obliging youth?" asked Sherlock Holmes.

"His name is Vincent Spaulding, and he's not such a youth, either. It's hard to say his age. I should not wish a smarter assistant, Mr. Holmes; and I know very well that he could better himself, and earn twice what I am able to give him. But, after all, if he is satis-fied, why should I put ideas in his head?"

"Why, indeed? You seem most fortunate in having an *employé* who comes under the full market price. It is not a common experi-ence among employers in this age. I don't know that your assistant is not as remarkable as your advertisement."

"Oh, he has his faults, too," said Mr. Wilson. "Never was such a fellow for photography. Snapping away with a camera when he ought to be improving his mind, and then diving down into the cellar like a rabbit into its hole to develop his pictures. That is his main fault; but, on the whole, he's a good worker. There's no vice in him."

"He is still with you, I presume?"

"Yes, sir. He and a girl of fourteen, who does a bit of simple cooking, and keeps the place clean—that's all I have in the house, for I am a widower, and never had any family. We live very quietly, sir, the three of us; and we keep a roof over our heads, and pay our debts, if we do nothing more.

"The first thing that put us out was that advertisement. Spaulding, he came down into the office just this day eight weeks, with this very paper in his hand, and he says:

"'I wish to the Lord, Mr. Wilson, that I was a red-headed man.'

"'Why that?' I asks.

"'Why,' says he, 'here's another vacancy on the League of the Red-headed Men. It's worth quite a little fortune to any man who gets it, and I understand that there are more vacancies than there are men, so that the trustees are at their wits' end what to do with the money. If my hair would only change color, here's a nice little crib all ready for me to step into.'

"'Why, what is it, then?' I asked. You see, Mr. Holmes, I am a very stay-at-home man, and as my business came to me instead of my having to go to it, I was often weeks on end without putting my foot over the door mat. In that way I didn't know much of what was going on outside, and I was always glad of a bit of news.

"'Have you never heard of the League of the Red-headed Men?' he asked, with his eyes open.

"'Never.'

"'Why, I wonder at that, for you are eligible yourself for one of the vacancies.'

"'And what are they worth?' I asked.

"'Oh, merely a couple of hundred a year, but the work is slight, and it need not interfere very much with one's other occupations.'

"Well, you can easily think that that made me prick up my ears, for the business has not been over good for some years, and an extra couple of hundred would have been very handy.

"'Tell me about it,' said I.

"'Well,' said he, showing me the advertisement, 'you can see for yourself that the League has a vacancy, and there is the address where you should apply for particulars. As far as I can make out, the League was founded by an American millionaire, Ezekiah Hopkins, who was very peculiar in his ways. He was himself red-headed, and he had a great sympathy for all red-headed men; so, when he died, it was found that he had left his enormous fortune in the hands of trustees, with instructions to apply the interest to the providing of easy berths to men whose hair is of that color. From all I hear it is splendid pay, and very little to do.'

"'But,' said I, 'there would be millions of red-headed men who would apply.'

"'Not so many as you might think,' he answered. 'You see it is really confined to Londoners, and to grown men. This American had started from London when he was young, and he wanted to do the old town a good turn. Then, again, I have heard it is no use your applying if your hair is light red, or dark red, or anything but real bright, blazing, fiery red. Now, if you cared to apply, Mr. Wilson, you would just walk in; but perhaps it would be hardly worth your while to put yourself out of the way for the sake of a few hundred pounds.'

"Now, it is a fact, gentlemen, as you may see for yourself, that my hair is of a very full and rich tint, so that it seemed to me that, if there was to be any competition in the matter, I stood as good a chance as any man that I had ever met. Vincent Spaulding seemed to know so much about it that I thought he might prove useful, so I just ordered him to put up the shutters for the day, and to come right away with me. He was very willing to have a holiday, so we shut the business up, and started off for the address in the advertisement.

"I never hope to see such a sight as that again, Mr. Holmes. From north, south, east, and west every man who had a shade of red in his hair had tramped into the city to answer the advertisement. Fleet Street was choked with red-headed folk, and Pope's Court looked like a coster's orange barrow. I should not have thought there were so many in the whole country as were brought together by that single advertisement. Every shade of color they were—straw, lemon, orange, brick, Irish setter, liver, clay; but, as Spaulding said, there were not many who had the real vivid flame-colored tint. When I saw how many were waiting, I would have given it up in despair; but Spaulding would not hear of it. How he did it I could not imagine, but he pushed and pulled and butted until he got me through the crowd, and right up to the steps which led to the office. There was a double stream upon the stair, some going up in hope, and some coming back dejected; but we wedged in as well as we could, and soon found ourselves in the office."

"Your experience has been a most entertaining one," remarked Holmes, as his client paused and refreshed his memory with a huge pinch of snuff. "Pray continue your very interesting statement."

"There was nothing in the office but a couple of wooden chairs and a deal table, behind which sat a small man, with a head that was even redder than mine. He said a few words to each candidate as he came up, and then he always managed to find some fault in them which would disqualify them. Getting a vacancy did not seem to be such a very easy matter, after all. However, when our turn came, the little man was much more favorable to me than to any of the others, and he closed the door as we entered, so that he might have a private word with us.

"'This is Mr. Jabez Wilson,' said my assistant, 'and he is willing to fill a vacancy in the League.'

"'And he is admirably suited for it,' the other answered. 'He has every requirement. I cannot recall when I have seen anything so fine.'

"He took a step backward, cocked his head on one side, and gazed at my hair until I felt quite bashful. Then suddenly he plunged forward, wrung my hand, and congratulated me warmly on my success.

"'It would be injustice to hesitate,' said he. 'You will, however, I am sure, excuse me for taking an obvious precaution.' With that he seized my hair in both his hands, and tugged until I yelled with the pain. 'There is water in your eyes,' said he, as he released me. 'I perceive that all is as it should be. But we have to be careful, for we have twice been deceived by wigs and once by paint. I could tell you tales of cobbler's wax which would disgust you with human nature.' He stepped over to the window, and shouted through it at the top of his voice that the vacancy was filled. A groan of disappointment came up from below, and the folk all trooped away in different directions, until there was not a red head to be seen except my own and that of the manager.

"'My name,' said he, 'is Mr. Duncan Ross, and I am myself one of the pensioners upon the fund left by our noble benefactor. Are you a married man, Mr. Wilson? Have you a family?'

"I answered that I had not.

"His face fell immediately.

"'Dear me!' he said, gravely, 'that is very serious indeed! I am sorry to hear you say that. The fund was, of course, for the propagation and spread of the redheads as well as for their maintenance. It is exceedingly unfortunate that you should be a bachelor.'

"My face lengthened at this, Mr. Holmes, for I thought that I was not to have the vacancy after all; but, after thinking it over for a few minutes, he said that it would be all right.

"'In the case of another,' said he, 'the objection might be fatal, but we must stretch a point in favor of a man with such a head of hair as yours. When shall you be able to enter upon your new duties?'

"'Well, it is a little awkward, for I have a business already,' said I.

"'Oh, never mind about that, Mr. Wilson!' said Vincent Spaulding. 'I shall be able to look after that for you.'

"'What would be the hours?' I asked.

"'Ten to two.'

"Now a pawnbroker's business is mostly done of an evening, Mr. Holmes, especially Thursday and Friday evening, which is just before payday; so it would suit me very well to earn a little in the mornings. Besides, I knew that my assistant was a good man, and that he would see to anything that turned up.

"'That would suit me very well,' said I. 'And the pay?'

"'Is £4 a week.'

"'And the work?'

"'Is purely nominal.'

"'What do you call purely nominal?'

"'Well, you have to be in the office, or at least in the building, the whole time. If you leave, you forfeit your whole position forever. The will is very clear upon that point. You don't comply with the conditions if you budge from the office during that time.'

"'It's only four hours a day, and I should not think of leaving,' said I.

"'No excuse will avail,' said Mr. Duncan Ross, 'neither sickness nor business nor anything else. There you must stay, or you lose your billet.'

"'And the work?'

"'Is to copy out the "Encyclopædia Britannica." There is the first volume of it in that press. You must find your own ink, pens, and blotting paper, but we provide this table and chair. Will you be ready tomorrow?'

"'Certainly,' I answered.

"'Then, good-bye, Mr. Jabez Wilson, and let me congratulate you once more on the important position which you have been fortunate enough to gain.' He bowed me out of the room, and I went home with my assistant, hardly knowing what to say or do, I was so pleased at my own good fortune.

"Well, I thought over the matter all day, and by evening I was in low spirits again; for I had quite persuaded myself that the whole affair must be some great hoax or fraud, though what its object might be I could not imagine. It seemed altogether past belief that anyone could make such a will, or that they would pay such a sum for doing anything so simple as copying out the 'Encyclopædia Britannica.' Vincent Spaulding did what he could to cheer me up, but by bedtime I had reasoned myself out of the whole thing. However, in the morning I determined to have a look at it anyhow, so I bought a penny bottle of ink, and with a quill pen, and seven sheets of foolscap paper, I started off for Pope's Court.

"Well, to my surprise and delight, everything was as right as possible. The table was set out ready for me, and Mr. Duncan Ross was there to see that I got fairly to work. He started me off upon the letter A, and then he left me; but he would drop in from time to time to see that all was right with me. At two o'clock he bade me good day, complimented me upon the amount that I had written, and locked the door of the office after me.

"This went on day after day, Mr. Holmes, and on Saturday the manager came in and planked down four golden sovereigns for my week's work. It was the same next week, and the same the week after. Every morning I was there at ten, and every afternoon I left at two. By degrees Mr. Duncan Ross took to coming in only once of a morning, and then, after a time, he did not come in at all. Still, of course, I never dared to leave the room for an instant, for I was not sure when he might come, and the billet was such a good one, and suited me so well, that I would not risk the loss of it.

"Eight weeks passed away like this, and I had written about Abbots and Archery and Armor and Architecture and Attica, and hoped with diligence that I might get on to the B's before very long. It cost me something in foolscap, and I had pretty nearly filled a shelf with my writings. And then suddenly the whole business came to an end."

"To an end?"

"Yes, sir. And no later than this morning. I went to my work as usual at ten o'clock, but the door was shut and locked, with a little square of cardboard hammered on to the middle of the panel with a tack. Here it is, and you can read for yourself."

He held up a piece of white cardboard about the size of a sheet of note paper. It read in this fashion:

THE RED-HEADED LEAGUE

IS

DISSOLVED.

*October* 9, 1890.

Sherlock Holmes and I surveyed this curt announcement and the rueful face behind it, until the comical side of the affair so completely overtopped every other consideration that we both burst out into a roar of laughter.

"I cannot see that there is anything very funny," cried our client, flushing up to the roots of his flaming head. "If you can do nothing better than laugh at me, I can go elsewhere."

"No, no," cried Holmes, shoving him back into the chair from which he had half risen. "I really wouldn't miss your case for the world. It is most refreshingly unusual. But there is, if you will excuse my saying so, something just a little funny about it. Pray what steps did you take when you found the card upon the door?"

"I was staggered, sir. I did not know what to do. Then I called at the offices round, but none of them seemed to know anything about it. Finally, I went to the landlord, who is an accountant living on the ground floor, and I asked him if he could tell me what had become of the Red-headed League. He said that he had never heard of any such body. Then I asked him who Mr. Duncan Ross was. He answered that the name was new to him.

"'Well,' said I, 'the gentleman at No. 4.'

"'What, the red-headed man?'

"'Yes.'

"'Oh,' said he, 'his name was William Morris. He was a solicitor, and was using my room as a temporary convenience until his new premises were ready. He moved out yesterday.'

"'Where could I find him?'

"'Oh, at his new offices. He did tell me the address. Yes, 17 King Edward Street, near St. Paul's.'

"I started off, Mr. Holmes, but when I got to that address it was a manufactory of artificial kneecaps, and no one in it had ever heard of either Mr. William Morris or Mr. Duncan Ross."

"And what did you do then?" asked Holmes.

"I went home to Saxe-Coburg Square, and I took the advice of my assistant. But he could not help me in any way. He could only say that if I waited I should hear by post. But that was not quite good enough, Mr. Holmes. I did not wish to lose such a place without a struggle, so, as I had heard that you were good enough to give advice to poor folk who were in need of it, I came right away to you."

"And you did very wisely," said Holmes. "Your case is an exceedingly remarkable one, and I shall be happy to look into it. From what you have told me I think that it is possible that graver issues hang from it than might at first sight appear."

"Grave enough!" said Mr. Jabez Wilson. "Why, I have lost four pounds a week."

"As far as you are personally concerned," remarked Holmes, "I do not see that you have any grievance against this extraordinary league. On the contrary, you are, as I understand, richer by some £30, to say nothing of the minute knowledge which you have gained on every subject which comes under the letter A. You have lost nothing by them."

"No, sir. But I want to find out about them, and who they are, and what their object was in playing this prank—if it was a prank—upon me. It was a pretty expensive joke for them, for it cost them two and thirty pounds."

"We shall endeavor to clear up these points for you. And, first, one or two questions, Mr. Wilson. This assistant of yours who first called your attention to the advertisement—how long had he been with you?"

"About a month then."

"How did he come?"

"In answer to an advertisement."

"Was he the only applicant?"

"No, I had a dozen."

"Why did you pick him?"

"Because he was handy, and would come cheap."

"At half-wages, in fact."

"Yes."

"What is he like, this Vincent Spaulding?"

"Small, stout-built, very quick in his ways, no hair on his face, though he's not short of thirty. Has a white splash of acid upon his forehead."

Holmes sat up in his chair in considerable excitement. "I thought as much," said he. "Have you ever observed that his ears are pierced for earrings?"

"Yes, sir. He told me that a gypsy had done it for him when he was a lad."

"Hum!" said Holmes, sinking back in deep thought. "He is still with you?"

"Oh, yes, sir; I have only just left him."

"And has your business been attended to in your absence?"

"Nothing to complain of, sir. There's never very much to do of a morning."

"That will do, Mr. Wilson. I shall be happy to give you an opinion upon the subject in the course of a day or two. Today is Saturday, and I hope that by Monday we may come to a conclusion."

"Well, Watson," said Holmes, when our visitor had left us, "what do you make of it all?"

"I make nothing of it," I answered frankly. "It is a most mysterious business."

"As a rule," said Holmes, "the more bizarre a thing is the less mysterious it proves to be. It is your commonplace, featureless crimes which are really puzzling, just as a commonplace face is the most difficult to identify. But I must be prompt over this matter."

"What are you going to do, then?" I asked.

*Frederick Dorr Steele*

"To smoke," he answered. "It is quite a three-pipe problem, and I beg that you won't speak to me for fifty minutes." He curled himself up in his chair, with his thin knees drawn up to his hawk-like nose, and there he sat with his eyes closed and his black clay pipe thrusting out like the bill of some strange bird. I had come to the conclusion that he had dropped asleep, and indeed was nodding myself, when he suddenly sprang out of his chair with the gesture of a man who has made up his mind, and put his pipe down upon the mantelpiece.

"Sarasate plays at the St. James's Hall this afternoon," he remarked. "What do you think, Watson? Could your patients spare you for a few hours?"

"I have nothing to do today. My practice is never very absorbing."

"Then put on your hat and come. I am going through the city first, and we can have some lunch on the way. I observe that there is a good deal of German music on the program, which is rather more to my taste than Italian or French. It is introspective, and I want to introspect. Come along!"

We traveled by the Underground as far as Aldersgate; and a short walk took us to Saxe-Coburg Square, the scene of the singular story which we had listened to in the morning. It was a pokey, little, shabby-genteel place, where four lines of dingy two-storied brick houses looked out into a small railed-in enclosure, where a lawn of weedy grass and a few clumps of faded laurel bushes made a hard fight against a smoke-laden and uncongenial atmosphere. Three gilt balls and a brown board with "JABEZ WILSON" in white letters, upon a corner house, announced the place where our red-headed client carried on his business. Sherlock Holmes stopped in front of it with his head on one side, and looked it all over, with his eyes shining brightly between puckered lids. Then he walked slowly up the street, and then down again to the corner, still looking keenly at the houses. Finally he returned to the pawnbroker's, and, having thumped vigorously upon the pavement with his stick two or three times, he went up to the door and knocked. It was instantly opened by a bright-looking, clean-shaven young fellow, who asked him to step in.

"Thank you," said Holmes, "I only wished to ask you how you would go from here to the Strand."

"Third right, fourth left," answered the assistant, promptly, closing the door.

"Smart fellow, that," observed Holmes, as we walked away. "He is, in my judgment, the fourth smartest man in London, and for daring I am not sure that he has not a claim to be third. I have known something of him before."

"Evidently," said I, "Mr. Wilson's assistant counts for a good deal in this mystery of the Red-headed League. I am sure that you inquired your way merely in order that you might see him."

"Not him."

"What then?"

"The knees of his trousers."

"And what did you see?"

"What I expected to see."

"Why did you beat the pavement?"

"My dear doctor, this is a time for observation, not for talk. We are spies in an enemy's country. We know something of Saxe-Coburg Square. Let us now explore the parts which lie behind it."

The road in which we found ourselves as we turned round the corner from the retired Saxe-Coburg Square presented as great a contrast to it as the front of a picture does to the back. It was one of the main arteries which convey the traffic of the city to the north and west. The roadway was blocked with the immense stream of commerce flowing in a double tide inward and outward, while the footpaths were black with the hurrying swarm of pedestrians. It was difficult to realize as we looked at the line of fine shops and stately business premises that they really abutted on the other side upon the faded and stagnant square which we had just quitted.

"Let me see," said Holmes, standing at the corner, and glancing along the line, "I should like just to remember the order of the houses here. It is a hobby of mine to have an exact knowledge of London. There is Mortimer's, the tobacconist, the little newspaper shop, the Coburg branch of the City and Suburban Bank, the Vegetarian Restaurant, and McFarlane's carriage-building depot. That carries us right on to the other block. And now, doctor, we've done our work, so it's time we had some play. A sandwich and a cup of coffee, and then off to violin-land, where all is sweetness and delicacy and harmony, and there are no red-headed clients to vex us with their conundrums."

My friend was an enthusiastic musician, being himself not only a very capable performer, but a composer of no ordinary merit. All the afternoon he sat in the stalls wrapped in the most perfect happiness, gently waving his long, thin fingers in time to the music, while his gently smiling face and his languid, dreamy eyes were as unlike those of Holmes, the sleuth-hound, Holmes the relentless, keen-witted, ready-handed criminal agent, as it was possible to conceive. In his singular character the dual nature alternately asserted itself, and his extreme exactness and astuteness represented, as I have often thought, the reaction against the poetic and contemplative mood which occasionally predominated in him. The swing of his nature took him from extreme languor to devouring energy; and, as I knew well, he was never so truly formidable as when, for days on end, he had been lounging in his armchair amid his improvisations and his black-letter editions. Then it was that the lust of the chase would suddenly come upon him, and that his brilliant reasoning power would rise to the level of intuition, until those who were unacquainted with his methods would look askance at him as on a man whose knowledge was not that of other mortals. When I saw him that afternoon so enwrapped in the music at St. James's Hall I felt that an evil time might be coming upon those whom he had set himself to hunt down.

"You want to go home, no doubt, doctor," he remarked, as we emerged.

"Yes, it would be as well."

"And I have some business to do which will take some hours. This business at Coburg Square is serious."

"Why serious?"

"A considerable crime is in contemplation. I have every reason to believe that we shall be in time to stop it. But today being Saturday rather complicates matters. I shall want your help tonight, Watson."

"At what time?"

"Ten will be early enough."

"I shall be at Baker Street at ten."

"Very well. And, I say, doctor, there may be some little danger, so kindly put your army revolver in your pocket." He waved his hand, turned on his heels, and disappeared in an instant among the crowd.

I trust that I am not more dense than my neighbors, but I was always oppressed with a sense of my own stupidity in my dealings with Sherlock Holmes. Here I had heard what he had heard, I had seen what he had seen, and yet from his words it was evident that he saw clearly not only what had happened, but what was about to happen, while to me the whole business was still confused and grotesque. As I drove home to my house in Kensington I thought over it all, from the extraordinary story of the red-headed copier of the "Encyclopædia" down to the visit to Saxe-Coburg Square, and the ominous words with which he had parted from me. What was this nocturnal expedition, and why should I go armed? Where were we going, and what were we to do? I had the hint from Holmes that this smooth-faced pawnbroker's assistant was a formidable man—a man who might play a deep game. I tried to puzzle it out, but gave it up in despair, and set the matter aside until night should bring an explanation.

It was a quarter past nine when I started from home and made my way across the Park, and so through Oxford Street to Baker Street. Two hansoms were standing at the door, and as I entered the passage I heard the sound of voices from above. On entering his room I found Holmes in animated conversation with two men, one of whom I recognized as Peter Jones, the official police agent, while the other was a long, thin, sad-faced man, with a very shiny hat and oppressively respectable frock coat. "Ha! our party is complete," said Holmes, buttoning up his pea-jacket, and taking his heavy hunting crop from the rack. "Watson, I think you know Mr. Jones, of Scotland Yard? Let me introduce you to Mr. Merryweather, who is to be our companion in tonight's adventure."

"We're hunting in couples again, doctor, you see," said Jones, in his consequential way. "Our friend here is a wonderful man for starting a chase. All he wants is an old dog to help him to do the running down."

"I hope a wild goose may not prove to be the end of our chase," observed Mr. Merryweather, gloomily.

"You may place considerable confidence in Mr. Holmes, sir," said the police agent, loftily. "He has his own little methods, which are, if he won't mind my saying so, just a little too theoretical and fantastic, but he has the makings of a detective in him. It is not too much to say that once or twice, as in that business of the Sholto murder and the Agra treasure, he has been more nearly correct than the official force."

"Oh, if you say so, Mr. Jones, it is all right," said the stranger, with deference. "Still, I confess that I miss my rubber. It is the first Saturday night for seven-and-twenty years that I have not had my rubber."

"I think you will find," said Sherlock Holmes, "that you will play for a higher stake tonight than you have ever done yet, and that the play will be more exciting. For you, Mr. Merryweather, the stake will be some £30,000; and for you, Jones, it will be the man upon whom you wish to lay your hands."

"John Clay, the murderer, thief, smasher, and forger. He's a young man, Mr. Merryweather, but he is at the head of his profession, and I would rather have my bracelets on him than on any criminal in London. He's a remarkable man, is young John Clay. His grandfather was a royal duke, and he himself has been to Eton and Oxford. His brain is as cunning as his fingers, and though we meet signs of him at every turn, we never know where to find the man himself. He'll crack a crib in Scotland one week, and be raising money to build an orphanage in Cornwall the next. I've been on his track for years, and have never set eyes on him yet."

"I hope that I may have the pleasure of introducing you tonight. I've had one or two little turns also with Mr. John Clay, and I agree with you that he is at the head of his profession. It is past ten, however, and quite time that we started. If you two will take the first hansom, Watson and I will follow in the second."

Sherlock Holmes was not very communicative during the long drive, and lay back in the cab humming the tunes which he had heard in the afternoon. We rattled through an endless labyrinth of gas-lit streets until we emerged into Farringdon Street.

"We are close there now," my friend remarked. "This fellow Merryweather is a bank director, and personally interested in the matter. I thought it as well to have Jones with us also. He is not a bad fellow, though an absolute imbecile in his profession. He has one positive virtue. He is as brave as a bulldog, and as tenacious as a lobster if he gets his claws upon anyone. Here we are, and they are waiting for us."

We had now reached the same crowded thoroughfare in which we had found ourselves in the morning. Our cabs were dismissed, and, following the guidance of Mr. Merryweather, we passed down a narrow passage and through a side-door, which he opened for us. Within there was a small corridor, which ended in a very massive iron gate. This also was opened, and led down a flight of winding stone steps, which terminated at another formidable gate. Mr. Merryweather stopped to light a lantern, and then conducted us down a dark, earth-smelling passage, and so, after opening a third door, into a huge vault or cellar, which was piled all round with crates and massive boxes.

"You are not very vulnerable from above," Holmes remarked, as he held up the lantern and gazed about him.

"Nor from below," said Mr. Merryweather, striking his stick upon the flags which lined the floor. "Why, dear me, it sounds quite hollow!" he remarked, looking up in surprise.

"I must really ask you to be a little more quiet," said Holmes, severely. "You have already imperiled the whole success of our expedition. Might I beg that you would have the goodness to sit down upon one of those boxes, and not to interfere?"

The solemn Mr. Merryweather perched himself upon a crate, with a very injured expression upon his face, while Holmes fell upon his knees upon the floor, and, with the lantern and a magnifying lens, began to examine minutely the cracks between the stones. A few seconds sufficed to satisfy him, for he sprang to his feet again, and put his glass in his pocket.

"We have at least an hour before us," he remarked; "for they can hardly take any steps until the good pawnbroker is safely in bed. Then they will not lose a minute, for the sooner they do their work the longer time they will have for their escape. We are at present, doctor—as no doubt you have divined—in the cellar of the city branch of one of the principal London banks. Mr. Merryweather is the chairman of directors, and he will explain to you that there are reasons why the more daring criminals of London should take a considerable interest in this cellar at present."

"It is our French gold," whispered the director. "We have had several warnings that an attempt might be made upon it."

"Your French gold?"

"Yes. We had occasion some months ago to strengthen our resources, and borrowed, for that purpose, 30,000 napoleons from the Bank of France. It has become known that we have never had occasion to unpack the money, and that it is still lying in our cellar. The crate upon which I sit contains 2,000 napoleons packed between layers of lead foil. Our reserve of bullion is much larger at present than is usually kept in a single branch office, and the directors have had misgivings upon the subject."

"Which were very well justified," observed Holmes. "And now it is time that we arranged our little plans. I expect that within an hour matters will come to a head. In the meantime, Mr. Merryweather, we must put the screen over that dark lantern."

"And sit in the dark?"

"I am afraid so. I had brought a pack of cards in my pocket, and I thought that, as we were a *partie carrée,* you might have your rubber after all. But I see that the enemy's preparations have gone so far that we cannot risk the presence of a light. And, first of all, we must choose our positions. These are daring men, and though we shall take them at a disadvantage, they may do us some harm unless we are careful. I shall stand behind this crate, and do you conceal yourselves behind those. Then, when I flash a light upon them, close in swiftly. If they fire, Watson, have no compunction about shooting them down."

I placed my revolver, cocked, upon the top of the wooden case behind which I crouched. Holmes shot the slide across the front of his lantern, and left us in pitch darkness—such an absolute darkness as I have never before experienced. The smell of hot metal remained to assure us that the light was still there, ready to flash out at a moment's notice. To me, with my nerves worked up to a pitch of expectancy, there was something depressing and subduing in the sudden gloom, and in the cold, dank air of the vault.

"They have but one retreat," whispered Holmes. "That is back through the house into Saxe-Coburg Square. I hope that you have done what I asked you, Jones?"

"I have an inspector and two officers waiting at the front door."

"Then we have stopped all the holes. And now we must be silent and wait."

What a time it seemed! From comparing notes afterwards it was but an hour and a quarter, yet it appeared to me that the night must have almost gone, and the dawn be breaking above us. My limbs were weary and stiff, for I feared to change my position; yet my nerves were worked up to the highest pitch of tension, and my hearing was so acute that I could not only hear the gentle breathing of my companions, but I could distinguish the deeper, heavier in-breath of the bulky Jones from the thin, sighing note of the bank director. From my position I could look over the case in the direction of the floor. Suddenly my eyes caught the glint of a light.

At first it was but a lurid spark upon the stone pavement. Then it lengthened out until it became a yellow line, and then, without any warning or sound, a gash seemed to open and a hand appeared; a white, almost womanly hand, which felt about in the center of the little area of light. For a minute or more the hand, with its writhing fingers, protruded out of the floor. Then it was withdrawn as suddenly as it appeared, and all was dark again save the single lurid spark which marked a chink between the stones.

Its disappearance, however, was but momentary. With a rending, tearing sound, one of the broad, white stones turned over upon its side, and left a square, gaping hole, through which streamed the light of a lantern. Over the edge there peeped a clean-cut, boyish face, which looked keenly about it, and then, with a hand on either side of the aperture, drew itself shoulder-high and waist-high, until one knee rested upon the edge. In another instant he stood at the side of the hole, and was hauling after him a companion, lithe and small like himself, with a pale face and a shock of very red hair.

"It's all clear," he whispered. "Have you the chisel and the bags? Great Scott! Jump, Archie, jump, and I'll swing for it!"

Sherlock Holmes had sprung out and seized the intruder by the collar. The other dived down the hole, and I heard the sound of rending cloth as Jones clutched at his skirts. The light flashed upon the barrel of a revolver, but Holmes's hunting crop came down on the man's wrist, and the pistol clinked upon the stone floor.

"It's no use, John Clay," said Holmes blandly. "You have no chance at all."

"So I see," the other answered, with the utmost coolness. "I fancy that my pal is all right, though I see you have got his coattails."

"There are three men waiting for him at the door," said Holmes.

"Oh, indeed! You seem to have done the thing very completely. I must compliment you."

"And I you," Holmes answered. "Your red-headed idea was very new and effective."

"You'll see your pal again presently," said Jones. "He's quicker at climbing down holes than I am. Just hold out while I fix the derbies."

"I beg that you will not touch me with your filthy hands," remarked our prisoner, as the handcuffs clattered upon his wrists. "You may not be aware that I have royal blood in my veins. Have the goodness, also, when you address me always to say 'sir' and 'please.'"

"All right," said Jones, with a stare and a snigger. "Well, would you please, sir, march upstairs, where we can get a cab to carry your highness to the police station?"

"That is better," said John Clay, serenely. He made a sweeping bow to the three of us, and walked quietly off in the custody of the detective.

"Really, Mr. Holmes," said Mr. Merryweather, as we followed them from the cellar, "I do not know how the bank can thank you or repay you. There is no doubt that you have detected and defeated in the most complete manner one of the most determined attempts at bank robbery that have ever come within my experience."

"I have had one or two little scores of my own to settle with Mr. John Clay," said Holmes. "I have been at some small expense over this matter, which I shall expect the bank to refund, but beyond that I am amply repaid by having had an experience which is in many ways unique, and by hearing the very remarkable narrative of the Red-headed League."

"You see, Watson," he explained, in the early hours of the morning, as we sat over a glass of whiskey-and-soda in Baker Street "it

was perfectly obvious from the first that the only possible object of
this rather fantastic business of the advertisement of the League, and
the copying of the 'Encyclopædia,' must be to get this not overbright
pawnbroker out of the way for a number of hours every day. It was
a curious way of managing it, but, really, it would be difficult to
suggest a better. The method was no doubt suggested to Clay's in-
genious mind by the color of his accomplice's hair. The £4 a week
was a lure which must draw him, and what was it to them, who
were playing for thousands? They put in the advertisement, one
rogue has the temporary office, the other rogue incites the man to
apply for it, and together they manage to secure his absence every
morning in the week. From the time that I heard of the assistant
having come for half wages, it was obvious to me that he had some
strong motive for securing the situation."

"But how could you guess what the motive was?"

"Had there been women in the house, I should have suspected
a mere vulgar intrigue. That, however, was out of the question.
The man's business was a small one, and there was nothing in his
house which could account for such elaborate preparations, and such
an expenditure as they were at. It must, then, be something out of
the house. What could it be? I thought of the assistant's fondness
for photography, and his trick of vanishing into the cellar. The
cellar! There was the end of this tangled clue. Then I made inquiries as to this mysterious assistant, and found that I had to deal
with one of the coolest and most daring criminals in London. He
was doing something in the cellar—something which took many
hours a day for months on end. What could it be, once more? I
could think of nothing save that he was running a tunnel to some
other building.

"So far I had got when we went to visit the scene of action. I
surprised you by beating upon the pavement with my stick. I was
ascertaining whether the cellar stretched out in front or behind.
It was not in front. Then I rang the bell, and, as I hoped, the assistant answered it. We have had some skirmishes, but we had never
set eyes upon each other before. I hardly looked at his face. His
knees were what I wished to see. You must yourself have remarked

how worn, wrinkled, and stained they were. They spoke of those hours of burrowing. The only remaining point was what they were burrowing for. I walked round the corner, saw that the City and Suburban Bank abutted on our friend's premises, and felt that I had solved my problem. When you drove home after the concert I called upon Scotland Yard, and upon the chairman of the bank directors, with the result that you have seen."

"And how could you tell that they would make their attempt tonight?" I asked.

"Well, when they closed their League offices that was a sign that they cared no longer about Mr. Jabez Wilson's presence—in other words, that they had completed their tunnel. But it was essential that they should use it soon, as it might be discovered, or the bullion might be removed. Saturday would suit them better than any other day, as it would give them two days for their escape. For all these reasons I expected them to come tonight."

"You reasoned it out beautifully," I exclaimed, in unfeigned admiration. "It is so long a chain, and yet every link rings true."

"It saved me from ennui," he answered, yawning. "Alas! I already feel it closing in upon me. My life is spent in one long effort to escape from the commonplaces of existence. These little problems help me to do so."

"And you are a benefactor of the race," said I.

He shrugged his shoulders. "Well, perhaps, after all, it is of some little use," he remarked. "'L'homme c'est rien—l'œuvre c'est tout,' as Gustave Flaubert wrote to Georges Sand."

# NEW YORK TO PARIS

## By *CHARLES AUGUSTUS LINDBERGH*

*Portrait by Hugo Gellert*

A T New York we checked over the plane, engine and instruments, which required several short flights over the field.

When the plane was completely inspected and ready for the transAtlantic flight, there were dense fogs reported along the coast and over Nova Scotia and Newfoundland, in addition to a storm area over the North Atlantic.

On the morning of May 19th, a light rain was falling and the sky was overcast. Weather reports from land stations and ships along the great circle course were unfavorable and there was apparently no prospect of taking off for Paris for several days at least. In the morning I visited the Wright plant at Paterson, New Jersey, and had planned to attend a theater performance in New York that evening. But at about six o'clock I received a special report from the New York Weather Bureau. A high pressure area was over the entire North Atlantic and the low pressure over Nova Scotia and Newfoundland was receding. It was apparent that the prospects of the fog clearing up were as good as I might expect for some time to come.

The North Atlantic should be clear with only local storms on the coast of Europe. The moon had just passed full and the percentage of days with fog over Newfoundland and the Grand Banks was increasing so that there seemed to be no advantage in waiting longer.

We went to Curtiss Field as quickly as possible and made arrangements for the barograph to be sealed and installed, and for the plane to be serviced and checked.

We decided partially to fill the fuel tanks in the hangar before towing the ship on a truck to Roosevelt Field, which adjoins Curtiss on the east, where the servicing would be completed.

I left the responsibility for conditioning the plane in the hands of the men on the field while I went into the hotel for about two and one-half hours of rest; but at the hotel there were several more details which had to be completed and I was unable to get any sleep that night.

I returned to the field before daybreak on the morning of the twentieth. A light rain was falling which continued until almost dawn; consequently we did not move the ship to Roosevelt Field until much later than we had planned, and the take-off was delayed from daybreak until nearly eight o'clock.

At dawn the shower had passed, although the sky was overcast, and occasionally there would be some slight precipitation. The tail of the plane was lashed to a truck and escorted by a number of motorcycle police. The slow trip from Curtiss to Roosevelt was begun.

The ship was placed at the extreme west end of the field heading along the east and west runway, and the final fueling commenced.

About 7:40 A.M. the motor was started and at 7:52 I took off on the flight for Paris. [May 20, 1927.]

The field was a little soft due to the rain during the night and the heavily loaded plane gathered speed very slowly. After passing the halfway mark, however, it was apparent that I would be able to clear the obstructions at the end. I passed over a tractor by about fifteen feet and a telephone line by about twenty, with a fair reserve of flying speed. I believe that the ship would have taken off from a hard field with at least five hundred pounds more weight.

I turned slightly to the right to avoid some high trees on a hill directly ahead, but by the time I had gone a few hundred yards I had sufficient altitude to clear all obstructions and throttled the engine down to 1750 R.P.M. I took up a compass course at once and soon reached Long Island Sound where the Curtiss Oriole with its photographer, which had been escorting me, turned back.

The haze soon cleared and from Cape Cod through the southern half of Nova Scotia the weather and visibility were excellent. I was flying very low, sometimes as close as ten feet from the trees and water.

*Portrait of Charles Augustus Lindbergh*

[See page **216**]

On the three hundred mile stretch of water between Cape Cod and Nova Scotia I passed within view of numerous fishing vessels.

The northern part of Nova Scotia contained a number of storm areas and several times I flew through cloudbursts.

As I neared the northern coast, snow appeared in patches on the ground and far to the eastward the coast line was covered with fog.

For many miles between Nova Scotia and Newfoundland the ocean was covered with caked ice, but as I approached the coast the ice disappeared entirely and I saw several ships in this area.

I had taken up a course for St. John's, which is south of the great Circle from New York to Paris, so that there would be no question of the fact that I had passed Newfoundland in case I was forced down in the north Atlantic.

I passed over numerous icebergs after leaving St. John's but saw no ships except near the coast.

Darkness set in about 8:15 New York time and a thin, low fog formed through which the white bergs showed up with surprising clearness. This fog became thicker and increased in height until within two hours I was just skimming the top of storm clouds at about ten thousand feet. Even at this altitude there was a thick haze through which only the stars directly overhead could be seen.

There was no moon and it was very dark. The tops of some of the storm clouds were several thousand feet above me and at one time, when I attempted to fly through one of the larger clouds, sleet started to collect on the plane and I was forced to turn around and get back into clear air immediately and then fly around any clouds which I could not get over.

The moon appeared on the horizon after about two hours of darkness; then the flying was much less complicated.

Dawn came at about 1 A.M. New York time and the temperature had risen until there was practically no remaining danger of sleet.

Shortly after sunrise the clouds became more broken although some of them were far above me and it was often necessary to fly through them, navigating by instruments only.

As the sun became higher, holes appeared in the fog. Through one the open water was visible, and I dropped down until less than a hundred feet above the waves. There was a strong wind blowing from the northwest and the ocean was covered with white caps.

After a few miles of fairly clear weather the ceiling lowered to zero and for nearly two hours I flew entirely blind through the fog at an altitude of about 1,500 feet. Then the fog raised and the water was visible again.

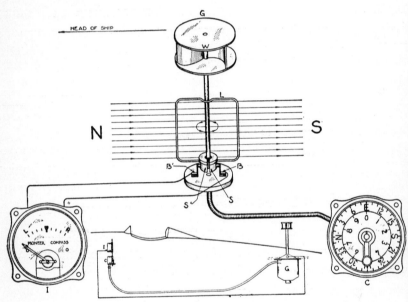

*Diagram of earth inductor compass used by Lindbergh.*

On several more occasions it was necessary to fly by instrument for short periods; then the fog broke up into patches. These patches took on forms of every description. Numerous shore lines appeared, with trees perfectly outlined against the horizon. In fact, the mirages were so natural that, had I not been in mid-Atlantic and known that no land existed along my route, I would have taken them to be actual islands.

As the fog cleared I dropped down closer to the water, sometimes flying within ten feet of the waves and seldom higher than two hundred.

There is a cushion of air close to the ground or water through which a plane flies with less effort than when at a higher altitude, and for hours at a time I took advantage of this factor.

Also, it was less difficult to determine the wind drift near the water. During the entire flight the wind was strong enough to produce white caps on the waves. When one of these formed, the foam would be blown off, showing the wind's direction and approximate velocity. This foam remained on the water long enough for me to obtain a general idea of my drift.

During the day I saw a number of porpoises and a few birds but no ships, although I understand that two different boats reported me passing over.

The first indication of my approach to the European coast was a small fishing boat which I first noticed a few miles ahead and slightly to the south of my course. There were several of these fishing boats grouped within a few miles of each other.

I flew over the first boat without seeing any signs of life. As I circled over the second, however, a man's face appeared, looking out of the cabin window.

I have carried on short conversations with people on the ground by flying low with throttled engine, shouting a question, and receiving the answer by some signal. When I saw this fisherman I decided to try to get him to point toward land. I had no sooner made the decision than the futility of the effort became apparent. In all likelihood he could not speak English, and even if he could he would undoubtedly be far too astounded to answer. However, I circled again and closing the throttle as the plane passed within a few feet of the boat I shouted, "Which way is Ireland?" Of course the attempt was useless, and I continued on my course.

Less than an hour later a rugged and semi-mountainous coast line appeared to the northeast. I was flying less than two hundred feet from the water when I sighted it. The shore was fairly distinct and not over ten or fifteen miles away. A light haze coupled with numerous local storm areas had prevented my seeing it from a long distance.

The coast line came down from the north, curved over toward

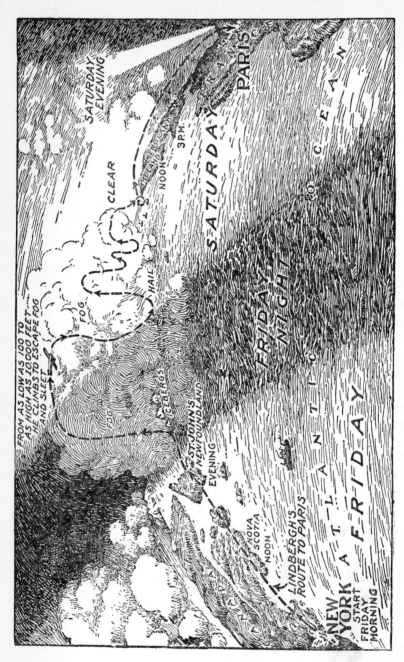

Graphic map of Lindbergh's flight (May 20-21, 1927).

the east. I had very little doubt that it was the southwestern end of Ireland but in order to make sure I changed my course toward the nearest point of land.

I located Cape Valentia and Dingle Bay, then resumed my compass course toward Paris.

After leaving Ireland I passed a number of steamers and was seldom out of sight of a ship.

In a little over two hours the coast of England appeared. My course passed over southern England and a little south of Plymouth; then across the English Channel, striking France over Cherbourg.

The English farms were very impressive from the air in contrast to ours in America. They appeared extremely small and unusually neat and tidy with their stone and hedge fences.

I was flying at about a fifteen hundred foot altitude over England and as I crossed the Channel and passed over Cherbourg, France, I had probably seen more of that part of Europe than many native Europeans. The visibility was good and the country could be seen for miles around.

People who have taken their first flight often remark that no one knows what the locality he lives in is like until he has seen it from above. Countries take on different characteristics from the air.

The sun went down shortly after passing Cherbourg and soon the beacons along the Paris-London airway became visible.

I first saw the lights of Paris a little before ten P.M.—or five P.M. New York time—and a few minutes later I was circling the Eiffel Tower at an altitude of about four thousand feet.

The lights of Le Bourget were plainly visible, but appeared to be very close to Paris. I had understood that the field was farther from the city, so continued out to the northeast into the country for four or five miles to make sure that there was not another field farther out which might be Le Bourget. Then I returned and spiraled down closer to the lights. Presently I could make out long lines of hangars, and the roads appeared to be jammed with cars.

I flew low over the field once, then circled around into the wind and landed.

After the plane stopped rolling I turned it around and started to taxi back to the lights. The entire field ahead, however, was covered with thousands of people all running toward my ship. When the first few arrived, I attempted to get them to hold the rest of the crowd back, away from the plane, but apparently no one could understand, or would have been able to conform to my request if he had.

I cut the switch to keep the propeller from killing someone, and attempted to organize an impromptu guard for the plane. The impossibility of any immediate organization became apparent, and when parts of the ship began to crack from the pressure of the multitude I decided to climb out of the cockpit in order to draw the crowd away.

Speaking was impossible; no words could be heard in the uproar and nobody apparently cared to hear any. I started to climb out of the cockpit, but as soon as one foot appeared through the door I was dragged the rest of the way without assistance on my part.

For nearly half an hour I was unable to touch the ground, during which time I was ardently carried around in what seemed to be a very small area, and in every position it is possible to be in. Everyone had the best of intentions but no one seemed to know just what they were.

The French military flyers very resourcefully took the situation in hand. A number of them mingled with the crowd; then, at a given signal, they placed my helmet on an American correspondent and cried: "Here is Lindbergh." That helmet on an American was sufficient evidence. The correspondent immediately became the center of attraction, and while he was being taken protestingly to the Reception Committee via a rather devious route, I managed to get inside one of the hangars.

Meanwhile a second group of soldiers and police had surrounded the plane and soon placed it out of danger in another hangar.

The French ability to handle an unusual situation with speed and capability was remarkably demonstrated that night at Le Bourget.

Ambassador Herrick extended me an invitation to remain at his Embassy while I was in Paris, which I gladly accepted. But grateful as I was at the time, it did not take me long to realize that a kind Providence had placed me in Ambassador Herrick's hands. The ensuing days found me in situations that I had certainly never expected to be in and in which I relied on Ambassador Herrick's sympathetic aid.

These situations were brought about by the whole-hearted welcome to me—an American—that touched me beyond any point that any words can express. I left France with a debt of gratitude which, though I cannot repay it, I shall always remember. If the French people had been acclaiming their own gallant airmen, Nungesser and Coli, who were lost only after fearlessly departing in the face of conditions insurmountably greater than those that confronted me, their enthusiastic welcome and graciousness could not have been greater.

In Belgium as well, I was received with a warmth which reflected more than simply a passing curiosity in a trans-Atlantic flight, but which was rather a demonstration by the people of their interest in a new means of transportation which eventually would bring still closer together the new world and the old. Their welcome, too, will be a cherished memory for all time.

In England, I experienced one final unforgettable demonstration of friendship for an American. That spontaneous wonderful reception during my brief visit seemed typical of what I had always heard of the good sportsmanship of the English.

My words to all those friends in Europe are inadequate, but my feelings of appreciation are boundless.


## CONCLUSION

When I was contemplating the flight to Paris I looked forward to making a short tour of Europe with especial regard to the various airports and aeronautical activities.

After I arrived, however, the necessity for returning to America in the near future became apparent and, after a consultation with Ambassador Houghton, who informed me that President Coolidge was sending the cruiser *Memphis* to Cherbourg for my return journey to America, I flew the "Spirit of St. Louis" to Gosport early one morning. There it was dismantled and crated, through the courtesy of the Royal Air Force which also placed a Woodcock pursuit plane at my disposal.

I returned to London in the Woodcock and a few days later flew to Paris in another R.A.F. machine of the same type.

I remained overnight in Paris, and early the next morning flew a French Breguet to Cherbourg where the cruiser *Memphis* was waiting.

Admiral Burrage met me at the dock, and after going aboard the *Memphis* I became acquainted with Captain Lackey and the officers of the ship. During the trip across they extended every courtesy and did everything within their power to make the voyage a pleasant one.

A description of my welcome back to the United States would, in itself, be sufficient to fill a larger volume than this. I am not an author by profession, and my pen could never express the gratitude which I feel toward the American people.

The voyage up the Potomac and to the Monument Grounds in Washington; up the Hudson River and along Broadway; over the Mississippi and to St. Louis—to do justice to these occasions would require a far greater writer than myself.

Washington, New York, and finally St. Louis and home. Each of these cities has left me with an impression that I shall never forget, and a debt of gratitude which I can never repay.

# FLYING OVER THE NORTH POLE

## By *RICHARD E. BYRD*

*Portrait by Rebecca L. Taylor*

WITH a total load of nearly 10,000 pounds we raced down the runway. The rough snow ahead loomed dangerously near but we never reached it. We were off for our great adventure!

Beneath us were our shipmates—everyone anxious to go along, but unselfishly wild with delight that we were at last off—running in our wake, waving their arms, and throwing their hats in the air. As long as I live I can never forget that sight, or those splendid fellows. They had given us our great chance.

For months previous to this hour, utmost attention had been paid to every detail that would assure our margin of safety in case of accident, and to the perfection of our scientific results in the case of success.

We had a short-wave radio set operated by a hand dynamo, should we be forced down on the ice. A handmade sledge presented to us by Amundsen was stowed in the fuselage, on which to carry our food and clothing should we be compelled to walk to Greenland. We had food for ten weeks. Our main staple, pemmican, consisting of chopped-up dried meat, fat, sugar and raisins, was supplemented by chocolate, pilot bread, tea, malted milk, powdered chocolate, butter, sugar and cream cheese, all of which form a highly concentrated diet.

Other articles of equipment were a rubber boat for crossing open leads if forced down, reindeer skin, polar bear and seal fur clothes, boots and gloves, primus stove, rifle, pistol, shotgun and ammunition; tent, knives, ax, medical kit and smoke bombs—all as compact as humanly possible.

If we should come down on the ice the reason it would take us so long to get back, if we got back at all, was that we could not return Spitzbergen way on account of the strong tides. We would have to march Etah way and would have to kill enough seal, polar bear and musk ox to last through the Arctic nights.

The first stage of our navigation was the simple one of dead reckoning, or following the well-known landmarks in the vicinity of Kings Bay, which we had just left. We climbed to 2,000 feet to get a good view of the coast and the magnificent snow-covered mountains inland. Within an hour of taking the air we passed the rugged and glacier-laden land and crossed the edge of the polar ice pack. It was much nearer to the land than we had expected. Over to the east was a point where the ice field was very near the land.

We looked ahead at the sea ice gleaming in the rays of the midnight sun—a fascinating scene whose lure had drawn famous men into its clutches, never to return. It was with a feeling of exhilaration that we felt that for the first time in history two mites of men could gaze upon its charms, and discover its secrets, out of reach of those sharp claws.

Perhaps! There was still that "perhaps," for if we should have a forced landing disaster might easily follow.

It was only natural for Bennett and me to wonder whether or not we would ever get back to this small island we were leaving, for all the airmen explorers who had preceded us in attempts to reach the Pole by aviation had met with disaster or near disaster.

Though it was important to hit the Pole from the standpoint of achievement, it was more important to do so from that of our lives, so that we could get back to Spitzbergen, a target none too big. We could not fly back to land from an unknown position. We must put every possible second of time and our best concentration on the job of navigating and flying a straight course—our very lives depended on it.

As there are no landmarks on the ice, Polar Sea navigation by aircraft is similar to that on the ocean, where there is nothing but sun and stars and moon from which to determine one's position. The altitude above the sea horizon of one of these celestial bodies is taken with the sextant. Then, by mathematical calculations, requiring an hour or so to work out, the ship is located somewhere on an

*Portrait of Admiral Richard Evelyn Byrd.*

[See page 225]

imaginary line. The Polar Sea horizon, however, cannot always be depended upon, due to roughness of the ice. Therefore we had a specially designed instrument that would enable us to take the altitude without the horizon. I used the same instrument that we had developed for the 1919 trans-Atlantic flight.

Again, should the navigator of a fast airplane take an hour to get his line of position, by the time he plotted it on his chart he would be a hundred miles or so away from the point at which he took the sight. He must therefore have quick means of making his astronomical calculations.

We were familiar with one means of calculation which takes advantage of some interesting astronomical conditions existing at the North Pole. It is a graphical method that does away largely with mathematical calculations, so that the entire operation of taking the altitude of the sun and laying down the line of position could be done in a very few minutes.

This method was taught me by G. W. Littlebales of the Navy Hydrographic Office and was first discovered by Arthur Hinks of the Royal Geographic Society.

So much for the locating of position in the Polar Sea by astronomy, which must be done by the navigator to check up and correct the course steered by the pilot. The compass is generally off the true course a greater or less degree, on account of faulty steering, currents, wind, etc.

Our chief concern was to steer as nearly due north as possible. This could not be done with the ordinarily dependable magnetic compass, which points only in the general direction of the North Magnetic Pole, lying on Boothia Peninsula, Canada, more than a thousand miles south of the North Geographical Pole.

If the compass pointed exactly toward the Magnetic Pole the magnetic bearing of the North Geographical Pole could be calculated mathematically for any place on the Polar Sea. But as there is generally some local condition affecting the needle, the variation of the compass from true north can be found only by actual trial.

Since this trial could not have been made over unknown regions, the true directions the compass needle would point along our route were not known. Also, since the directive force of the earth's magnetism is small in the Far North, there is a tendency of the needle toward sluggishness in indicating a change in direction of the plane, and toward undue swinging after it has once started to move.

Nor would the famous gyroscopic compass work up there, as when nearing the Pole its axis would have a tendency to point straight up in the air.

There was only one thing to do—to depend upon the sun. For this we used a sun-compass: the same type instrument that had been invented and constructed for our 1925 expedition by Albert H. Bumstead, chief cartographer of the National Geographic Society. I do not hesitate to say that without it we could not have reached the Pole; it is even doubtful if we could have hit Spitzbergen on our return flight.

Of course, the sun was necessary for the use of this compass. Its principle is a kind of reversal of that of the sundial. In the latter, the direction of north is known and the shadow of the sun gives the time of day. With the sun-compass, the time of day is known, and the shadow of the sun, when it bisects the hand of the 24-hour clock, indicates the direction after the instrument has been set.

Then there was the influence of the wind that had to be allowed for. An airplane, in effect, is a part of the wind, just as a ship in a current floats with the speed of the current. If, for example, a thirty-mile-an-hour wind is blowing at right angles to the course, the plane will be taken 30 miles an hour to one side of its course. This is called "drift" and can be compensated for by an instrument called the drift-indicator, which we had also developed for the first trans-Atlantic flight.

We used the drift-indicator through the trapdoor in the plane, and had so arranged the cabin that there was plenty of room for navigating. There was also a fair-sized chartboard.

As exact Greenwich time was necessary, we carried two chronometers that I had kept in my room for weeks. I knew their error to within a second. There seems to be a tendency for chronometers to slow up when exposed to the cold. With this in mind we had taken their cold-weather error.

As we sped along over the white field below I spent the busiest and most concentrated moments of my life. Though we had confidence in our instruments and methods, we were trying them for the first time over the Polar Sea. First, we obtained north and south bearings on a mountain range on Spitzbergen which we could see for a long distance out over the ice. These checked fairly well with the sun-compass. But I had absolute confidence in the sun-compass.

We could see mountains astern gleaming in the sun at least a hundred miles behind us. That was our last link with civilization. The unknown lay ahead.

Bennett and I took turns piloting. At first Bennett was steering, and for some unaccountable reason the plane veered from the course time and time again, to the right. He could glance back where I was working, through a door leading to the two pilots' seats. Every minute or two he would look at me, to be checked if necessary, on the course by the sun-compass. If he happened to be off the course I would wave him to the right or left until he got on it again. Once every three minutes while I was navigating, I checked the wind drift and ground speed, so that in case of a change in wind I could detect it immediately and allow for it.

We had three sets of gloves which I changed constantly to fit the job in hand, and sometimes removed entirely for short periods to write or figure on the chart. I froze my face and one of my hands in taking sights with the instruments from the trapdoors. But I noticed these frostbites at once and was more careful thereafter in the future. Ordinarily a frostbite need not be dangerous if detected in time and if the blood is rubbed back immediately into the affected parts. We also carried leather helmets that would cover the whole face when necessary to use them.

We carried two sun-compasses. One was fixed to a trapdoor in the top of the navigator's cabin; the other was movable, so when the great wing obscured the sun from the compass on the trapdoor, the second could be used in the cabin, through the open windows.

Every now and then I took sextant sights of the sun to see where the lines of position would cross our line of flight. I was very thankful at those moments that the Navy requires such thorough navigation training, and that I had made air navigation my hobby.

Finally, when I felt certain we were on our course, I turned my attention to the great ice pack, which I had wondered about ever since I was a youngster at school. We were flying at about 2,000 feet, and I could see at least 50 miles in every direction. There was no sign of land. If there had been any within 100 miles' radius we would have seen its mountain peaks, so good was the visibility.

The ice pack beneath was crisscrossed with pressure ridges, but here and there were stretches that appeared long and smooth enough to land on. However, from 2,000 feet pack ice is very deceptive.

The pressure ridges that looked so insignificant from the plane varied from a few feet to 50 or 60 feet in height, while the average thickness of the ice was about 40 feet. A flash of sympathy came over me for the brave men who had in years past struggled northward over that cruel mass.

We passed leads of water recently opened by the movement of the ice, and so dangerous to the foot traveler, who never knows when the ice will open up beneath and swallow him into the black depths of the Polar Sea.

I now turned my mind to wind conditions, for I knew they were a matter of interest to all those contemplating the feasibility of a polar airway. We found them good. There were no bumps in the air. This was as we had anticipated, for the flatness of the ice and the Arctic temperature were not conducive to air currents, such as are sometimes found over land. Had we struck an Arctic gale, I cannot say what the result would have been as far as air roughness is concerned. Of course we still had the advantage of spring and 24-hour daylight.

It was time now to relieve Bennett again at the wheel, not only that he might stretch his legs, but so that he could pour gasoline into the tanks from the five-gallon tins stowed all over the cabin. Empty cans were thrown overboard to get rid of the weight, small though it was.

Frequently I was able to check myself on the course by holding the sun-compass in one hand and steering with the other.

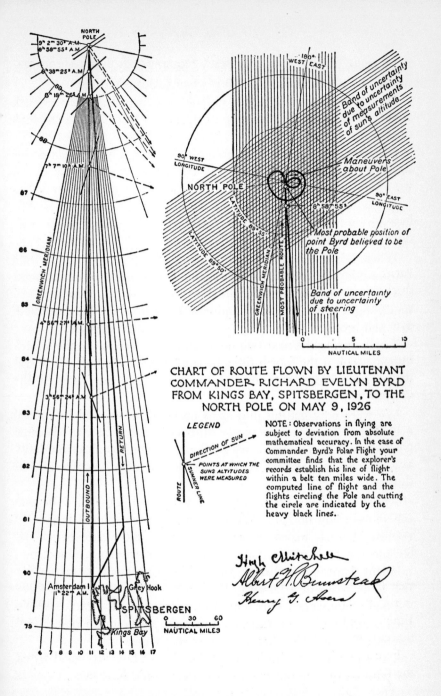

**CHART OF ROUTE FLOWN BY LIEUTENANT COMMANDER RICHARD EVELYN BYRD FROM KINGS BAY, SPITSBERGEN, TO THE NORTH POLE ON MAY 9, 1926**

LEGEND

DIRECTION OF SUN

POINTS AT WHICH THE SUNS ALTITUDES WERE MEASURED

ROUTE

SUMNER LINE

NOTE: Observations in flying are subject to deviation from absolute mathematical accuracy. In the case of Commander Byrd's Polar Flight your committee finds that the explorer's records establish his line of flight within a belt ten miles wide. The computed line of flight and the flights circling the Pole and cutting the circle are indicated by the heavy black lines.

I had time now to examine the ice pack and eagerly sought signs of life, a polar bear, a seal, or birds flying, but could see none.

On one occasion, as I turned to look over the side, my arm struck some object in my left breast pocket. It was filled with good-luck pieces!

I am not superstitious, I believe. No explorer, however, can go off without such articles. Among my trinkets was a religious medal put there by a friend. It belonged to his fiancée and he firmly believed it would get me through. There was also a tiny horseshoe made by a famous blacksmith. Attached to the pocket was a little coin taken by Peary, pinned to his shirt, on his trip to the North Pole.

When Bennett had finished pouring and figuring the gasoline consumption, he took the wheel again. I went back to the incessant navigating. So much did I sight down on the dazzling snow that I had a slight attack of snow blindness. But I need not have suffered, as I had brought along the proper kind of amber goggles.

Twice during the next two hours I relieved Bennett at the wheel. When I took it the fourth time, he smiled as he went aft. "I would rather have Floyd with me," I thought, "than any man in the world."

We were now getting into areas never before viewed by mortal eye. The feelings of an explorer superseded the aviator's. I became conscious of that extraordinary exhilaration which comes from looking into virgin territory. At that moment I felt repaid for all our toil.

At the end of this unknown area lay our goal, somewhere beyond the shimmering horizon. We were opening unexplored regions at the rate of nearly 10,000 square miles an hour, and were experiencing the incomparable satisfaction of searching for new land. Once, for a moment, I mistook a distant, vague, low-lying cloud formation for the white peaks of a far-away land.

I had a momentary sensation of great triumph. If I could explain the feeling I had at this time, the much-asked question would be answered: "What is this Arctic craze so many men get?"

The sun was still shining brightly. Surely fate was good to us, for without the sun our quest of the Pole would have been hopeless.

To the right, somewhere, the rays of the midnight sun shone down on the scenes of Nansen's heroic struggles to reach the goal that we were approaching with the ease of an eagle at the rate of nearly 100 miles an hour. To our left, lay Peary's oft-traveled trail.

When I went back to my navigating, I compared the magnetic compass with the sun-compass and found that the westerly error in the former had nearly doubled since reaching the edge of the ice pack, where it had been eleven degrees westerly.

When our calculations showed us to be about an hour from the Pole, I noticed through the cabin window a bad leak in the oil tank of the starboard motor. Bennett confirmed my fears. He wrote: "That motor will stop."

Bennett then suggested that we try a landing to fix the leak. But I had seen too many expeditions fail by landing. We decided to keep on for the Pole. We would be in no worse fix should we come down near the Pole than if we had a forced landing where we were.

When I took to the wheel again I kept my eyes glued on that oil leak and the oil-pressure indicator. Should the pressure drop, we would lose the motor immediately. It fascinated me. There was no doubt in my mind that the oil pressure would drop at any moment. But the prize was actually in sight. We could not turn back.

At 9:02 A.M., May 9, 1926, Greenwich civil time, our calculations showed us to be at the Pole! The dream of a lifetime had at last been realized.

We headed to the right to take two confirming sights of the sun, then turned and took two more.

After that we made some moving and still pictures, then went on for several miles in the direction we had come, and made another larger circle to be sure to take in the Pole. We thus made a non-stop flight around the world in a very few minutes. In doing that we lost a whole day in time and of course when we completed the circle we gained that day back again.

Time and direction became topsy-turvy at the Pole. When crossing it on the same straight line we were going north one instant and south the next! No matter how the wind strikes you at the North Pole it must be traveling north and however you turn your head you must be looking south and our job was to get back to the small island of Spitzbergen which lay somewhere south of us!

There were two great questions that confronted us now: Were we exactly where we thought we were? If not—and could we be absolutely certain?—we would miss Spitzbergen. And even if we were on a straight course, would the engine stop? It seemed certain it would.

As we flew there at the top of the world, we saluted the gallant, indomitable spirit of Peary and verified his report in every detail.

Below us was a great eternally frozen, snow-covered ocean, broken into ice fields or cakes of various sizes and shapes, the boundaries of which were the ridges formed by the great pressure of one cake upon another. This showed a constant ice movement and indicated the non-proximity of land. Here and there, instead of a pressing together of the ice fields, there was a separation, leaving a water-lead which had been recently frozen over and showing green and greenish-blue against the white of the snow. On some of the cakes were ice hummocks and rough masses of jumbled snow and ice.

At 9:15 A.M. we headed for Spitzbergen, having abandoned the plan to return via Cape Morris Jesup on account of the oil leak.

But, to our astonishment, a miracle was happening. That motor was still running. It is a hundred to one shot that a leaky engine such as ours means a motor stoppage. It is generally an oil lead that breaks. We afterwards found out the leak was caused by a rivet jarring out of its hole, and when the oil got down to the level of the hole it stopped leaking. Flight Engineer Noville had put an extra amount of oil in an extra tank.

The reaction of having accomplished our mission, together with the narcotic effect of the motors, made us drowsy when we were steering. I dozed off once at the wheel and had to relieve Bennett several times because of his sleepiness.

I quote from my impressions cabled to the United States on our return to Kings Bay:

"The wind began to freshen and change direction soon after we left the Pole, and soon we were making over 100 miles an hour.

"The elements were surely smiling that day on us, two insignificant specks of mortality flying there over that great, vast, white area in a small plane with only one companion, speechless and deaf from the motors, just a dot in the center of 10,000 square miles of visible desolation.

"We felt no larger than a pinpoint and as lonely as the tomb; as remote and detached as a star.

"Here, in another world, far from the herds of people, the smallnesses of life fell from our shoulders. What wonder that we felt no great emotion of achievement or fear of death that lay stretched beneath us, but instead, impersonal, disembodied. On, on we went. It seemed forever onward.

"Our great speed had the effect of quickening our mental processes, so that a minute appeared as many minutes, and I realized fully then that time is only a relative thing. An instant can be an age, and age an instant."

We were aiming for Grey Point, Spitzbergen, and finally when we saw it dead ahead, we knew that we had been able to keep on our course! That we were exactly where we had thought we were!

It was a wonderful relief not to have to navigate any more. We came into Kings Bay flying at about 4,000 feet. The tiny village was a welcome sight, but not so much as the good old *Chantier* that looked so small beneath. I could see the steam from her welcoming and, I knew, joyous whistle.

It seemed but a few moments until we were in the arms of our comrades, who carried us with wild joy down the snow runway they had worked so hard to make.

# DAWN OVER ZERO

### By W. L. LAURENCE

#### Illustration by Tom Hall

THE Atomic Age began at exactly 5.30 Mountain War Time on the morning of July 16, 1945, on a stretch of semi-desert land about fifty air-miles from Alamogordo, New Mexico, just a few minutes before the dawn of a new day on that part of the earth. At that great moment in history, ranking with the moment when man first put fire to work for him, the vast energy locked within the heart of the atoms of matter was released for the first time in a burst of flame such as had never before been seen on this planet, illuminating earth and sky, for a brief span that seemed eternal, with the light of many super-suns.

The elemental flame, first fire ever made on earth that did not have its origin in the sun, came from the explosion of the first atomic bomb. It was a full-dress rehearsal preparatory to dropping the bomb over Hiroshima and Nagasaki—and other Japanese military targets, if Japan refused to accept the Potsdam Declaration for her surrender.

The rehearsal marked the climax in the penultimate act of one of the greatest dramas in our history and the history of civilized man —a drama in which our scientists, under the direction of the Army Corps of Engineers, were working against time to create an atomic bomb ahead of our German enemy. The collapse of Germany marked the end of the first act of this drama. The successful completion of our task, in the greatest challenge by man to nature so far, brought down the curtain on the second act. The grand finale came three weeks afterward in the skies over Japan, with a swift descent of the curtain on the greatest war in history.

The atomic flash in New Mexico came as a great affirmation to the prodigious labors of our scientists during the past four years. It came as the affirmative answer to the until then unanswered question: "Will it work?"

With the flash came a delayed roll of mighty thunder, heard, just as the flash was seen, for hundreds of miles. The roar echoed and reverberated from the distant hills and the Sierra Oscuro range near by, sounding as though it came from some supramundane source as well as from the bowels of the earth. The hills said yes and the mountains chimed in yes. It was as if the earth had spoken and the suddenly iridescent clouds and sky had joined in one affirmative answer. Atomic energy—yes. It was like the grand finale of a mighty symphony of the elements, fascinating and terrifying, uplifting and crushing, ominous, devastating, full of great promise and great forebodings.

I watched the birth of the era of atomic power from the slope of a hill in the desert land of New Mexico, on the northwestern corner of the Alamogordo Air Base, about 125 miles southeast of Albuquerque. The hill, named Compania Hill for the occasion, was twenty miles to the northwest of Zero, the code name given to the spot chosen for the atomic bomb test. The area embracing Zero and Compania Hill, twenty-four miles long and eighteen miles wide, had the code name Trinity.

I joined a caravan of three buses, three automobiles, and a truck carrying radio equipment at 11 P.M. on Sunday, July 15, at Albuquerque. There were about ninety of us in that strange caravan, traveling silently and in the utmost secrecy through the night on probably as unusual an adventure as any in our day. With the exception of myself the caravan consisted of scientists from the highly secret atomic bomb research and development center in the mesas and canyons of New Mexico, twenty-five miles northwest of Santa Fe, where we solved the secret of translating the fabulous energy of the atom into the mightiest weapon ever made by man. It was from there that the caravan set out at 5:30 that Sunday afternoon for its destination, 212 miles to the south.

The caravan wound its way slowly over the tortuous roads overlooking the precipitous canyons of northern New Mexico, passing through Espagnola, Santa Fe, and Bernalillo, arriving at Albuquerque at about 10 P.M.

The night was dark with black clouds, and not a star could be seen. Occasionally a bolt of lightning would rend the sky and reveal for an instant the flat semi-desert landscape, rich with historic lore of past adventure. We rolled along on U.S. Highway 85, running between Albuquerque and El Paso, through sleeping ancient Spanish-American towns, their windows dark, their streets deserted—towns with music in their names, Los Lunas, Belen, Bernardo, Alamillo, Socorro, San Antonio. At San Antonio we turned east and crossed "the bridge on the Rio Grande with the detour in the middle of it." From there we traveled ten and one-half miles eastward on U.S. Highway 380, and then turned south on a specially built dirt road, running for twenty-five miles to the base camp at Trinity.

The end of our trail was reached after we had covered about five and one-fifth miles on the dirt road. Here we saw the first signs of life since leaving Albuquerque about three hours earlier, a line of silent men wearing helmets. A little farther on, a detachment of military police examined our special credentials. We got out of the buses and looked around us. The night was still pitch-black save for an occasional flash of lightning in the eastern sky, outlining for a brief instant the Sierra Oscuro Range directly ahead of us. We were in the middle of the New Mexico desert, miles away from nowhere, with hardly a sign of life, not even a blinking light on the distant horizon. This was to be our caravansary until the zero hour.

From a distance to the southeast the beam of a searchlight probed the clouds. This gave us our first sense of orientation. The bomb-test site, Zero, was a little to the left of the searchlight beam, twenty miles away. With the darkness and the waiting in the chill of the desert the tension became almost unendurable.

We gathered in a circle to listen to directions on what we were to do at the time of the test, directions read aloud by the light of a flashlight:

At a short signal of the siren at minus five minutes to zero, "all personnel whose duties did not specifically require otherwise" were to prepare "a suitable place to lie down on." At a long signal of the siren at minus two minutes to zero, "all personnel whose duties did not specifically require otherwise" were to "lie prone on the ground immediately, the face and eyes directed toward the ground and with the head away from Zero. Do not watch for the flash directly," the directions read, "but turn over after it has occurred and watch the cloud. Stay on the ground until the blast wave has passed (two minutes). At two short blasts of the siren, indicating the passing of all hazard from light and blast, all personnel will prepare to leave as soon as possible.

"The hazard from blast is reduced by lying down on the ground in such a manner that flying rocks, glass and other objects do not intervene between the source of blast and the individual. Open all car windows.

"The hazard from light injury to eyes is reduced by shielding the closed eyes with the bended arms and lying face down on the ground. If the first flash is viewed a 'blind spot' may prevent your seeing the rest of the show.

"The hazard from ultraviolet light injuries to the skin is best overcome by wearing long trousers and shirts with long sleeves."

David Dow, assistant to the scientific director of the Atomic Bomb Development Center, handed each of us a flat piece of colored glass such as is used by arc welders to shield their eyes. Dr. Edward Teller of George Washington University cautioned us against sunburn. Someone produced sunburn lotion and passed it around. It was an eerie sight to see a number of our highest-ranking scientists seriously rubbing sunburn lotion on their faces and hands in the pitch-blackness of the night, twenty miles away from the expected flash. These were the men who, more than anybody else, knew the potentialities of atomic energy on the loose. It gave one an inkling of their confidence in their handiwork.

The bomb was set on a structural steel tower one hundred feet high. Ten miles away to the southwest was the Base Camp. Here were erected barracks to serve as living-quarters for the scientists, a mess hall, a commissary, a post exchange, and other buildings. Here the vanguard of the atomists lived like soldiers at the front, supervising the enormously complicated details involved in the epoch-making tests.

At the Base Camp was a dry, abandoned reservoir, about five hundred feet square, surrounded by a mound of earth about eight feet high. Within this mound bulldozers dug a series of slit trenches, each about three feet deep, seven feet wide, and twenty-five feet long. At a command over the radio at zero minus one minute all observers at Base Camp lay down in their assigned trenches, "face and eyes directed toward the ground and with the head away from Zero." But most of us on Compania Hill remained on our feet.

Three other posts had been established, south, north, and west of Zero, each at a distance of 10,000 yards (5.7 miles). These were known, respectively, as South-10,000, North-10,000, and West-10,000, or S-10, N-10, and W-10. Here the shelters were much more elaborate—wooden structures, their walls reinforced by cement, buried under a massive layer of earth.

S-10 was the control center. Here Professor Oppenheimer, as scientific commander-in-chief, and his field commander, Professor Bainbridge, issued orders and synchronized the activities of the other sites. Here the signal was given and a complex of mechanisms was set in motion that resulted in the greatest burst of energy ever released by man on earth up to that time. No switch was pulled, no button pressed, to light this first cosmic fire on this planet.

At forty-five seconds to zero, set for 5:30 o'clock, young Dr. Joseph L. McKibben, at a signal from Professor Bainbridge, activated a master robot that set off a series of other robots, until, at last, strategically spaced electrons moved to the proper place at the proper split second.

Forty-five seconds passed and the moment was zero.

Meanwhile at our observation post on Compania Hill the atmosphere had grown tenser as the zero hour approached. We had spent the first part of our stay eating an early morning picnic breakfast that we had taken along with us. It had grown cold in the desert, and many of us, lightly clad, shivered. Occasionally a

Tom Hall

*First test of the atomic bomb, July 16, 1945, in New Mexico,
drawn from official photograph of the explosion.*

drizzle came down, and the intermittent flashes of lightning made us turn apprehensive glances toward Zero. We had had some disturbing reports that the test might be called off because of the weather. The radio we had brought with us for communication with Base Camp kept going out of order, and when we had finally repaired it some blatant band would drown out the news we wanted to hear. We knew there were two specially equipped B-29 Superfortresses high over head to make observations and recordings in the upper atmosphere, but we could neither see nor hear them. We kept gazing through the blackness.

Suddenly, at 5.29.50, as we stood huddled around our radio, we heard a voice ringing through the darkness, sounding as though it had come from above he clouds: "Zero minus ten seconds!" A green flare flashed out through the clouds, descended slowly, opened, grew dim, and vanished into the darkness.

The voice from the clouds boomed out again: "Zero minus three seconds!" Another green flare came down. Silence reigned over the desert. We kept moving in small groups in the direction of Zero. From the east came the first faint signs of dawn.

And just at that instant there rose from the bowels of the earth a light not of this world, the light of many suns in one. It was a sunrise such as the world had never seen, a great green super-sun climbing in a fraction of a second to a height of more than eight thousand feet, rising ever higher until it touched the clouds, lighting up earth and sky all around with a dazzling luminosity.

Up it went, a great ball of fire about a mile in diameter, changing colors as it kept shooting upward, from deep purple to orange, expanding, growing bigger, rising as it expanded, an elemental force freed from its bonds after being chained for billions of years. For a fleeting instant the color was unearthly green, such as one sees only in the corona of the sun during a total eclipse. It was as though the earth had opened and the skies had split. One felt as though one were present at the moment of creation when God said: "Let there be light."

To another observer the spectacle was "the nearest thing to doomsday that one could possibly imagine. I am sure," he said, "that at the end of the world—in the last millisecond of the earth's existence—the last man will see what we have just seen!"

A great cloud rose from the ground and followed the trail of the great sun. At first it was a giant column, which soon took the shape of a supramundane mushroom. For a fleeting instant it took the form of the Statue of Liberty magnified many times. Up it went, higher, higher, a giant mountain born in a few seconds instead of millions of years, quivering convulsively. It touched the multicolored clouds, pushed its summit through them, kept rising until it reached a height of 41,000 feet, 12,000 feet higher than the earth's highest mountain.

All through this very short but extremely long time-interval not a sound was heard. I could see the silhouettes of human forms motionless in little groups, like desert plants in the dark. The newborn mountain in the distance, a giant among the pygmies of the Sierra Oscuro Range, stood leaning at an angle against the clouds, a vibrant volcano spouting fire to the sky.

Then out of the great silence came a mighty thunder. For a brief interval the phenomena we had seen as light repeated themselves in terms of sound. It was the blast from thousands of blockbusters going off simultaneously at one spot. The thunder reverberated all through the desert, bounced back and forth from the Sierra Oscura, echo upon echo. The ground trembled under our feet as in an earthquake. A wave of hot wind was felt by many of us just before the blast and warned us of its coming.

The big boom came about one hundred seconds after the great flash—the first cry of a newborn world. It brought the silent, motionless silhouettes to life, gave them a voice. A loud cry filled the air. The little groups that had hitherto stood rooted to the earth like desert plants broke into a dance—the rythm of primitive man dancing at one of his fire festivals at the coming of spring. They clapped their hands as they leaped from the ground—earthbound man symbolizing the birth of a new force that for the first time gives man means to free himself from the gravitational pull of the earth that holds him down.

The dance of the primitive man lasted but a few seconds, during which an evolutionary period of about 10,000 years had been telescoped. Primitive man was metamorphosed into modern man —shaking hands, slapping his fellow on the back, all laughing like happy children.

The sun was just rising above the horizon as our caravan started on its way back to Albuquerque and Los Alamos. We looked at it through our dark lenses to compare it with what we had seen.

"The sun can't hold a candle to it!" one of us remarked.

# THE MAKING OF AN EXPLORER

*By ROY CHAPMAN ANDREWS*

ALMOST every day someone asks me: "How did you start exploring and digging up dinosaur eggs in the Gobi Desert?" I can answer simply enough: "I couldn't help it. I happen to have been born to do it. I am sure that I would have been a rotten failure doing anything else."

Ever since I remember I always intended to be a naturalist and explorer. Nothing else ever had a place in my mind. My first shotgun was given to me when I was nine years old. My mother was terrified at the thought, but very wisely my father said: "We can't keep him away from guns. He will get one somewhere and keep it hidden. It will be much less dangerous if I buy him one and teach him how to use it." Father was right. Nothing could have kept me away from firearms and he taught me their danger and use in the best possible way. If he ever saw me point a gun, even a wooden one, at a person or handle it carelessly, it was taken away for a day or more.

I lived in Beloit, a southern Wisconsin town. Every moment that I could steal from school was spent in the woods along the banks of Rock River or on the water itself. Sundays I was not allowed to take my gun, so field glasses and notebook were substituted. I kept a record of bird migrations and knew every species of bird and animal of the region; also much first-hand information as to their habits.

Taxidermy was a necessity, so I taught myself from books. The first bird-skin I ever "made up" is now in the American Museum of Natural History with the rest of my collections. Mounting birds and mammals came to be very important to me, for I was the only one who "practiced the art" in that vicinity. I reaped a harvest during the shooting season and made all the money that I needed.

After preparatory school I entered Beloit College. During the junior year came the first tragedy of my life and the first real adventure. I was duck shooting with one of the young instructors of the college, Montague White, when the canoe we were in upset in the swollen river. White was carried by the current directly to the shore, but drowned from cramp in the ice-cold water when almost safe. I was swept out into the middle of the river. There did not seem to be a chance, but I fought the deadly numbness of freezing limbs until I reached some half submerged willow trees. There was still a quarter of a mile of brown water between me and dry land. Some way, I reached it; I never quite knew how. But that hour in the icy water nearly did for me.

The next year, in June of 1906, I graduated from college and a month later came to New York. I had thirty dollars but no job. My father would have given me money but I had a boyish superstition about taking any. The thirty dollars I had made myself, stuffing deer heads and birds. I thought it would bring me luck, for to enter the American Museum of Natural History was my life ambition.

Doctor H. C. Bumpus was then director of the Museum. He said that he had no job for me. "You have to have someone to scrub the floors, don't you?" I asked.

"Of course," said he, "but a man with a college education doesn't want to begin his career scrubbing floors."

"No," I said, "I don't want to wash just any floors, but the Museum floors are different." Mentally I pictured the floors that had been walked on by my scientific gods. I would wash those floors and love it.

And scrub them I did. Dr. Bumpus took me at my word and put me in the taxidermy department with the rising young animal sculptor, James L. Clark. Part of my work was to keep the floor clean; the rest of the time I mixed clay for modeling, helped prepare animal-and bird-skins for mounting and did any odd job. Never before or since have I been as happy.

The day I was introduced to Frank Chapman I nearly suffocated with delight. He had written my bible, the "Handbook of North American Birds." I used to hang about the meteorites in the foyer at one o'clock to get a sight of Professor Osborn when he went to luncheon. I never hoped to really meet him.

Director Bumpus did not forget me down there in the taxidermy department. He would send for me frequently to write special labels or to do some other bit of work for him. He used to inspect my floor now and then to see if the college diploma had got in the way of the mop.

A few months after I entered the Museum, my chance came. Dr. Bumpus called me to his office and introduced me to a gray-haired gentleman who, he said, was to build a life-sized model of a whale out of paper. It was to hang in the gallery-well of the third floor, and I was to be the gentleman's understudy. I was considerably frightened but tried not to show it. My acquaintance with whales was less than nothing. You don't often meet a whale during your evening walk out in the woods of Wisconsin!

From the director's office I dashed to the Museum library and got every book I could find on whales. Most of them discussed in learned terms the skeletons of whales, but we were to build a model. I soon found that very little had been published on the external anatomy of whales and almost nothing about their habits.

But my lack of knowledge made little difference for we were actually only to enlarge a scale model of a sulphur-bottom whale, which was to be made by James L. Clark under the immediate supervision of Dr. F. A. Lucas, then director of the Brooklyn Museum. Dr. Lucas had been to Newfoundland, where he had cut up whales and knew every inch of them from flukes to blowhole.

The huge model became a long job. The skeleton of angle-iron and wood grew apace but the paper covering did not work. It just couldn't be kept from buckling and sinking in between the ribs. Our whale looked perfectly awful. It seemed to be in the last stages of starvation. I used to dream about it at night, and the director was in despair.

Finally he called Jimmie Clark and me to his office. "This whale is getting on my nerves," said he, "it is beyond all endurance. What shall we do?"

Jimmie and I knew exactly what to do, for we were living together then and had spent many hours discussing that emaciated whale.

"Fire the paper gentleman," we chorused, "and let us finish it with wire netting and *papier-mâché.*"

The director beamed "Done. If you turn that wreck of a cetacean into a fat respectable whale, I'll give you both a knighthood."

Jimmie and I hopped to it with a crew of twelve men. It was amazing what a well regulated diet of wire screen and *papier-mâché* did for that whale. He lost the pitiful starved appearance, his sides filled out and became as smooth as a rubber boot; we could almost feel him roll and blow as we built him up with our new tonic.

Jimmie Clark is now Assistant Director of the Museum, in charge of preparation, and I am a wanderer on the face of the earth; but our old whale still hangs in the gallery-well where he may be seen by one and all. For twenty-two years he has hung there and the inspectors report him to be in the best of health. God help those below if he ever falls, for he is seventy-six feet long and weighs several tons!

He is a good whale, too. I know, because during the next few years I was destined to see many hundreds of whales. One might say that I had a speaking acquaintance with some for I studied them at sea with field glasses and camera, while they played and ate and slept. It was almost indecent the way I spied upon their private lives. And on shore, at the stations, I investigated them both inside and out as they were hauled from the water to be carved up. I even went so far as to crawl into the tummies of several just to see what sort of apartments Jonah had rented. After all that, I can still be proud of our *papier-mâché* whale in the American Museum.

Building that whale marked an episode in my life. For one thing it graduated me from floor-scrubbing; for another, it set me to thinking very definitely about whales. Then fate dealt me a second ace. A real honest-to-goodness whale was killed just off the Long Island coast at Amagansett.

For many years Captain Josh Edwards, a fine old retired whaling captain, had lived there with his sons. Although seventy-six years old he could not quite give up the sea. The village kept a fully-rigged whaleboat in a shack on the beach. Sometimes the fishermen discovered a whale cruising along the shore. At the long-drawn cry of "There she blows" gallant old Captain Josh took his place in the bow of the boat and hurled the harpoon that made them fast. It was his arm, still strong under the weight of years, that thrust the lance into the Leviathan's heart.

All this happened just as it had happened half a dozen times before, only with one important difference. I was at the American Museum and the director wanted the whale. He wanted everything; photographs, measurements, skeleton, baleen, all there was that could be used for scientific study or exhibition.

The morning papers told of the capture and two hours later Jimmie Clark and I were on the way to Amagansett. We were picked, naturally, for were we not even then building a whale? The director's instructions, as we dashed into and out of his office were, "Get the whole thing—every bone."

We did not learn until afterwards that he never believed we could do just that. He and Dr. Lucas knew a lot about beached whales and how quickly the great bones sink into the sand. He thought we might get most of the skeleton but we never would have lost our jobs if some of the bones had been missing.

I was the most excited and the proudest boy in all New York State as we journeyed toward Amagansett. Only seven months in the Museum and off on an expedition. True, it was not an expedition to the arctic or the tropics, but it was an expedition none the less.

Arrived at the village the business of buying the whale was quickly ended. The baleen or "whalebone" was the valuable part, for at that time it was still being used for corsets and carriage whips. I believe it cost us thirty-two hundred dollars, which was only a little more than the commercial value. They threw in the skeleton but we were obligated to get the bones ourselves. The captors took the blubber, which they tried out for oil.

The carcass was beached just at the edge of low tide. We knew it was a North Atlantic right whale but the creature was so huge and so curious that at first we could hardly distinguish the head from the tail (the "flukes" had been cut off before we arrived). Finally, with the aid of the illustrations in our books, we discovered that the animal lay on its back and left side. The balleen or whalebone interested me most of all. It hung in parallel plates on either side of the mouth and was frayed out on the inner edges to form a thick mat of bristles. This mat acted as a sieve to strain from the water the tiny crustaceans upon which the beast fed.

After the fishermen had stripped off the fat, or blubber, which lies between the skin and the flesh and acts as a blanket to keep the animal warm, they went away. Jimmie and I were faced with a real problem for the skeleton lay embedded in some fifty tons of flesh. Of course we could do nothing alone and the fishermen were not at all keen to work even for high wages. The thermometer stood at twenty above zero and the wind was bitter. Finally we did persuade half a dozen men to hack away at the carcass with great knives. A horse helped to drag off huge chunks of meat by means of ropes and hooks. It was a slow business but finally the head was separated and on the beach, also the ribs of the upper side. Then the worst happened. A storm blew up from the east beating upon the exposed coast with hurricane force. We saw it coming and anchored our whale as best we could, working waist deep in the icy water. For three days the shore was a smother of white surf. Anxiously we waited. Only half the skeleton was on the beach and that would be well-nigh worthless if the remainder were lost. The fourth day was dead calm but very cold; twelve degrees above zero at noon. When we got to the beach a smooth expanse of sand, innocent of whale, met our eyes. The bones had disappeared. Jimmie and I were frantic but the anchor ropes extended down into the sand where the bones had been. A little shoveling exposed the skeleton, deeply buried. It would have been difficult enough in the best of circumstances to uncouple the huge vertebræ and get the ribs of the lower side but now it was almost impossible. As soon as we dug out a shovelful of sand to get at a bone, the depression filled with water. We had to grope blindly with small knives, our arms in the freezing water up to the elbows, to disarticulate each vertebræ. None of the fishermen would work at any price. It was too cold and they just sat by the fire smoking. Jimmie and I carried on alone for three days, warming our hands every few minutes over a driftwood fire. It seemed hopeless, and I don't mind saying that I have never suffered more in any experience of my life than I did then. But the director had told us to get every bone and we simply couldn't give up.

At last some of the fishermen decided to help when they saw us two kids struggling hopelessly in that icy water. I believe it was more shame than the high wages which brought them to our assistance. Anyway, half a dozen men came and we began to make real progress. At the end of a week a huge pile of bones lay well up on the beach. We checked them off one by one on a drawing from a skeleton in the Smithsonian Institution. They were all there, except that Dr. Bumpus had told us to watch particularly for the pelvic bones. The Smithsonian drawing did not show them, but we knew what they looked like. Two small bones about a foot in length which lay somewhere in the mass of flesh about the genital organs. They are the last vestiges of the hind limbs which used to exist sixty or seventy millions of years ago when the ancestors of whales traveled the land on four legs. Of course they did not look like whales in those days: probably they were small shore mammals, living like the seals partly in the water and partly out of it. As they spent more and more of the time in the sea the flukes, or tail, developed as a swimming organ and the useless legs entirely disappeared. But the pelvic rudiments still persist as two slender angular rods. Nodules of bone representing the femur are also present in some species. They are so small and so deeply embedded in flesh that they are seldom preserved in museum skeletons.

Search as we would, Jimmie and I could not find those wretched bones. They were all that remained to prevent us from doing a perfect job. Suddenly I had the idea that the flesh containing them might have been pulled off with the blubber by the fishermen who flensed the whale. We got to the try-works just in time. That particular part of the blubber had already been thrown into the huge iron caldron. With a long-handled wire net we fished about in the pot and triumphantly brought out not only the two pelvic bones but the femoral rudiments still attached in their proper places.

Jimmie and I breathed several sighs of relief. Now we could go back to New York with a clean bill of bones.

The Amagansett whale was a female fifty-four feet long. She had with her a baby only a few months old, thirty-eight feet in length. The calf had left when its mother was killed and swam aimlessly along the shore toward the village of Wainscott. There it had been killed by other fishermen. The day after our arrival at Amagansett I had driven over to Wainscott and purchased the skeleton from the captors. John Nichols, now curator of fishes in the Museum, had been sent up to get the bones, which he did without much difficulty. Later, it was traded to the British Museum (Natural History) for the skeleton of a dodo, that extinct bird of which you may have heard!

Cleaning up the skeleton of the whale at the American Museum was quite a job, for at that time we were not equipped as we are to-day to handle such huge bones. But by spring the work was done and our sulphur-bottom model had been completed. As a reward for services rendered the director let me study and describe the skeleton we had obtained. It was my first job in real science. Of course, I could read French and German and all winter I had absorbed every bit of literature regarding our species, much of which was written in those languages. Norwegian rather stumped me but I learned enough to find out what they were talking about.

By this study of the literature I was amazed to discover how little was actually known about whales. Almost everything pertained to technical description of such incomplete skeletons as had found their way into museums. Almost never had these been collected by the men who described them. Virtually nothing had been published about the life history and habits of the mammals except as whalers' accounts. It was all closet-naturalist stuff.

Here was the most extraordinary group from the standpoint of adaptation and evolutionary history in the entire animal kingdom just waiting for somebody to expose its secrets. I had made up my mind long before the study of the Amagansett whale was finished that the best opportunity for a young scientist lay with whales. The men who had worked in that subject were too old. It needed youth, enthusiasm and the willingness to undergo hardships, to get out on the sea and really find out things. Moreover, the American Museum of Natural History wanted whales. It had recently been presented with a considerable sum of money by Mr. George H. Bowdoin to make such a collection. I figured that with the start which the big model and the Long Island whale had given me, I ought to get the job. It was not just "opportunism" on my part. I had become fascinated with the subject.

Our Amagansett specimen belonged to a group known as the right whales, so called by the early Basque hunters because since they have the longest and finest whalebone and the fattest blubber they were the right kind of whales to kill.

"The wrong" whales are technically known as the Balænopteras or rorquals, all members of which have short, coarse whalebone and thin blubber. The sulphur-bottom, a model of which we had made, is one of the wrong whales.

Then there is still another great division called the toothed whales, of which the sperm is the best known representative. It also includes the dolphins and porpoises. Until comparatively recently the wrong whales or rorquals had been left severely alone by the commercial whalers. They gave too little money and by their great speed and agility wrecked too many boats. They are the greyhounds of the sea, while the right and sperm whales are slow and ponderous in their movements.

But a Norwegian by the name of Svend Foyn had invented a harpoon gun which could be fired from the deck of a small steamer. By this means the rorquals could be killed with comparative safety, towed into definite ports and there converted into oil and fertilizer at great plants. This was known as shore whaling. It first started on the coasts of Scandinavia and later extended to Newfoundland. It was there that the late Dr. Frederick W. True of the Smithsonian Institution and Dr. F. A. Lucas had made a study of certain Atlantic species. As the whales were drawn completely out of the water on to a slip by means of a steam winch, they gave opportunities to a scientist such as he never had had before for photographs, studies and measurements.

True had written a superb monograph on the Atlantic rorquals. However, the Pacific whales remained almost unknown. One interesting question was whether or not the large whales migrated from one ocean to another. Two shore stations had been established on the coast of Vancouver Island and one in southeastern Alaska. I made up my mind to go there.

In the meantime I had been transferred to the Department of Birds and Mammals under the wonderful pioneer naturalist, Dr. J. A. Allen. Frank M. Chapman was his associate having charge of birds, while Dr. Allen devoted himself to mammals. No sweeter character or truer scientist ever lived than Dr. Allen. The days I spent at his side were all too few, due to my restless adventurous spirit, but to work with him was one of the greatest privileges of my life. When I was admitted to this constant association with Dr. Allen and Frank Chapman, I seemed to have reached my greatest ambition.

My work consisted chiefly of revising and rearranging the study collections of small mammals. This gave me a general and valuable perspective of mammalogy, but my thoughts were always centered upon the opportunities presented by a study of whales.

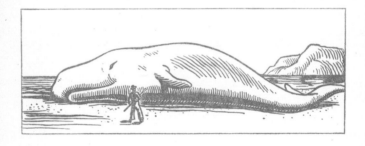

# WITH HELMET AND HOSE

### By WILLIAM BEEBE

I AM twenty feet under water with a huge copper helmet on my head, tilting with my trident against an olive-green grouper over a yard long, who is much too fearless and inquisitive for my liking. Not until I have pricked him sharply with the grains does he leave off nosing my legs with his mean jaws and efficient teeth. It suddenly occurs to me how knightlike I am as far as the metal cask goes, and then in spite of the strange world all about, my mind goes back to the long-ago Christmases when a new-published Henty book was an invariable and almost the best gift. I instantly know that if ever I succeed in shackling these divings to mere, awkward words it must be called "With Helmet and Hose," and if any modern boy, grown-up or gentle reader does not know why, explanations will do no good.

I wish I could credit my present passionate enthusiasm for diving beneath strange tropical waters to a life-long suppressed desire—an *idée fixe* which would not be gainsaid. But unfortunately this is not so. My only excuse is that I suffer intermittently from what my artist once offered as a definition of a monkey, a desire to be somewhere else than I am.

Considering carefully this whirling ball of mud upon which I found myself, I read in books and saw pictures of jungles and deserts, and my desire to see them was just a little stronger than the many obstacles between; I had breathed the air and watched birds fly for an unconscionable number of years before I began my first wobbly taxiing across a flying field. Since then I have left the earth under pleasant and unpleasant conditions over three hundred times, and, except twice, returned safely.

Without shame I confess that I have lain awake nights and spent innumerable hours of my life in gazing at the moon and planets— nay, even at the Small Magellanic Cloud with desire and longing, for if one wishes to visit interstellar space, one might as well hold the thought of a passage on Tomlinson's route as on a measurable moon trip. Up to the present, twenty-two thousand feet is as far as I have been able to rise above solid ground.

Another realm which has always seemed as remote as the moon is the depth of the ocean. My reading and wishing never took any concrete, definite direction until the trip I made to the Galápagos on the *Noma*. Then I first realized the glories and desirability of the submarine world. This at once encouraged and then disheartened me—the encouragement coming from the ease of diving from a boat or a pier and watching for a brief moment the fish and sea-things, simultaneously with the realization of the futility of such a brief, blurred glimpse.

I inspected a number of diver's outfits one day and found nothing tempting in the enormously cumbersome suits. Then, just before I sailed on the *Arcturus,* I bought my helmet. The paraphernalia accompanying it were so simple that I doubted its efficiency, but at least it was an effort in the right direction of investigation of a new world.

During the first part of the *Arcturus* adventure the sea was too rough to think of using it, even a few feet below the gangway, but when we moored close under the cliffs of Darwin Bay at Tower Island—our old Galápagos anchorage—I brought up the box from the hold and unlimbered the diving apparatus. The helmet was a big, conical affair of copper, made to rest on the shoulders, with a hose connection on the right side and two oblique windows in front. Around the bottom extended a flange on which four flattened pieces of lead were hung, each weighing ten pounds. This made a total weight of sixty pounds for the entire thing. The hose, which was of the ordinary common or garden variety, was attached at one end to the helmet and at the other to a double-action automobile pump, which screwed to a board, and was operated by a long iron lever, pushed back and forth. Almost at once we elaborated a method of operation which was so simple and satisfactory, even to the slightest details, that no change was necessary after weeks and months of use.

Our regular mode of diving is as follows: We start out from the *Arcturus* in a flat-bottomed boat which has a square, eighteen-inch glass set in the bottom amidships. To the stern is fastened a long, metal Jacob's-ladder, rolled up when not in use. We are towed or we row to the shore, preferably to the base of cliffs or steep rocks, as that affords considerable depth close inshore and rocky places are beloved by hosts of fish. We anchor as close to the cliffs as is safe, and roll out the ladder, so that it sways in midwater or rests upon the bottom. The pump is in the bow, the handle fixed, and the leather washer carefully screwed in. The hose is cleared of kinks, and is looped, partly overboard. A hand line is tied to the top of the helmet, and the inside of the glass windows is coated with a film of glycerine to prevent the breath of the diver from condensing and so clouding it. The four lead weights are slipped over the flange on the helmet base and all is ready for the diver. A hand waterglass is near for constant lookout for danger, and one or two long-handled harpoons.

In bathing suit I climb down the ladder over the stern, and dip to my neck, being careful not to wet my head. Then John lifts the helmet; I give a last, quick look around, draw a deep breath, duck into it, and as it settled firmly on my shoulders, I climb slowly down. The sensation just above water is of unbearable weight, but the instant I immerse this goes and the weight of the helmet with all the lead is only a gentle pressure, sufficient to give perfect stability. Meanwhile Ruth Rose has started the pump.

From a blurred view of the water surface and the boat's stern, I sink instantly to clear vision under water. I descend three rungs and reach up for the short harpoon of grains which is put into my hand. At the fourth or fifth rung the air presses perceptibly on my ears and I relieve it by swallowing. I descend slowly, swallowing now and then, and when the last rung has been reached, I lower myself easily by one arm, and lightly rest on the bottom. If serious danger threatens or the pumping should go wrong for any reason, I have only to lift up the helmet, duck out from under it and swim to the surface. The level of the water keeps constantly at the level of my neck or throat, and if I lean far forward it gradually rises to my mouth. But there is no splashing, no sense of oppression.

In most of the great changes or experiences which come to us humans, such as seeing our first palm tree or circus or volcano, the first reading of "Alice," diving, a battle, discovering the method of complete relaxation or really being *in* the only Borneo in the world, it is not, as so many people think, the first few minutes which are the most wonderful. It is the subsequent gradual appreciation which develops that realization of the wonder and the beauty of the thing close at hand. It is so easy to miss this almost conscious appraisement, and after the trip or performance or experience is past, we long for just one moment of the actuality, so that this or that could be seen again and remembered more clearly. Before I started on my trip around the world in my search for wild pheasants, some one gave me one of the most valuable hints I have ever had. It seems a foolish little game when I come to write it down, but it is based on a very sound realization of a great human weakness—the contempt bred by myopic familiarity, the absolute necessity for even an artificial perspective. It consists merely in shutting your eyes when you are in the midst of a great moment, or close to some marvel of time or space, and convincing yourself that you are at home again with the experience over and past; and what would you wish most to have examined or done if you could turn time and space back again. A hundred questions rush into this inducted mental vacuum—what were the color and shape of the wild blossoms upon which that pheasant fed? What was the sound of the anti-aircraft shells? At what speed did the lava flow? etc.

And so, as I said, I swung myself lightly down from the ladder and stood on the bottom. I gazed out with interest on the rocks and fish about me, but I felt a vague feeling of disappointment. I was breathing so easily; the water outside might have been correctly heated air as far as any bodily sensation went; I was looking through a pane of glass at fish swimming about—exactly what I have done and seen a hundred times in our aquarium in New York. I felt only as if I were in a very small, strange, but perfectly comfortable room, looking upon a wonderful tank of living fish with a most excellently painted background. The shock of entrance into this long-anticipated world had not been as radical as my imagination had pictured, even although I cannot recall having visualized instant attacks by huge sharks, or the feel of the snaky tentacle of an approaching great octopus. The fact of my bodily comfort and the vivid memory of aquariums all over the world had deadened the stupendous marvel of it all.

I sat down on a convenient rock, shut my eyes, and recited my lesson: *I am not at home, nor near any city or people; I am far out in the Pacific on a desert island, sitting on the bottom of the ocean; I am deep down under the water in a place where no human being has ever been before; it is one of the greatest moments of my whole life; thousands of people would pay large sums, would forego much for five minutes of this!*

This was enough. I opened my eyes and saw, resting on a rock not more than three inches away from my face, the red bull of Kim. It was the strangest little blenny in the world, five inches long and mostly all head, with tail enough only to steady him in his place on the bowlder. His long snout with nostrils flaring at the tip, his broad, flat crown surmounted by two curving horns, made him absurdly like a prize bull. He was dull scarlet with splashes of golden brown along his sides, which was well enough, but a bull does not have tatters and fringes of blue and yellow scattered all over him (unless we choose to consider the cruel banderillos as ornamental). My blenny's eyes were silver with hieroglyphics of purple in them, and as I looked, he puffed a puff of water at my window and was gone.

I was quite reoriented now. The hardest thing was to realize that I was *wet*. It was the old story of the value of comparison. All of me was wet and I could not reach up into dry air, so I had no sensation of wetness. I looked at my fingers, however, and saw the beginning of washerwoman's wrinkles, so was convinced! I reached out and picked a starfish from the rock in front, and as it slowly crawled over my hand, I realized to the full that this was a wild starfish and not one brought from somewhere else and placed there for me to look at.

It was the morning of April ninth when I went down for the first time, on a coral bank in Darwin Bay. I made five descents but recall very few details, because at the moment when I was ducking inside the helmet for the second time, I saw, a few yards away, one of the largest gray sharks I have ever seen, a giant of a generous eleven or twelve feet, cutting the water with his great dark fin. My companions did not fail to remind me of my notorious scorn of sharks, so with a rather sickly grin I went down. The dominant impression of this first experience was of the disconcertingly narrow field of vision—the oblique panes of glass in the helmet permitting only about sixty degrees. What I had seen at the surface kept my imagination busy with the keenest desire to see what was transpiring in the remaining three hundred degrees of my visual circle. I am certain that from above I must have looked like some strange sort of owl, whose head continually revolved first in one and then in the opposite direction.

It is idle to say that I, and I think all of us who went down, did not feel at first exceedingly nervous. It was disconcerting, as I have said, not to be able to see directly behind by a quick turn of the head, and until I became accustomed to the nibbling touch of some little fish who was investigating this strange creature so new to its world, I would often leap up in expectation of seeing some monster of the deep about to attack me. This stage passed and I soon felt perfectly at home. On the very few occasions when some creatures seemed tempted to make a tentative hostile approach, it appeared to be the snaky hose extending to the surface and the constant stream of bubbles which deterred it.

In the afternoon of the same April day I submerged near the foot of the great cliffs, and, as I have described it, disciplined myself into a greater realization of the wonder of it. I think my first surprise was of the constant movement of everything, not so much individually as of the whole in relation to the rocks and bottom. I knew of course that the boat was rising and falling with every surge, which heaved and settled in turn as each wave passed, to break against the cliffs. I found this same motion extended downward, with less and less force, until at thirty feet it all but died away. At present in about twenty feet of water I felt it strongly. I would be sitting quietly without the slightest tremor, when, gently and without shock, every fish in sight, every bit of weed or hydroid, the anchor rope, the shadow of the boat, the hose and myself swayed toward the land. One could resist it by clinging firmly to the rock, but the supreme joy, because of its impossibility in the air above, was to balance carefully and let oneself be wafted through space and deposited safely on the next rock. There followed a period of complete rest, and back again everything would come. It was so soothing, so rhythmical, that one yielded to it at times in a daze of sheer enjoyment. Where the water is not too deep and the bottom is sand or powdered shells, it is evident that the great surges are not a simple, compact movement, for here are made visible little, individual whirlwinds and casual, separate breezes which twist the shell-dust about or send up clouds of sand about my body.

In days to come I was to find the surge sometimes a very real danger, as when at Cocos I went down in a smashing thrashing sea and was scraped and torn back and forth across lacerating knife-points of coral and poisonous spines of urchins until flesh and blood could no longer stand it. Like getting one's sea legs it soon became second nature to anticipate the swell, to lean against it, to shift the balance, so that everything moved except myself and the eternal rocks.

Now, day by day, occurred the accidents by which I learned how to do things, little by little relinquishing the ideas which, on dry land, had seemed feasible and important. For a day or two I could not understand why, during certain dives, the fish were so much tamer than at other times. The clew came to me when a rather heavy swell was running and I found that if I gave to the movement of the water, all the inhabitants, from gobies to groupers, from shrimps to sharks, accepted me as something new but harmless which the waves had washed in, but if I resisted the aquatic wind and maintained place and posture, I became an object of suspicion. This was the first of many radical differences which I was to find between the world of dry land and that of the underwater; on land, to move is to arouse fear among the wild creatures, here I did it by remaining still.

I walked or half-walked, half-floated, toward the cliffs. The rocks were almost bare in this bay, like those between tides, and the multitudes of lesser aquatic creatures were concealed beneath them. The water was quiet, and between surges was often perfectly clear, so that I could see plainly the cliffs rising high in air above that narrow straight line which marked the division between the two kingdoms. I went as far as my hose tether would permit and reached a bowlder on which, the day before, at low tide, I had sat comfortably in the clear, cool air of the upper world.

Turning back, I saw that I had become a Pied Piper of sorts, leading a host of fish which followed in my train. The sun was out now in full strength and no fish, however strange and unknown to me, could hold my eyes from the marvel of distance. As I walked toward the cliffs I had also worked a little toward the east and the view I had, as I turned, was of another slope than that over which I had come.

The bottom thus far was not wholly unlike the cliff above the water, but before me now the slope fell away in a manner which was beyond all experience—a breath-stopping fall, down which one could not topple headlong, but only roll and slide slowly, to be overcome, not by swift speed of descent or smashing blow, but by a far more terrible slow increase of pressure of the invisible medium, whose very surface film is death to us. To detect a faint, colorless shape now and then, through the azure curtain, and never to know whether it was rock or living creature—things such as this made every descent an ineradicable memory.

My range of vision was perhaps fifty feet in every direction, but for all I could tell it might have been fifty feet or fifty miles. The sun's rays filtered down as though through the most marvelous cathedral ever imagined—intangible, oblique rays which the eye could perceive but no lip describe. With distance, these became more and more luminous, more wondrously brilliant, until rocks died away in a veritable purple glory. No sunset, no mist on distant mountains that I have seen, could compare with this. One had to sit quietly and absorb these beauties before one could remember to be an ichthyologist.

As I was reveling in pure sensuous delight at this color of colors, a small object appeared in midwater close by my little glass window, and was instantly obscured by half a dozen little fish which darted

about it, some actually flicking my helmet with their tails. Just as I
saw that the suspended object was a baited hook, a baby scarlet snapper snatched at it, darted downward, and was at once drawn up into
the boat. As I looked after it an idea came to me and I followed the
snapper upward by way of the ladder. When the helmet was lifted
off and I could speak, I expressed my wants, and descended again.
Soon there fell slowly at my feet a small stone to which was tied a
juicy and scarcely dead crab. I picked this up, waved it back and
forth so as to scatter the impelling incense of its body and as if by
magic, from behind me, from crevices upon which I was seated,
seemingly materializing from the clear water, came fish and fish and
fish. It is far from my intention to give a detailed list of all of these.
The effect upon the reader in this connection would be much the
same as my own sensations at this time, if, by chance, my friend
working the pump in the boat above had suddenly dropped off to
sleep. Their names, numbers, colors and habits are all set down elsewhere in a more suitable place—*Zoölogica*.

Even if I wished to speak of them in a homely way I could not,
for most of them have had visited upon them the names only of the
official, scientific census-taker, while the rest have no names at all. So
Adam-like, I had to give them all temporary names, until I could
identify them, or christen them with my own binominal terms. It
was long before I could disentangle individual characteristics from
the whirling mass. The first four fishes rushed for the bait—

> "And yet another four;
>     And thick and fast they came at last,
>   And more, and more, and more—"

so that until I could shut my mind to the abstract marvel of it and
my eyes to the kaleidoscopic, hypnotic effect, ichthyology gained little of specific factual contribution. I waved my magic crab, I may
have murmured Plop! Glub! and Bloob! which is what the bubbles
say when I first immerse—and the hosts came. Within three minutes from the time when the crab first fell into my hand, I had five
hundred fish swirling around my crab and hand and head. Similes
failed. I thought of the hosts of yellow butterflies I have seen flutter-

ing at arm's length on Boom-boom Point; I thought of the maze of wings of the pigeons of St. Mark's, but no memory of the upper world was in place here—this was a wholly new thing.

Often there was a central nucleus a foot or more in diameter, of solid fish, so that the bait and my arm to the elbow were quite invisible. Twenty or twenty-five species were represented, and, like birds, they were graded with exquisite exactness as to correlation of fear and size. The great majority were small, from two to four inches in length, and these were wholly without fear, nibbling my hand—passing between my fingers but always just avoiding capture, no matter how quickly I shut my fist. Six- and eight-inch fish also came near, but were more ready to dart off at any sudden movement of mine. On the outskirts hung a fringe of still larger fish, hungry, and rushing in now and then for a snap at the delicious morsel which they saw their lesser fellows enjoying, but always with less abandon to the temptation of the moment. The tameness of the little chaps, however, was so astounding that the relatively greater wariness of the larger fish scarcely deserved the name of suspicion, not to say fear. Another unexpected thing was the rapidity with which these fish lost even this slight suspicion and learned to connect my appearance with food. If I dived in the same spot several times a day and several days in succession, fish would approach in numbers and investigate my hands and trident with much greater eagerness and, I presume, with expectancy, than they ever displayed on the occasion of the first dive, before I had repeatedly tempted them with freshly killed crabs. I could even recognize certain individuals, characterized by some peculiarity of color or form.

Before I go on to speak, even casually, of the fish themselves, I must tell of my second discovery. As with the crab baiting and so much else in my life, it was by sheer accident that I learned of the possibility of spearing fish twenty to thirty feet under water. The first few times I dived I carried a powerful harpoon with a long metal handle, thinking I could lay it down and pick it up more readily than if it had been buoyant. The big, green grouper which I mentioned in my opening sentence was bothering me, shoving his big jaws close to my arms and legs, so I struck idly at him, missing of course, and to my astonishment, he instantly attacked the prongs of the trident. Again I stabbed when he was broadside on and struck him so hard that he tore away with difficulty, whereupon he took himself off, and sulked under a great mushroom coral.

I remembered this incident and the following day had a special grains made out of three large, straightened fishhooks, fixed in the end of a yard-long wooden handle. This I took down with me and waited until my regular crab bait came sailing down. I caught the stone and wedged it in a crevice of the rock, where the crab was only partly exposed. The fact of the invisibility of the food made little difference in the swiftness and the numbers of the arrivals. Their keen powers of scent drew them like filings to a magnet, and although only three or four fish could find room for a simultaneous nibble, yet scores waited behind, or pushed and wedged themselves in, reminding me of the buffet at a supper dance.

At last I decided to try my new weapon. On several former descents I had noticed a very common fish which was new to me, and now there were twenty or thirty in sight, nibbling at the crab, swimming in and out of crevices, and doing all the things which are imperative for small fish to do on occasions such as this. They were smug little fellows, high-backed like sunfish, brownish-black, with only two outstanding features—delicately beautiful bright orange tips to the pectoral fins and a white base to the tail. Twice I leveled my trident and stabbed, and twice I missed. Then I found a new point of balance along the handle, struck again, and had a fish caught fast—my first *Pomacentrus leucorus*.

And now my undersea sprang a new surprise on me. Although I am a scientist and a hunting scientist, I hate to take life. Under the provocation of extreme danger to me or mine, I have always valued human life at less than nothing, but shooting down a savage as he is rushing you is one thing and deliberately spearing a fish which you have been watching and which swims about close to your face and hands in perfect fearlessness is quite another. However, one can be tender-hearted without being sentimental and if I need the facts for science, to complete the life-history of a whole species, I will shoot a dove on her eggs without compunction. I sympathize, on the other hand, with the Hindoo fishermen of the Laccadives who are not allowed by their faith to take life, and hence, when they have drawn their nets, they rush ashore and lay the still living fish gently upon leaves and moss. Later they return, and finding, to their surprise, a lot of fish which are quite dead, it is permitted that they gather them up to sell or to eat.

So it was not with the unmixed feelings of a triumphant Neptune or a successful ichthyologist that I clambered up the ladder, and when near the surface held out my trident with the impaled fish. My pleasure in the feat was heightened when I finally ascended and found my fish swimming unconcernedly about in the well of the boat. As a matter of fact, a much greater percentage of my speared individuals recovered and survived, living and feeding contentedly for weeks in our aquaria, than of those we caught on hook and line. Almost invariably the tip of the grains would penetrate only the mass of back muscles, leaving quite untouched the head and the vital organs of the body.

I experimented with all sorts of methods, such as putting a bit of crab on the trident itself. This was a complete failure, for the fish would crowd around it head-on, and with all my efforts I never succeeded in even touching a fish when in this position. It can very naturally shoot forward and backward with infinitely greater speed and facility, than move sideways against such a heavy medium. So my efforts were always directed at fish broadside on. This method of attack was so new to their experience, that even when just missed, they darted aside only far enough to escape the thrust, then returned at once and examined the trident with deep interest. Sometimes I would scrape off a few scales and then these most astounding creatures would rush back in great excitement, and snap up, one by one, each floating scale, "getting a bit of their own back," as it were.

The smaller fish were as easy to reach with the prongs as if they were blackberries fastened to a stem, but they were so small and agile that they slipped between and around the barbs. The easiest of all to secure were the medium-sized herbivorous fish such as the yellow-tailed surgeons and the gorgeously colored angel fish. These came inspired only by curiosity and drifted about me aimlessly or nibbled at the rock by my elbow. The sign of Cancer meant nothing to them, and their efficient poisonous spines or defense of whatever kind wrought a self-confidence which carried them through life calmly and without fear. I had merely to wait until they approached and turned their broad profiles when a quick flick of the wrist meant their transference to life in one of our aquariums—where they continued to live placidly and undisturbed by any change which fate had brought to them. The number of the surgeons which I took was limited only by my desire for specimens or the capacity of our aquariums, for my capture of one conveyed no alarm or sense of insecurity, and when I again climbed down the ladder the chances were that I would find the remainder of the school in the same spot, undisturbed.

The best sport was to be had with the brilliantly colored wrasse. They were among the most active and swift, slender and supple as eels, with an abundance of fins for doing everything that perfect control demands. Two species in particular were always about, although never more than a half dozen were in sight at once. Nature must have relegated the coloring of some of these fish to an amateur assistant, for it was crude, blatant and, judged by human ideas of ornamentation, in execrably bad taste. Yet as I saw it—a living organism—winding in and out of dark crevices, or twisting almost on its back to get a nibble at crab meat, it seemed rather an exquisite mass of palette splashes. The head was scarlet, the body, fins and tail mostly bright grass green. The head was outlined in dark blue, and from the lips, which were solidly of the same color, five blue lines streamed backward, flowing in irregular bands through the eye and across the cheeks, saturating the pectoral fins. The whole green body was thickly banded with irregular vertical lines of an unnamable dull maroon—like thick heavy streaks of some awful rain or acid stains. The tail had a stiff, unnatural pattern, like a great scarlet H drawn crudely over the green. I was happy when at last I outwitted a six-inch green wrasse, and put him aboard, where he lived for two months, allowing us to paint and study him at our leisure.

The other wrasse was simpler, but even more striking in pattern and coloration, and to the last defied my every effort. Twice I struck and marked them, and day after day the same individuals would come about as bold as ever, flaunting their scars and wounds in my face. One of these had two jagged holes well into his side, yet they apparently gave him no concern, nor interfered at all with his speed and control, and he easily avoided every attack which I launched. These fish were about five inches in length, bright tyrian purple over all, with a broad vertical band of sulphur yellow extending down from the neck around the body and including the pectoral fins. While I was exerting every muscle to get him, I called him many names in the quiet of my helmet, but these are neither here nor there. No written description fits him, and until I return and with greater skill succeed in overcoming his cleverness, he can be called only the Yellow-banded Purple Wrasse.

The little round, brownish-black *Pomacentrus* fish of two species were the most abundant of the four-inchers, and were the most absolute home bodies, each living in his particular crack or crevice, from which he frequently rushed out and attacked ferociously any fish which approached too near, regardless of its size.

Another field of work of tremendous interest was suggested when I turned over the first stone and saw the mass of life covering the underside and filling the crevices. I arranged to have a pail lowered on a rope, and squatting low on the floor of the bay I filled the pail and gave the signal to draw it up. Five pailfuls provided a tub of rocks. This was left standing in the sun for a day and at the end of that time there had crept out an amazing array of interesting beings —beautiful sea worms, starfishes, squillas, hermit crabs, and shrimps of every hue, a number of strange larval fish and an adult formed, wonderfully patterned, quite fearless moray eel exactly one and one-half inches in length. This tapped a fertile and untouched field, providing organisms which cannot be dredged because of their shelter under and within coral and stones, and not to be gathered by wading along shore at low tide, since twenty feet of water lay above them.

The obliquity of the two windows in the helmet made it necessary to look out of either one or the other exclusively, when engaged in observation or work which required accurate correlation of eye and hand. Seldom have I seen a funnier sight than the earnest efforts of any of our party before they learned of this optical effect. Through the water glass a pale figure would be seen crouched on the bottom, industriously picking up stones and carefully dropping them about two feet from the bucket. After much hard labor, the helmeted creature would raise the empty bucket and gaze at it in puzzled astonishment. In imagination we could see the large question mark poised in midwater over his head. Another labor-saving individual decided to pick the specimens themselves off the rocks, and long streamers of algæ and clumps of hydroids were gathered and carefully placed in the bucket, only to float instantly out and up to us, while he was looking for other equally buoyant specimens. Don Quixote's horse was nothing compared to the worker's ultimate idea of the capacity of that pail.

From first to last I could never guess, from examining the bottom through a water glass, what a submersion would yield, or even look like, except in the most general, superficial way. It was like judging a shore line from a ship with all the indentations flattened, all the coves and little bays concealed in the optical straightening, and the wicked, crashing breakers smoothed from behind into harmless appearing ripples. In many lights, the bottom, even only twenty feet down, appears merely undulating or paved with huge stones.

One of the last dives I made in Darwin Bay showed such an aspect from above. I went down rather deeply, but very slowly, for I always came under the spell of the ever wonderful blueness of distance. It seemed impossible, even after all the times I had studied it, that invisibility or opacity of whatever distance could result from such a luminous medium. When at last I rested on the bottom I watched three white-striped angel fish chasing one another in sheer play. They drew my attention upward to where they were breaking the surface film, not far from the boat whose keel was bobbing absurdly up and down. The angel fish then curved downward, the long filaments streaming from the fins above and below, and giving the appearance of even greater speed. They rose and fell, circled about, turned on their backs and fell into nose dives as easily as I sat still. Finally, the emotion over, whatever it was, they all came to rest still high up in midwater. It occurred to me that in comparison, our own world is practically one of two planes, while this is really the one of three. It is fair to compare fish only with birds, and even birds need two perching props, and do not dare to develop wings or feather fins beneath the body, for, sooner or later, they must alight, while a fish can live, eat and sleep poised in midwater.

I turned my attention from the fish to the scene behind me and the absurdity of my appraisement from the water glass became apparent. I was standing a few yards away from a bowlder as big as a cottage, and my heart gave a leap as I saw a curved flight of steps—giant steps like those up which I had once climbed Cheops. They began on my side at the doorless entrance of the sinister cottage, slowly encircled it and vanished behind it in a soul-stirring abyss of blueness, which, from a delicate shade near at hand, blued more and more clearly into infinite depth and space. I believe that Sime would have loved this scene, and Dunsany would have deemed it not unfitting for the habitation of Gnoles. Töten Insel treasured no more mystery in its perspective than did this. As I watched, a bit of greenish-black coral which projected eavelike, began to move and crawl slowly downward, and with it went dangling things which I had taken for strands of dead seaweed, but which on this edifice might well have been awful stalactites or icicles of sorts. The octopus climbed down, hesitated, felt about in different directions, and then descended the steps, flowing along the angles like some horrid viscid fluid in animal form. The most active imagination could not have set the scene better, or found a more appropriate actor.

But like the double miracle of the stars falling into the volcano the end was not yet. A mist of yellow-tailed surgeons drifted across the stairs and the dread bowlder, and for a moment their calm matter-of-factness lessened the sinister feeling of the whole thing. A strong desire arose to look around the corner of the stair for myself. I was submerged so deeply that as I stood, I could barely reach the lowest rung of the ladder, indeed I was occasionally lifted a few inches from the ground as the boat rose to a greater swell. But I knew the hose was new and stout and even if I began to fall with that terrible slowness, as seemed easily possible to my imagination, I could surely climb back up my own string. One finger relaxed and I was about to take the chance when a mote, very faint and pale, stirred the blueness as if some wondrous tapestry curtain were troubled by a breath of air.

The thing grew denser, took form and became concrete, and a flat, round-fronted head, lazily undulating, wound through the water over the steps, a nine-foot shark weaving along where I would have been a minute later. My common-sense theory of the harmlessness of these beings still held good; in the last few days dozens of them had approached within a few yards of me, but the eerie character of this place had penetrated even my prison of copper and glass, and when I realized where my precious ladder would drift to when I relinquished my hold, looked down at my unprotected limbs and realized that I had not even a trident with me, I decided to go through life with the mystery of the stairway unsolved. The great, gray being, wafting along its hundreds of pounds of body by slow, gentle undulations, kept on and on until again hidden by the blue light. When I ascended to a world of greater reality, I took with me the memory of the beings to which legend and fact have brought the greatest notoriety of anything in the sea, and the setting in which I found them will never pass from mind—the Edge of the Edge of the World.

# SUMMIT OF THE WORLD: THE FIGHT FOR EVEREST

## By JAMES RAMSEY ULLMAN

IN THE early afternoon of June 8, 1924, a man stood on a crag in the freezing sub-stratosphere, 26,000 feet above the sea, raised his eyes and stared. On a ridge high overhead he saw two human figures, black and tiny against the sky. Less than 800 feet above them was the snow-plumed summit of the highest mountain on earth.—A minute, two minutes the watcher gazed, while the climbers crept upward. Then clouds swept in upon the mountain-top, blotting them from view.

They were never seen again.

So ended the most splendid and tragic of many attempts to conquer Everest, king of mountains. To this day no one knows whether George Leigh-Mallory and Andrew Irvine reached the top before death overtook them. No one, probably, will ever know. One thing is certain: no man has ever reached the summit and returned to tell the tale.

The story of Mount Everest begins in 1852, when a clerk in the office of the Indian Trigonometrical Survey looked up excitedly from a page of figures and cried to his superior, "Sir, I have discovered the highest mountain in the world!" A careful checking of his calculations proved him right. The remote Himalayan summit listed prosaically on the charts as "Peak XV" was found to be 29,002 feet high—almost a thousand feet higher than its closest rival. Later observers corrected its altitude to 29,141 feet and named it for Sir George Everest, first Surveyor-General of India. But its supremacy remained, and remains today, unchallenged.

What began as an exercise in higher mathematics was to become, as years passed, one of the great adventures of the human spirit.

For a half century after its discovery Everest was a mountain of mystery. Tibet and Nepal, on whose frontiers it rises, were both rigorously closed to outsiders, and, far from climbing it, men of the West were unable even to approach it or learn anything about it. All they knew were the tantalizing figures of the Trigonometrical Survey. All they could see was a remote pinnacle of rock and ice, one of thousands in the great sea of peaks to the north of the Indian plain. The mountain itself—its structure and appearance, its surroundings and approaches—was as unknown as if it stood upon another planet.

Then, in the late 1890's, as we have seen, the full tide of mountaineering interest and activity turned toward the Himalayas. Soon a thin trickle of pioneers began to penetrate into the great passes and gorges where no white man had ever been before; adventurous spirits crossed the frontiers into forbidden Tibet and Nepal, disguised as Hindu or Mohammedan traders; men like Freshfield, Kellas and Longstaff turned their attention from the Sikkim and Garhwal foothills to the greater peaks that lay beyond. Slowly the net closed in about the remote, secret place where rose the highest mountain in the world. Mountaineers had heard the siren call of the mysterious and the unknown, and all the obstacles of man and nature were not going to stop them in their quest.

A lone traveler might slip into Tibet without official sanction; not so a large expedition equipped to tackle Everest. The permission of the Tibetan government was essential, and for long years this permission was not forthcoming. At last, in 1913, it appeared that the way was clear, and an exploring party was about to be organized by Freshfield; but the project was ended before it began by the outbreak of the First World War. It was not until seven years later that men were again able to turn their eyes and thoughts to the greatest mountain.

Early in 1920 the Royal Geographical Society of London and the British Alpine Club joined forces to form the Mount Everest Committee and after prolonged negotiations secured permission for an all-English party to approach and, if possible, ascend the mountain. Preparations were immediately begun on an elaborate scale.

It was planned to send out two expeditions, a year apart, the first to explore and reconnoitre, the second to climb. As it eventually turned out, there was a third, and it was this final attack that was to end, a scant few hundred feet from triumph, in mystery and tragedy.

It was Mallory who was to become the foremost of the "Everesters" and the most famous mountaineer of his day. He was the only man to participate in all three of the great expeditions between 1921 and 1924, and although never the official leader (he was only thirty-eight when he died), his marvellous climbing accomplishments and his flaming spirit made him the outstanding figure in every one of them. Everest became *his* mountain, as completely as the Matterhorn, sixty years before, had been Whymper's. His climbing companions, to a man, believed that if any one of them was to achieve conquest of the highest summit on earth Mallory would be the one, and many of them, in later days, clung staunchly to the belief that he attained his goal before death overtook him in the clouds.

There was nothing of the conventional athlete about Mallory. Slight and slim, with a round boyish face, he was anything but the popular conception of a rugged outdoor man. Again like Whymper, climbing to him was not exercise or amusement, but passionate devotion, and, like all great mountaineers, less a physical than a spiritual adventure. His explanation of why men climb remains today the simplest, and at the same time perhaps the most profound, that has ever been given.

"But *why?*" a friend asked him as he set out for a renewed assault on Everest. "Why do you try to climb this mountain?"

Mallory's answer consisted of four words: "Because it is there."

"There," however, was a remote, unknown corner of the earth, and it required an arduous journey of many weeks before the Everesters of the 1921 reconnoitering party came even within sight of their goal. Beginning at Darjeeling in the middle of May their march carried them first through the steaming tropical jungles of Sikkim, then up through great mountain passes onto the desolate, windswept wilderness of the Tibetan plateau. In a straight line the distance from Darjeeling to Everest is only a hundred miles, but they had to journey more than three hundred, threading their way among the great peaks and gorges of the eastern Himalayas.

These were days of endless toil and hardship, and they took their toll in sudden and tragic fashion. Dr. Kellas, whose health was no longer robust, strained his heart while crossing the high passes and died in the Tibetan village of Kampa Dzong. Soon after, Raeburn became seriously ill and had to return to India, with Wollaston accompanying him. These two were not able to rejoin the expedition until the middle of the summer. Everest had begun to claim her victims even before they had had so much as a glimpse of her.

The others struggled on, saddened but resolute. There were only six white men now, at the head of a vast cavalcade of Sherpa porters, Tibetan guides and helpers, ponies, donkeys, bullocks and yaks. Day after day they pushed northward and westward across as savage country as exists anywhere on the earth's surface—through sandstorms and raging, glacial torrents, across vast boulder-strewn plains and passes 20,000 feet above the sea. At night they camped under the stars or enjoyed the primitive hospitality of Buddhist monasteries and village headmen. Their passports from the Tibetan authorities in Lhassa assured them kindly and courteous treatment, but the announcement of the purpose of their journey elicited only a dubious shaking of heads and a solemn turning of prayer wheels. To these devout and superstitious orientals, Everest was more than a mountain. Chomolungma, they called it—Goddess-Mother-of-the-World. It was sacrilege, they believed, for mere mortals even to approach it.

At last, late in June, the expedition arrived at the great Rongbuk Monastery, where an isolated colony of priests and hermits dwelt, some twenty miles due north of Everest. And from here, at last, they saw their mountain head on, in its titanic majesty—the first white men ever to have a close-up view of the summit of the world. "We paused," wrote Mallory, "in sheer astonishment. The sight of it banished every thought; we asked no questions and made no comment, but simply looked. . . . At the end of the valley and above the glacier Everest rises, not so much a peak as a prodigious mountain-mass. There is no complication for the eye. The highest of the world's mountains, it seems, has to make but a single gesture of magnificence to be the lord of all, vast in unchallenged and isolated supremacy. To the discerning eye other mountains are visible, giants between 23,000 and 26,000 feet high. Not one of their slenderer heads even reaches their chief's shoulder; beside Everest they escape notice—such is the pre-eminence of the greatest."

The explorers set themselves at once to their tasks, reconnoitering, surveying, studying the colossal rock-and-ice mass that towered before them and probing the possible routes to its summit. They were already at an altitude of 18,000 feet—far higher than the highest summit in the Alps or Rockies—and the slightest exertion set their lungs to heaving and their hearts to pounding. The world around them was a trackless wilderness of peaks, ridges and glaciers, and wind and snow roared down from the heights with hurricane fury. And still there remained two vertical miles of mountain soaring above them into the sky.

Working slowly around its base Mallory and Bullock discovered that Everest was constructed as an almost perfect pyramid, with three faces and three main ridges sweeping downward from the summit like vast buttresses. The faces were all built up in tiers of precipices which no man could even dream of scaling, and the south and northwest ridges, miles in length and flanked by vertical ice-walls, appeared almost equally hopeless. In addition, the whole southern half of the mountain lay in Nepal and was therefore politically closed to them.

Only on the northeast did Mallory detect any possibilities whatever. Here, bordering the ten-thousand-foot precipice of the north face, a jagged arête descended from a great rocky shoulder near the summit to a high snow saddle on the east of the Rongbuk Glacier. The angle of the arête was steep, but not so steep that experienced mountaineers could not ascend it, and from the shoulder upward the main east ridge and the wedgelike summit pyramid seemed to present no insuperable obstacles. The first great question mark was whether a way could be found to reach the saddle.

A way was found, but the finding required two long months

of planning and toil. The saddle—or North Col, as it came to be known—rose from the Rongbuk Glacier as an almost perpendicular ice-wall 4,000 feet high, and even the dauntless Mallory realized that it could never be scaled from that side. His only hope was that the far, or eastern, side might prove more feasible. The next and greatest job was to get there.

The Rongbuk Glacier was a narrow avenue of ice walled in by tremendous mountains in which no break appeared to exist. Actually there was a break, and if Mallory had found it he would have been able to reach the far side of the col in a day or two. But it was so tiny and obscure a passage that he missed it. The result was a circuitous journey of more than a hundred miles, back across the plateau and passes which they had traveled before, and then south and west again toward the base of Everest.

This last stage of their journey took them through a mountain wonderland such as no man had ever been privileged to look upon before. The Kama and Kharta valleys, up which they pushed, were great gashes in the earth, so deep at their lower ends that their floors were covered with lush, tropical vegetation, so lofty at their apexes that the explorers found themselves struggling in snow up to their armpits. At their head loomed the mighty upper slopes of Everest, flanked by the pinnacles of Makalu, Chomolönzo and Lhotse, themselves among the highest summits in the world.

At last, after innumerable delays and hardships, the climbers reached the apex of the Kharta Valley—a wild, blizzard-racked pass known as the Lhakpa La, 22,000 feet above the sea. From here they could see the long-sought eastern approach to the North Col, and it was indeed as Mallory had hoped: the great saddle of snow and ice rose on this side to a height of only 1,500 feet above the glacier floor, as against 4,000 feet on the Rongbuk side. It appeared not impossible to scale. A cheer went up from the lips of the frozen, exhausted men, for they knew they had found the key to the mountain.

By this time it was late August and the brief Himalayan summer was almost over. The work of the expedition, however, would not be done until they had reached the col, and so the three strongest climbers, Mallory, Bullock and Wheeler, pushed on over the Lhakpa La, down its far side and across the glacier below. On their way they made a second important discovery: that there was, after all, a passage from the Rongbuk Glacier to the eastern side of the col. It was of course too late for it to be of help to them that year, but the narrow defile was used by all subsequent Everest expeditions.

Once found, the eastern wall of the North Col did not prove a particularly formidable obstacle—at least not in 1921. The outer surface of the wall was composed of frozen avalanche snow, and up it the three climbers hacked their way, slanting carefully to right and left to avoid the gaping blue abysses with which it was scarred. At noon on the twenty-fourth of August they stood upon the top, at an altitude of 23,000 feet—higher than any mountain-top in the world outside of the Himalayas.

The pinnacle of Everest, however, was still 6,000 feet above them and two and a half miles away. Scanning the northeast ridge, the shoulder and the summit pyramid, they saw that Mallory's earlier surmise had been right: the upper mountain slanted upward in a fairly easy gradient of rock and snow, seeming to present neither difficulty nor great danger. The temptation was strong to venture still higher, but they were almost done in from their evertions as it was and realized they could not hope to match their strength against the wild wind and blizzards of the exposed heights. After taking as complete observations as they could they descended from the col, rejoined their companions on the Lhakpa La and began the long return journey to India.

The members of the 1921 expedition had never once actually set foot on Everest itself; their highest point on the North Col was where subsequent expeditions would begin their real work. Yet, except for the untimely death of Dr. Kellas, the venture had been a complete and distinguished success. The trail to the mountain had been blazed, the weakness in its armor found. Everyone was agreed that, as far as actual climbing problems were concerned, the greatest mountain *might* be climbed. That "might" was all the Everesters needed. No sooner had the reconnaissance party returned to England than preparations for the real assault began.

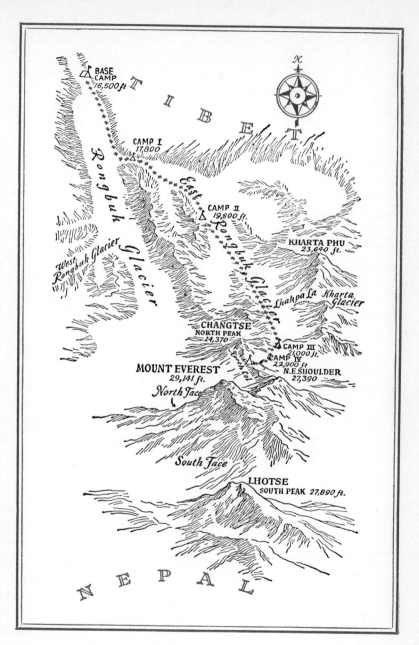

The Route to Everest.

On May 1, 1922, the first Mount Everest climbing expedition pitched its base camp within sight of the great lamasery near the snout of the Rongbuk Glacier. It was composed of thirteen Englishmen, sixty hillmen from Nepal and northern India, a hundred-odd Tibetan helpers and more than three hundred pack animals— a veritable army in miniature. Remote and isolated Tibet had not witnessed such a sight in the thousands of years of its history.

In the preceding year the purpose had been to explore, reconnoitre and learn. Now, however, all else was to be subordinated to one great purpose: to reach the top of Everest. To this end, the personnel of the party had been almost completely changed, with only Mallory and Morshead remaining from the original group. Of these, Norton, Somervell and Finch were climbers in the prime of their careers and were expected, together with Mallory, to make the final bid for the summit.

As we have repeatedly seen, the climbing of a great mountain is far more than a matter of putting one foot in front of the other and moving uphill. Indeed, in the case of a giant like Everest, climbing in itself may be said to be of merely secondary importance. Two-thirds of the 1922 expedition's battles had to be fought before a single man set foot on the mountain proper.

First, there was the all-important problem of weather. No man, to be sure, could hope to prophesy the day-by-day variations of calm and storm in those wild Himalayan uplands, but the observations of the previous year had convinced everyone concerned that Everest was climbable, if at all, only during a very brief period of the year. Until early May the whole region was locked in savage, blizzard-driven winter; after the middle of June the eastern Himalayas received the full brunt of the Indian monsoon and remained through the summer a death-trap of snow and sleet and rotten, melting ice. A period of only some six weeks intervened in which the climbers might hope for reasonably clear skies, a minimum of wind and at least a fighting chance for success. It was therefore not an accident, but careful planning, that brought the 1922 expedition to the skirts of Everest on May first. Their next great task was to get onto the mountain itself as quickly as possible. The race with the monsoon was on.

For two long weeks climbers and porters crept back and forth along the vast northern glaciers, transporting food, supplies and equipment. Mallory, in an analysis of the problems of Everest, had likened a climbing expedition to a ladder, in which the higher rungs were useless unless the rungs below were dependable and strong. It was these lower rungs which now had to be fashioned—a chain of camps, not more than an easy day's march apart, extending as high as human strength could take them. Camp I was pitched between the Rongbuk and East Rongbuk Glaciers, in the narrow defile which Mallory had missed the previous year. Camp II was established halfway up the East Rongbuk Glacier, and Camp III near its head, close by the eastern wall of the North Col. The older and less acclimatized members of the party were left behind to staff and maintain communication between these lower stations, while the stronger climbers and porters proceeded to the establishment of Camp IV on top of the col.

This in itself was a feat more difficult than the ascent to the summit of a lesser mountain. Mallory and Somervell led the way, chopping countless steps in the glaring ice-cliffs, edging their way around bottomless, dark crevasses and snow-masses as vast as toppled buildings. The porters followed, straining on the ropes, scarcely more than creeping under their heavy loads. On their return to civilization the Everesters were unanimous in declaring that without these sturdy Sherpas from the hill country of northern India their assault on the mountain would have bogged down before it even began. Unlike the Tibetans, who refused even to set foot on Chomolungma, the haunted mountain, these men climbed doggedly and cheerfully to heights where no men had ever stood before and in 1924 achieved the almost incredible feat of carrying packs and establishing a camp at an altitude of more than 27,000 feet. "Tigers," the Englishmen called them, and they richly deserved the name.

With a huddle of tiny green tents established on the col, the assault on Everest proper was at last at hand. Mallory, Somervell, Norton and Morshead were selected for the first attempt, and at dawn on May twentieth, accompanied by a group of the strongest porters, they set out for the unknown, untrodden heights. The cold was almost unendurable; the wild west wind roared down upon them like an invisible avalanche; and their goal was still a mile above them, remote and tantalizing in the sky. But their hopes and hearts were high. "No end," wrote Mallory, "was visible or even conceivable to this kingdom of adventure!"

Hour after hour the climbers toiled up the northeast ridge. The going underfoot was not technically difficult, but constant care was necessary to guard against a slip on the steep, ice-coated slabs. The wind tore at them relentlessly, and, worse yet, as they ascended it grew more difficult to breathe. Later expeditions were to learn an important lesson from their ordeal and allow themselves more time for acclimatization before storming the almost oxygen-less heights.

They had hoped to pitch their highest camp close under the northeast shoulder, but at 25,000 feet cold and exhaustion forced a halt. Sending their faithful "tigers" down to Camp IV they pitched their two tiny tents in as sheltered a spot as they could find and crawled into their sleeping bags. All night they lay there, while the wind howled and the mercury in their thermometers dropped to seven degrees above zero.

At first daylight they were moving upward again through thick mist and gusts of windblown snow. After an hour's climbing Morshead reached the limit of his endurance and had to turn back, but Mallory, Somervell and Norton still struggled on. Their progress consisted of fifteen or twenty minutes' slow, painful climbing, a long rest, another period of climbing, another rest. Before long their hands and feet grew numb and their mouths hung wide open, gasping for air. Even their minds and senses, they reported later, were affected by oxygen starvation: ambition, judgment and will disappeared, and they moved forward mechanically, like men in a trance.

By mid-afternoon they had reached a height of 27,000 feet. They had ascended two-thirds of the vertical distance between the North Col and the summit and were a full 2,400 feet higher than any man had ever stood before. Physically they could have gone even farther, but to have done so at that late hour, without food or shelter, would have been suicidal. Too exhausted to feel disappointment, or any other emotion, they turned their backs on their goal and began the descent.

As it was they were lucky to return to their companions alive. At Camp IV they found Morshead so crippled by frostbite that he had almost to be carried down to the col. Then, crossing a steep snow-slope lower down, one of them slipped, and the four were carried to the very brink of the precipitous north face before Mallory succeeded in jamming his ax into the snow and holding the rope fast. As a crowning misfortune, night overtook them before they reached the col, and it was past midnight when at last they groped their way into their tents.

The same day that the first attempt ended in heroic failure, the second was launched. The climbers now were Finch, Geoffrey Bruce and Tejbir Bura, a Gurkha corporal who had proved himself a first-class mountaineer. Captain Noel ascended with them to the North Col camp, where he remained in reserve, and twelve porters set up a fifth camp for them at 25,500 feet—a full 500 feet higher than where Mallory and his companions had bivouacked a few nights before. This headstart for the final dash, added to the advantage that they were supplied with tanks of oxygen to aid their breathing, gave the second party high hopes of success.

They were hopes, however, that were to be quickly shattered. No sooner had Finch, Bruce and Tejbir crawled into their tent for the night than a blizzard swooped down upon the mountain. For more than twenty-four hours the wind shrieked, the snow drove down in an almost solid mass, and the climbers struggled desperately with ripping canvas and breaking guy-ropes. It was little less than a miracle that men, tent and all were not blown bodily off the mountain into the mile-deep gulfs below.

After two nights and a day the weather at last cleared, and the climbers made their delayed start in a still, frozen dawn. At 26,000 feet Tejbir collapsed and had to return to the tent, Finch and Bruce continuing. The oxygen which they carried spared them the tortures which their predecessors had endured, but this advantage was more than nullified by the thirty pounds of tank and apparatus which each carried on his back. Worse than this, Bruce's apparatus was almost the cause of his death, for without warning, at an altitude of about 26,500 feet, something went wrong with it and the flow of oxygen stopped. Accustomed by then to artificial breathing, Bruce would have been able to live for only a few minutes without it. Finch, however, quickly connected Bruce's mouthpiece to his own tank, and between them they were able to make the necessary repairs.

Hoping to escape the full brunt of the wind, they left the northeast ridge a few hundred feet below the shoulder and headed diagonally upward across the smooth slabs and powdered snow of Everest's north face. They made remarkable progress and by midday had gained a point only half a mile from the summit and a scant 1,900 feet below it. But here they reached the end of their tether. Their bodies and brains were numb; their limbs were ceasing to function and their eyes to focus; each additional foot upward would probably be a foot that they could never return. They turned back defeated, like their companions before them, but in defeat they had set a new world's climbing record of 27,235 feet.

One more attempt the expedition of 1922 was to make. It was doomed to be the most short-lived and disastrous one that has ever been made against the king of mountains.

The dreaded monsoon came early that year, and already in the first days of June dark banks of clouds appeared above the mountains to the south and the snow fell in billowing drifts on the upper slopes of Everest. A final thrust, if it were to be made at all, must be made quickly.

The main base, at which the whole expedition now gathered, resembled a field hospital more than a mountaineers' camp; of the high climbers only Mallory and Somervell were fit for further work. Resolved on a last try, however, they again pushed up the glaciers and, with Crawford, Wakefield and a squad of porters helping, resumed the laborious task of packing supplies up to the North Col. A night of sub-zero temperature had apparently solidified the fresh snow on the great wall, and they had reason to believe the going would be comparatively easy.

Starting early one morning from Camp III, Mallory, Somervell, Crawford and fourteen heavily loaded porters began the ascent. The Englishmen were on one rope, cutting steps and leading the way; three roped groups of porters followed. All went well until they had reached a point some 600 feet below the summit of the col. Then suddenly they were startled by a deep rumbling sound beneath them. An instant later there was a dull, ominous explosion, and the rampart of snow and ice to which they clung seemed to shudder along its entire face. An ocean of soft, billowing snow poured down upon them, knocked them from their feet and swept them away.

By miraculous good fortune, Mallory, Somervell and Crawford were not in the direct path of the avalanche. Caught by its flank, they were carried down a distance of some fifty feet; but by striking out like swimmers they were at last able to struggle to the surface and gain a secure foothold. Not so the unfortunate porters. Struck by the full force of the snowslide, they were catapulted down the steep slope to the lip of the sheer ice-wall below. A moment before there had been a gaping crevasse beneath the wall; now it was filled by the avalanche. Hurtling over the brink, the porters plunged into the soft, hissing sea of snow, disappearing from sight one by one as thousands of more tons poured down after them.

Grim and heroic work was carried out on the ice-wall that day. Hour after hour the climbers floundered through the great drifts, burrowing, straining at ropes, expending their last reserve of strength to find and rescue the buried porters. One or two they found almost uninjured. A few more, who at first appeared dead from suffocation, they were able to revive. But seven were beyond help. To this day their bodies lie entombed in the snow beneath the North Col, tragic victims of the wrath of the greatest mountain.

So the 1922 attack on Everest ended, not only in defeat but in disaster. Any further attempt on the peak that year was unthinkable, and it was a silent, saddened band of mountaineers who, a few days later, began the long trek across Tibet toward India and home. Behind them the summit of the greatest mountain loomed white and lonely in the sky, its snow-plume streaming in the wild west wind.

The curtain drops for two years on Chomolungma, Goddess-Mother-of-the-World. No expedition was sent out in 1923, but the struggle was by no means at an end. The Mount Everest Committee continued with its work—planning, financing, organizing—and in late March of 1924 a third expedition set out from Darjeeling on the high, wild trail to the heart of the Himalayas. Before it returned it was destined to write the most famous chapter in the history of mountaineering.

Several of the old Everesters were back again in harness: the indefatigable Mallory, of course; Somervell, Norton and Geoffrey Bruce; Noel with his cameras. General Bruce had again been appointed leader, but early in the march through Tibet he was stricken with malaria and had to return to India while Norton carried on as first-in-command. Almost three hundred men, all told, were in the party when at the end of April it set up its base camp beside the great moraines of the now familiar Rongbuk Glacier.

The preliminary moves of the campaign were carried out according to the same plan as before—but more methodically and rapidly. The first three advance camps were established a day's march apart on the glaciers, and within two weeks the advance guard was ready to tackle the North Col. The whole organization was functioning like an oiled machine; there were no accidents or illness, and the weather was fine. According to their schedule they would be on the northeast ridge by the middle of May and have almost a full month for climbing before the arrival of the monsoon. Even the most sceptical among them, staring eagerly at the heights above, could not but believe that Everest at last was theirs.

This time, however, misfortune struck even before they reached the mountain.

Scarcely had Camp III been set up below the col than a blizzard swept down from the north, wrecking everything in its path, turning camps and communication lines into a shambles. The porters, many of them caught unprepared and without adequate clothing or shelter, suffered terribly from exposure and exhaustion. Two of them died. The climbers, who were supposed to be conserving their energies for the great effort higher up, wore themselves out in their efforts to save men and supplies. Two weeks after the vanguard had left the base camp, full of strength and optimism, they were back again where they started, frostbitten, battered and fagged out.

A major blow had been dealt their chances for success, but the Everesters pulled in their belts and went at it again. The porters' drooping spirits were raised by a blessing from the Holy Lama of the Rongbuk Monastery, and a few days later a second assault was begun. At the beginning all went well, and the three glacier camps were re-established and provisioned in short order. But trouble began again on the great ice-wall beneath the North Col. The storms and avalanches of two years had transformed the thousand-foot face into a wild slanting chaos of cliffs and chasms. No vestige of their former route remained.

Then followed days of killing labor. Thousands of steps had to be chopped in the ice and snow. An almost perpendicular chimney, a hundred feet high, had to be negotiated. Ladders and ropes had to be installed so that the porters could come up with their loads. There many narrow escapes from disaster, notably on one occasion when Mallory, descending the wall alone, plunged through a snow-bridge into a gaping hole beneath. Luckily his ice-ax jammed against the sides of the crevasse after he had fallen only ten feet, for below him was only blue-black space. As it was, his companions were all too far away to hear his shouts for help and he was barely able to claw his way upward to the surface snow and safety.

At last, however, the route up the wall was completed. The body of climbers retired to Camp III, at its foot, for a much-needed rest, leaving Hazard and twelve porters in the newly established camp on the col. During the night the mercury fell to twenty-four below zero and at dawn a heavy snowfall began; but Geoffrey Bruce and Odell nevertheless decided to ascend to the col. They did not get far. Halfway up they encountered Hazard and eight of the porters coming down. They were near collapse after the night of frightful cold and wind on the exposed col. Worse yet, four of the porters were still up there, having absolutely refused to budge downward over the treacherous fresh snow of the chimney.

A sombre council of war ensued at Camp III. Snow and wind were now driving down the mountain in wild blasts, and it was obvious that the marooned men could not long survive. All plans had to be set aside and every effort devoted to getting them down.

What followed constitutes one of the most remarkable and courageous rescues in mountaineering annals. Mallory, Norton and Somervell, the three outstanding climbers of the expedition, fought their way up the ice-wall and came out at last upon a steep snow-slope a short distance below the top and immediately above a gaping crevasse. At the top of the slope the porters huddled, half-dead from exposure, but afraid to move. The snow between them and the rescuing party was loose and powdery, liable to crumble away at any moment.

At this point Somervell insisted on taking the lead. Roping up, he crept toward the porters along the upper lip of the crevasse, while Mallory and Norton payed out behind him. But the rope's two hundred feet were not enough; when he had reached its end he was still ten yards short of the men. There was nothing for it but that they must risk the unbridged stretch on their own. After long persuasion two of them began edging across. And made it. Somervell passed them along the rope to Mallory and Norton. Then the other two started over, but at their first step the snow gave way and they began sliding toward the abyss below. Only a patch of solid snow saved them. They brought up at the very edge of the crevasse, gasping, shaken, unable to move an inch.

Now Somervell called into action all his superb talents as a mountaineer. He jammed his ice-ax into the snow and, untying the rope from his waist, passed it around the ax and strained it to its fullest length. Then he lowered himself down the slope until he was clinging to its last strands with one hand. With the other he reached out and, while the snow shuddered ominously underfoot, seized each porter in turn by the scruff of the neck and hauled him up to safety. Within a few hours climbers and porters were back in Camp III, all of them still alive, but little more.

After this harrowing experience a few days' rest at lower altitudes was absolutely necessary, and for the second time in two weeks the Everesters found themselves driven back to the base camp. Their situation could scarcely have been more discouraging. They had planned to be on the northeast ridge by the middle of May, and now it was already June and no man had yet set foot on the mountain proper. In another ten days, at most, the monsoon would blow in and all hope of success would be gone. They must strike hard and strike fast, or go down to defeat.

The next week witnessed climbing such as the world had never seen before.

The plan called for an assault in continuous waves, each climbing party consisting of two men, each attempt to begin the day after the preceding one. The base of operations was to be Camp IV on the North Col. Camp V was to be set up on the ridge, near the site of the 1922 bivouac, and a sixth camp higher yet— as near to the summit as the porters could possibly take it. The climbers believed that the establishment of Camp VI was the key to the ascent; the experiences of the previous expedition had convinced them that the top could be reached only if the final "dash" were reduced to not more than 2,000 feet. In the first fine weather they had experienced in weeks the band of determined men struggled back up the glaciers.

Mallory and Geoffrey Bruce were chosen for the first attack. With Odell, Irvine and nine porters they reached the North Col safely, spent the night there, and the next morning struck out up the ridge, accompanied by eight of the "tigers." Odell, Irvine and one helper remained on the col in support. The climbers made good progress the first day and set up their tents at 25,300 feet—a mere 200 feet lower than the highest camp of 1922. A night of zero cold and shrieking wind, however, was too much for the porters, and the next morning no amount of persuasion would induce them to go higher. Seething with frustration, Mallory and Bruce were forced to descend with them.

Meanwhile the second team of Norton and Somervell had started up from the col, according to plan. They passed the first party on its way down, reached Camp V and spent the night there. In the morning their porters, too, refused at first to go on, but after four solid hours of urging three of them at last agreed to make a try. The work they subsequently did that day has seldom been matched anywhere for endurance, courage and loyalty. Step by gasping step they struggled upward with their packs—freezing, leaden-footed, choking for air—until at last Camp VI was pitched at the amazing altitude of 26,800 feet. Their task completed, they then descended to the North Col, to be hailed as heroes by all below: Lhakpa Chede, Napoo Yishay and Semchumbi, greatest of all "tigers."

That night Norton and Somervell slept in a single tiny tent, higher than men had ever slept before. Their hearts were now pounding with more than the mere physical strain of their exertions: the long dreamed-of summit loomed in the darkness only 2,300 feet above them; victory was at last within their reach. Carefully, for the hundredth time, they reviewed their plans for the final day. There were two opinions in the expedition as to the best route to be followed. Mallory and some of the others were in favor of ascending straight to the northeast shoulder and then following the crest of the main east ridge to the base of the summit pyramid. Norton and Somervell, however, believed that by keeping a few hundred feet below the ridge they would not only find easier climbing, but also escape the full fury of the west wind; and it was this route that they now determined to take.

Dawn of the next day broke clear and still. By full sunrise they were on their way, creeping upward and to the west over steeply tilted, snow-powdered slabs. As they had hoped, they were protected from the wind, but the cold was bitter and both men coughed and gasped in the thin, freezing air. They could take only a dozen steps in succession before pausing to rest. While moving, they were forced to take from four to ten breaths for each single step. Yet they kept going for five hours: to 27,000 feet— 27,500—28,000—

At noon Somervell succumbed. His throat was a throbbing knot of pain and it was only by the most violent effort that he was able to breathe at all. Another few minutes of the ordeal would have been the end of him. Sinking down on a small ledge in a paroxysm of coughing, he gestured to his companion to go on alone.

With the last ounce of his strength Norton tried. An hour's climbing brought him to a great couloir, or gully, which cuts the upper slopes of Everest between the summit pyramid and the precipices of the north face below. The couloir was filled with soft, loose snow, and a slip would have meant a 10,000-foot plunge to the Rongbuk Glacier. Norton crossed it safely, but, clinging feebly to the ledges on the far side, he knew that the game was up. His head and heart were pounding as if any moment they might literally explode. In addition, he had begun to see double, and his leaden feet would no longer move where his will directed them. In his clouded consciousness he was just able to realize that to climb farther would be to die.

For a few moments Norton stood motionless. He was at an altitude of 28,126 feet—higher than any man had ever stood before; so high that the greatest mountain range on earth, spreading endlessly to the horizon, seemed flattened out beneath him. Only a few yards above him began the culminating pyramid of Everest. To his aching eyes it seemed to present an easy slope—a mere thousand feet of almost snow-free slanting rock beckoning him upward to the shining goal. If only his body possessed the strength of his will; if only he were more than human—

Somehow Norton and Somervell got down the terrible slopes of Everest. By nine-thirty that night they were back in the North Col camp in the ministering hands of their companions, safe, but more dead than alive. Somervell was a seriously sick man. Norton was suffering the tortures of snow-blindness and did not regain

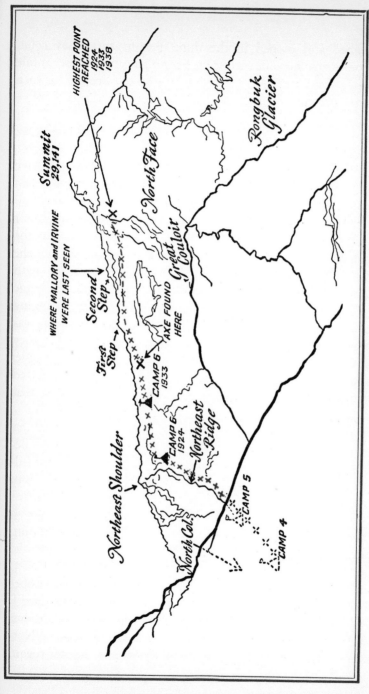

*Ultima Thule.*

The upper north face of Everest as seen by telephoto from the base camp below.
The routes and camps of the highest climbers are shown in the corresponding diagram.

Summit
29,141

HIGHEST POINT
REACHED
1924
1933
1938

WHERE MALLORY and IRVINE
WERE LAST SEEN

North Face

Rongbuk Glacier

Second Step

First Step

Great Couloir

AXE FOUND
HERE

CAMP 6
1933

CAMP 6
1924

Northeast Shoulder

Northeast Ridge

North Col.

CAMP 5

CAMP 4

his sight for several days. Both had given all they had. That it was not enough is surely no reflection on two of the most determined and courageous mountaineers who ever lived.

Norton and Somervell's assault was the next-to-last in the adventure of 1924. One more was to come—and, with it, mystery and tragedy.

Bitterly chagrined at the failure of his first effort, Mallory was determined to have one last fling before the monsoon struck. Everest was *his* mountain, more than any other man's. He had pioneered the way to it and blazed the trail to its heights; his flaming spirit had been the principal driving force behind each assault; the conquest of the summit was the great dream of his life. His companions, watching him now, realized that he was preparing for his mightiest effort.

Mallory moved with characteristic speed. With young Andrew Irvine as partner he started upward from the col the day after Norton and Somervell had descended. They spent the first night at Camp V and the second at Camp VI, at 26,800 feet. Unlike Norton and Somervell, they planned to use oxygen on the final dash and to follow the crest of the northeast ridge instead of traversing the north face to the couloir. The ridge appeared to present more formidable climbing difficulties than the lower route, particularly near the base of the summit pyramid where it buckled upward in two great rock-towers which the Everesters called the First and Second Steps. Mallory, however, was all for the frontal attack and had frequently expressed the belief that the steps could be surmounted. The last "tigers" descending that night from the highest camp to the col brought word that both climbers were in good condition and full of hope for success.

One man only was to have another glimpse of Mallory and Irvine.

On the morning of June eighth—the day set for the assault on the summit—Odell, the geologist, who had spent the night alone at Camp V, set out for Camp VI with a rucksack of food. The day was as warm and windless as any the expedition had experienced, but a thin gray mist clung to the upper reaches of the mountain, and Odell could see little of what lay above him. Presently, however, he scaled the top of a small crag at about 26,000 feet, and, standing there, he stopped and stared. For a moment the mist cleared. The whole summit ridge and final pyramid of Everest were unveiled, and high above him, on the very crest of the ridge, he saw two tiny figures outlined against the sky. They appeared to be at the base of one of the great steps, not more than seven or eight hundred feet below the final pinnacle. As Odell watched, the figures moved slowly upward. Then, as suddenly at it had parted, the mist closed in again, and they were gone.

The feats of endurance that Odell performed during the next forty-eight hours are unsurpassed by those of any mountaineer. That same day he went to Camp VI with his load of provisions, and then even higher, watching and waiting. But the mountain-top remained veiled in mist and there was no sign of the climbers returning. As night came on, he descended all the way to the col, only to start off again the following dawn. Camp V was empty. He spent a solitary night there in sub-zero cold and the next morning ascended again to Camp VI. It was empty too. With sinking heart he struggled upward for another thousand feet, searching and shouting, to the very limits of human endurance. The only answering sound was the deep moaning of the wind. The great peak above him loomed bleakly in the sky, wrapped in the loneliness and desolation of the ages. All hope was gone. Odell descended to the highest camp and signalled the tidings of tragedy to the watchers far below.

So ended the second attempt on Everest—and, with it, the lives of two brave men. The bodies of George Mallory and Andrew Irvine lie somewhere in the vast wilderness of rock and ice that guards the summit of the world. Where and how death overtook them no one knows. And whether victory came before the end no one knows either. Our last glimpse of them is through Odell's eyes—two tiny specks against the sky, fighting upward.

The rest is mystery.

The story of Everest from 1924 onward continues as it began. The greatest mountain still works its magic on the imaginations of men, and the fight for its conquest goes on. Again and again, through the 'Thirties, bands of brave and determined climbers have come to challenge it, struggling through the passes and gorges of the Himalayas, penetrating its inner fastnesses along the great glaciers, storming the North Col, creeping doggedly upward through wind and blizzard and avalanche. Each successive expedition has added something to the store of man's knowledge. Some have performed feats of unexcelled skill and endurance. But every one has failed of its goal. All the determination of the human spirit, all the ingenuity of science, have not yet been able to get a man up the final thousand feet of that gleaming, snow-plumed summit— and down.

For nine years after the 1924 assault no climbers approached Everest. Tibet again closed its gates rigidly to white men, and it was not until 1933 that permission was once more granted for an expedition to try its luck. By this time most of the veterans of the previous attempts were too old for another ordeal on the mountain, but a capable team of younger climbers was assembled by the Mount Everest Committee. The new leader was Hugh Ruttledge, an experienced Himalayan climber.

Following the by now traditional route, the 1933 party battled its way along the glaciers, up the ice-wall to the North Col, and established its higher camps close to the northeast ridge. From Camp VI, at 27,400 feet—600 feet above the highest previous bivouac—two successive assaults were made on the summit. The first, by Harris and Wager, carried across the brow of the north face to the far side of the great couloir and ended, with both men near collapse, at almost the identical spot at which Norton had turned back nine years before. The second, by Shipton and Smythe, got no farther. Shipton succumbed to the efforts of altitude soon after leaving Camp VI, and was forced to descend, while Smythe, struggling on alone, reached the end of his endurance just beyond the couloir, as had the others before him. It seemed almost as if Everest were ringed by a magic wall a thousand feet beneath the summit, beyond which no man could venture and live.

A dramatic discovery was made by Harris and Wager an hour's climb above Camp VI. On the tilted slabs just below the summit ridge they came suddenly upon a solitary, rusted ice-ax. The name of the Swiss maker, still plainly stamped on its head, left no possibility of doubt as to how it had come there; it was either Mallory's or Irvine's. Some mountaineers have claimed this to be an indication that Mallory and Irvine reached the top. Odell, they argue, saw them at a point much farther along the ridge; neither climber, presumably, would have attempted to go on without his ax, and the logical supposition, therefore, is that it was dropped in an accident on the way down. Others merely shrug their shoulders. Whatever one chooses to believe, there is no proof. The ax is no more than a tantalizing hint at the fate of the lost climbers.

The 1933 Everesters were favored by no better weather than their predecessors. Immediately after Smythe and Shipton's "all out" attempt, the monsoon struck in a fury of blizzards and all further climbing was out of the question. The expedition had accomplished notable work and suffered not a single fatality or serious accident. But the world's climbing record was still 28,126 feet, and Everest was still 29,141 feet high.

For many years men had looked longingly upward at the summit of the highest mountain. Now, in the same year as the third climbing expedition, men were to look *down* upon it.

Almost since the beginning of aviation airmen had been considering the possibilities of a flight over Everest, and in April of 1933 the first attempt was made. It was completely successful. Under the leadership of the Marquis of Clydesdale (now the Duke of Hamilton) and Air-Commodore Fellowes of the Royal Air Force two specially designed planes took off from Purnea, in northern India, and reached the peak in a mere hour. A treacherous down-current of wind almost crashed them against the slopes of the summit pyramid, but at the last moment they succeeded in gaining sufficient altitude to clear it. Then, fortunately, the weather improved, and they spent the next fifteen minutes circling the pinnacle, making observations and taking close-range photographs. In another hour they were safely back at their airport.

A remarkable flying achievement in itself, the flight was of importance to mountaineers chiefly in that it confirmed their belief that the topmost thousand feet of Everest did not present impossible climbing difficulties—provided a human being could reach them with any strength or breath left in his body. The highest pinnacle, viewed from above, was a gentle crest of white, windblown snow. No human relic could be seen.

The year 1934 saw only one short-lived attempt on the mountain—an attempt so foolhardy and hopeless that it appears less an actual climbing venture than an elaborate suicide. The would-be climber was Maurice Wilson, an English aviator who had never been on a high peak in his life. Like the ill-fated Farmer on Kanchenjunga, he smuggled himself into the forbidden regions of the Himalayas, hired a handful of natives to pack his supplies and launched a one-man assault on the mountain. Somehow he succeeded in struggling up the glaciers, but cold and exhaustion caught up with him below the ice-cliffs of the North Col. His body was discovered and buried the following spring.

In 1935 and 1936 the real Everesters returned to the wars. Because of long delays in gaining the sanction of the Tibetan government only a reconnaissance was undertaken the first year,[1] but in late April of '36 a full-fledged climbing party was once more at the Rongbuk base camp, ready for battle. Ruttledge was again the leader, and the climbing personnel was virtually the same as in 1933.

The earlier expeditions had had bad luck with the weather; this one had no luck at all. Wind-storms, blizzards and avalanches thundered down upon them from the first day on, and—crowning blow—the monsoon blew up from the south a full month earlier than expected. After a few hairbreadth escapes on the crumbling deathtrap of the North Col, the climbers were forced to withdraw without having even set foot on the mountain itself.

---

[1] The 1935 expedition, however, performed many remarkable feats, among them the ascent of more peaks of over 22,000 feet than had ever been climbed before.

In 1938 came still another expedition—the seventh and, to date, the last. The leadership had passed on to H. W. Tilman, of Nanda Devi fame, but several of the old guard were again on hand— notably Smythe, Shipton and the veteran Odell, now well on into middle age, yet back for another try after fourteen years.

The venture was favored by slightly better weather than its predecessors. The North Col was reached in short order, the northeast ridge ascended, and Camp VI pitched at 27,000 feet. Beyond it, however, the climbers were up against the same invincible defenses that had defeated every previous effort; and with the same result. Two summit assaults were launched—the first by the old team of Smythe and Shipton, the second by Tilman and young Peter Lloyd, who had climbed with him on Nanda Devi. In each case, however, the climbers were turned back short of the final pyramid by exhaustion, oncoming darkness and the slanting, snow-powdered slabs of the north face. Then, before they could reorganize their forces for still another try, the monsoon struck, putting an end to their hopes.

So stands the fight for Everest up to the present time. Seven great expeditions have come and challenged, struggled and failed. Many brave men, white and brown, have lost their lives. And the summit of the greatest mountain still soars into the sky, untouched and unconquered.

When and how the mountain will be climbed is the secret of the future, but that it *will* be climbed is sure—as sure as that the oceans have been crossed, the continents spanned, the poles discovered. Perhaps the victory will be won on the next attempt, perhaps not for generations. But still men will come, and more men, and at last the day will come when the weather is right and the mountain is right and the men are right, and those men will get to the top.

Meanwhile, there is something better than victory—something that should make us almost thankful that the summit of the world has not yet been trodden by the foot of man. For until that happens Everest is more than the highest mountain. It is one of the great unfinished adventures of mankind.

# ADRIFT ON AN ICE PAN

## By WILFRED T. GRENFELL

*Illustration by Warren Chappell*

IT WAS Easter Sunday at St. Anthony in the year 1908, but with us in northern Newfoundland still winter. Everything was covered with snow and ice. I was walking back after morning service, when a boy came running over from the hospital with the news that a large team of dogs had come from sixty miles to the southward, to get a doctor on a very urgent case. It was that of a young man on whom we had operated about a fortnight before for an acute bone disease in the thigh. The people had allowed the wound to close, the poisoned matter had accumulated, and we thought we should have to remove the leg. There was obviously, therefore, no time to be lost. So, having packed up the necessary instruments, dressings, and drugs, and having fitted out the dog-sleigh with my best dogs, I started at once, the messengers following me with their team.

My team was an especially good one. On many a long journey they had stood by me and pulled me out of difficulties by their sagacity and endurance. To a lover of his dogs, as every Christian man must be, each one had become almost as precious as a child to its mother. They were beautiful beasts: "Brin," the cleverest leader on the coast; "Doc," a large gentle beast, the backbone of the team for power; "Spy," a wiry, powerful black and white dog; "Moody," a lop-eared black-and-tan, in his third season, a plodder that never looked behind him; "Watch," the youngster of the team, long-legged and speedy, with great liquid eyes and a Gordon-setter coat; "Sue," a large, dark Eskimo, the image of a great black wolf, with her sharp-pointed and perpendicular ears, for she "harked back" to her wild ancestry; "Jerry," a large roan-colored slut, the quickest of all my dogs on her feet, and so affectionate that her overtures of joy had often sent me sprawling on my back; "Jack," a jet-black, gentle-natured dog, more like a retriever, that always ran next the sledge, and never looked back but everlastingly pulled straight ahead, running always with his nose to the ground.

It was late in April, when there is always the risk of getting wet through the ice, so that I was carefully prepared with spare outfit, which included a change of garments, snowshoes, rifle, compass, ax, and oilskin overclothes. The messengers were anxious that their team should travel back with mine, for they were slow at best and needed a lead. My dogs, however, being a powerful team, could not be held back, and though I managed to wait twice for their sleigh, I had reached a village about twenty miles on the journey before nightfall, and had fed the dogs, and was gathering a few people for prayers when they caught me up.

During the night the wind shifted to the northeast, which brought in fog and rain, softened the snow, and made traveling very bad, besides heaving a heavy sea into the bay. Our drive next morning would be somewhat over forty miles, the first ten miles on an arm of the sea, on salt-water ice.

In order not to be separated too long from my friends, I sent them ahead two hours before me, appointing a rendezvous in a log tilt that we have built in the woods as a halfway house. There is no one living on all that long coast line, and to provide against accidents —which have happened more than once—we built this hut to keep dry clothing, food, and drugs in.

The first rain of the year was falling when I started, and I was obliged to keep on what we call the "ballicaters," or ice barricades, much farther up the bay than I had expected. The sea of the night before had smashed the ponderous covering of ice right to the land-wash. There were great gaping chasms between the enormous blocks, which we call pans, and half a mile out it was all clear water.

An island three miles out had preserved a bridge of ice, however, and by crossing a few cracks I managed to reach it. From the island it was four miles across to a rocky promontory—a course that would be several miles shorter than going round the shore. Here as far as the eye could reach the ice seemed good, though it was very rough. Obviously, it had been smashed up by the sea and then packed in again by the strong wind from the northeast, and I thought it had frozen together solid.

All went well till I was about a quarter of a mile from the landing-point. Then the wind suddenly fell, and I noticed that I was traveling over loose "sish," which was like porridge and probably many feet deep. By stabbing down I could drive my whip-handle through the thin coating of young ice that was floating on it. The sish ice consists of the tiny fragments where the large pans have been pounding together on the heaving sea, like the stones of Freya's grinding mill.

So quickly did the wind now come off shore, and so quickly did the packed "slob," relieved of the wind pressure, "run abroad," that already I could not see one pan larger than ten feet square; moreover, the ice was loosening so rapidly that I saw that retreat was absolutely impossible. Neither was there any way to get off the little pan I was surveying from.

There was not a moment to lose. I tore off my oilskins, threw myself on my hands and knees by the side of the komatik to give a larger base to hold, and shouted to my team to go ahead for the shore. Before we had gone twenty yards, the dogs got frightened, hesitated for a moment, and the komatik instantly sank into the slob. It was necessary then for the dogs to pull much harder, so that they now began to sink in also.

Earlier in the season the father of the very boy I was going to operate on had been drowned in this same way, his dogs tangling their traces around him in the slob. This flashed into my mind, and I managed to loosen my sheath-knife, scramble forward, find the traces in the water, and cut them, holding on to the leader's trace wound round my wrist.

Being in the water I could see no piece of ice that would bear anything up. But there was as it happened a piece of snow, frozen together like a large snowball, about twenty-five yards away, near where my leading dog, "Brin," was wallowing in the slob. Upon this he very shortly climbed, his long trace of ten fathoms almost reaching there before he went into the water.

This dog had weird black markings on his face, giving him the appearance of wearing a perpetual grin. After climbing out on the snow, as if were the most natural position in the world, he deliberately shook the ice and water from his long coat, and then turned round to look for me. As he sat perched up there out of the water, he seemed to be grinning with satisfaction. The other dogs were hopelessly bogged. Indeed, we were like flies in treacle.

Gradually, I hauled myself along the line that was still tied to my wrist, till without any warning the dog turned round and slipped out of his harness, and then once more turned his grinning face to where I was struggling.

It was impossible to make any progress through the sish ice by swimming, so I lay there and thought all would soon be over, only wondering if anyone would ever know how it happened. There was no particular horror attached to it, and in fact I began to feel drowsy, as if I could easily go to sleep, when suddenly I saw the trace of another big dog that had himself gone through before he reached the pan, and though he was close to it was quite unable to force his way out. Along this I hauled myself, using him as a bow anchor, but much bothered by the other dogs as I passed them, one of which got on my shoulder, pushing me farther down into the ice. There was only a yard or so more when I had passed my living anchor, and soon I lay with my dogs around me on the little piece of slob ice. I had to help them on to it, working them through the lane that I had made.

The piece of ice we were on was so small, it was obvious we must soon all be drowned, if we remained upon it as it drifted seaward into more open water. If we were to save our lives, no time was to be lost. When I stood up, I could see about twenty yards away a larger pan floating amidst the sish, like a great flat raft, and if we could get on to it we should postpone at least for a time the death that already seemed almost inevitable. It was impossible to reach it without a life line, as I had already learned to my cost, and the next problem was how to get one there. Marvelous to relate, when I had first fallen through, after I had cut the dogs adrift without any hope left of saving myself, I had not let my knife sink, but had fastened it by two half hitches to the back of one of the dogs. To my great joy there it was still, and shortly I was at work cutting all the seal-skin traces still hanging from the dogs' harnesses, and splicing them together into one long line. These I divided and fastened to the backs of my two leaders, tying the near ends round my two wrists. I then pointed out to "Brin" the pan I wanted to reach and tried my best to make them go ahead, giving them the full length of my lines from two coils. My long sealskin moccasins, reaching to my thigh, were full of ice and water. These I took off and tied separately on the dogs' backs. My coat, hat, gloves, and overalls I had already lost. At first, nothing would induce the two dogs to move, and though I threw them off the pan two or three times, they struggled back upon it, which perhaps was only natural, because as soon as they fell through they could see nowhere else to make for. To me, however, this seemed to spell "the end." Fortunately, I had with me a small black spaniel, almost a featherweight, with large furry paws, called "Jack," who acts as my mascot and incidentally as my retriever. This at once flashed into my mind, and I felt I had still one more chance for life. So I spoke to him and showed him the direction, and then threw a piece of ice toward the desired goal. Without a moment's hesitation he made a dash for it, and to my great joy got there safely, the tough scale of sea ice carrying his weight bravely. At once I shouted to him to "lie down," and this, too, he immediately did, looking like a little black fuzz ball on the white setting. My leaders could now see him seated there on the new piece of floe, and when once more I threw them off they understood what I wanted, and fought their way to where they saw the spaniel, carrying with them the line that gave me the one chance for my life. The other dogs followed them, and after painful struggling, all got out again except one. Taking all the run that I could get on my little pan, I made a dive, slithering with the impetus along the surface till once more I sank through. After a long fight, however, I was able to haul myself by the long traces on to this new pan, having taken care beforehand to tie the harnesses to which I was holding under the dogs' bellies, so that they could not slip them off. But alas! the pan I was now on was not large enough to bear us and was already beginning to sink, so this process had to be repeated immediately.

I now realized that, though we had been working toward the shore, we had been losing ground all the time, for the off-shore wind had already driven us a hundred yards farther out. But the widening gap kept full of the pounded ice, through which no man could possibly go.

I had decided I would rather stake my chances on a long swim even than perish by inches on the floe, as there was no likelihood whatever of being seen and rescued. But keenly though I watched, not a streak even of clear water appeared, the interminable sish rising from below and filling every gap as it appeared. We were now resting on a piece of ice about ten by twelve feet, which, as I found when I came to examine it, was not ice at all, but simply snow-covered slob frozen into a mass, and I feared it would very soon break up in the general turmoil of the heavy sea, which was increasing as the ice drove off shore before the wind.

At first we drifted in the direction of a rocky point on which a heavy surf was breaking. Here I thought once again to swim ashore. But suddenly we struck a rock. A large piece broke off the already small pan, and what was left swung round in the backwash, and started right out to sea.

There was nothing for it now but to hope for a rescue. Alas! there was little possibility of being seen. As I have already mentioned, no one lives around this big bay. My only hope was that the other komatik, knowing I was alone and had failed to keep my tryst, would perhaps come back to look for me. This, however, as it proved, they did not do.

The westerly wind was rising all the time, our coldest wind at this time of year, coming as it does over the Gulf ice. It was tantalizing, as I stood with next to nothing on, the wind going through me and every stitch soaked in ice water, to see my well-stocked komatik some fifty yards away. It was still above water, with food, hot tea in a thermos bottle, dry clothing, matches, wood, and everything on it for making a fire to attract attention.

It is easy to see a dark object on the ice in the daytime, for the gorgeous whiteness shows off the least thing. But the tops of bushes and large pieces of kelp have often deceived those looking out. Moreover, within our memory no man has been thus adrift on the bay ice. The chances were about one in a thousand that I should be seen at all, and if I were seen, I should probably be mistaken for some piece of refuse.

To keep from freezing, I cut off my long moccasins down to the feet, strung out some line, split the legs, and made a kind of jacket,

Warren Chappell

*It was scarcely safe to move on my small raft.*

which protected my back from the wind down as far as the waist. I have this jacket still, and my friends assure me it would make a good Sunday garment.

I had not drifted more than half a mile before I saw my poor komatik disappear through the ice, which was every minute loosening up into the small pans that it consisted of, and it seemed like a friend gone and one more tie with home and safety lost. To the northward, about a mile distant, lay the mainland along which I had passed so merrily in the morning—only, it seemed, a few moments before.

By mid-day I had passed the island to which I had crossed on the ice bridge. I could see that the bridge was gone now. If I could reach the island I should only be marooned and destined to die of starvation. But there was little chance of that, for I was rapidly driving into the ever widening bay.

It was scarcely safe to move on my small ice raft, for fear of breaking it. Yet I saw I must have the skins of some of my dogs—of which I had eight on the pan—if I was to live the night out. There was now some three to five miles between me and the north side of the bay. There, immense pans of Arctic ice, surging to and fro on the heavy ground seas, were thundering into the cliffs like medieval battering-rams. It was evident that, even if seen, I could hope for no help from that quarter before night. No boat could live through the surf.

Unwinding the sealskin traces from my waist, round which I had wound them to keep the dogs from eating them, I made a slipknot, passed it over the first dog's head, tied it round my foot close to his neck, threw him on his back, and stabbed him in the heart. Poor beast! I loved him like a friend—a beautiful dog—but we could not all hope to live. In fact, I had no hope any of us would, at that time, but it seemed better to die fighting.

In spite of my care the struggling dog bit me rather badly in the leg. I suppose my numb hands prevented my holding his throat as I could ordinarily do. Moreover, I must hold the knife in the wound to the end, as blood on the fur would freeze solid and make the skin useless. In this way I sacrificed two more large dogs, receiving only one more bite, though I fully expected that the pan I was on would break up in the struggle. The other dogs, who were licking their coats and trying to get dry apparently took no notice of the fate of their comrades—but I was very careful to prevent the dying dogs crying out, for the noise of fighting would probably have been followed by the rest attacking the down dog, and that was too close to me to be pleasant. A short shrift seemed to me better than a long one, and I envied the dead dogs whose troubles were over so quickly. Indeed, I came to balance in my mind whether, if once I passed into the open sea, it would not be better by far to use my faithful knife on myself than to die by inches. There seemed no hardship in the thought. I seemed fully to sympathize with the Japanese view of hara-kiri.

Working, however, saved me from philosophizing. By the time I had skinned these dogs, and with my knife and some of the harness had strung the skins together, I was ten miles on my way, and it was getting dark.

Away to the northward I could see a single light in the little village where I had slept the night before, where I had received the kindly hospitality of the simple fishermen in whose comfortable homes I have spent many a night. I could not help but think of them sitting down to tea, with no idea that there was any one watching them, for I had told them not to expect me back for three days.

Meanwhile I had frayed out a small piece of rope into oakum, and mixed it with fat from the intestines of my dogs. Alas, my match box, which was always chained to me, had leaked, and my matches were in pulp. Had I been able to make a light, it would have looked so unearthly out there on the sea that I felt sure they would see me. But that chance was now cut off. However, I kept the matches, hoping that I might dry them if I lived through the night. While working at the dogs, about every five minutes I would stand up and wave my hands toward the land. I had no flag, and I could not spare my shirt, for, wet as it was, it was better than nothing in that freezing wind, and, anyhow, it was already nearly dark.

Unfortunately, the coves in among the cliffs are so placed that only for a very narrow space can the people in any house see the sea. Indeed, most of them cannot see it at all, so that I could not in the least expect any one to see me, even supposing it had been daylight.

Not daring to take any snow from the surface of my pan to break the wind with, I piled up the carcasses of my dogs. With my skin rug I could now sit down without getting soaked. During these hours I had continually taken off all my clothes, wrung them out, swung them one by one in the wind, and put on first one and then the other inside, hoping that what heat there was in my body would thus serve to dry them. In this I had been fairly successful.

My feet gave me most trouble, for they immediately got wet again because my thin moccasins were easily soaked through on the snow. I suddenly thought of the way in which the Lapps who tend our reindeer manage for dry socks. They carry grass with them, which they ravel up and pad into their shoes. Into this they put their feet, and then pack the rest with more grass, tying up the top with a binder. The ropes of the harness for our dogs are carefully sewed all over with two layers of flannel in order to make them soft against the dogs' sides. So, as soon as I could sit down, I started with my trusty knife to rip up the flannel. Though my fingers were more or less frozen, I was able also to ravel out the rope, put it into my shoes, and use my wet socks inside my knickerbockers, where, though damp, they served to break the wind. Then, tying the narrow strips of flannel together, I bound up the top of the moccasins, Lapp-fashion, and carried the bandage on up over my knee, making a ragged though most excellent puttee.

As to the garments I wore, I had recently opened a box of football clothes I had not seen for twenty years. I had found my old Oxford University football running shorts and a pair of Richmond Football Club red, yellow, and black stockings, exactly as I wore them twenty years ago. These with a flannel shirt and sweater vest were now all I had left. Coat, hat, gloves, oilskins, everything else, were gone, and I stood there in that odd costume, exactly as I stood twenty years ago on a football field, reminding me of the little girl of a friend, who, when told she was dying, asked to be dressed in her Sunday frock to go to heaven in. My costume, being very light, dried all the quicker, until afternoon. Then nothing would dry anymore, everything freezing stiff. It had been an ideal costume to struggle through the slob ice. I really believe the conventional garments missionaries are supposed to affect would have been fatal.

My occupation till what seemed like midnight was unraveling rope, and with this I padded out my knickers inside, and my shirt as well, though it was a clumsy job, for I could not see what I was doing. Now, getting my largest dog, Doc, as big as a wolf and weighing ninety-two pounds, I made him lie down, so that I could cuddle round him. I then wrapped the three skins around me, arranging them so that I could lie on one edge, while the other came just over my shoulders and head.

My own breath collecting inside the newly flayed skin must have had a soporific effect, for I was soon fast asleep. One hand I had kept warm against the curled-up dog, but the other, being gloveless, had frozen, and I suddenly awoke, shivering enough, I thought, to break my fragile pan. What I took at first to be the sun was just rising, but I soon found out it was the moon, and then I knew it was about half-past twelve. The dog was having an excellent time. He hadn't been cuddled so warm all winter, and he resented my moving with low growls till he found out it wasn't another dog.

The wind was steadily driving me now toward the open sea, and I could expect, short of a miracle, nothing but death out there. Somehow, one scarcely felt justified in praying for a miracle. But we have learned down here to pray for things we want, and, anyhow, just at that moment the miracle occurred. The wind fell off suddenly, and came with a light air from the southward, and then dropped stark calm. The ice was now "all abroad," which I was sorry for, for there was a big safe pan not twenty yards away from me. If I could have got on that, I might have killed my other dogs when the time came, and with their coats I could hope to hold out for two or three days more, and with the food and drink their bodies would offer me need not at least die of hunger or thirst. To tell the truth, they were so big and strong I was half afraid to tackle them with only a sheath-knife on my small and unstable raft.

But it was now freezing hard. I knew the calm water between us would form into cakes, and I had to recognize that the chance of getting near enough to escape on to it was gone. If, on the other hand, the whole bay froze solid again I had yet another possible chance. For my pan would hold together longer and I should be opposite another village, called Goose Cove, at daylight, and might possibly be seen from there. I knew that the komatiks there would be starting at daybreak over the hills for a parade of Orangemen about twenty miles away. Possibly, therefore, I might be seen as they climbed the hills. So I lay down, and went to sleep again.

It seems impossible to say how long one sleeps, but I woke with a sudden thought in my mind that I must have a flag; but again I had no pole and no flag. However I set to work in the dark to disarticulate the legs of my dead dogs, which were now frozen stiff, and which were all that offered a chance of carrying anything like a distress signal. Cold as it was, I determined to sacrifice my shirt for that purpose with the first streak of daylight.

It took a long time in the dark to get the legs off, and when I had patiently marled them together with old harness rope and the remains of the skin traces, it was the heaviest and crookedest flagpole it has ever been my lot to see. I had had no food from six o'clock the morning before, when I had eaten porridge and bread and butter. I had however, a rubber band which I had been wearing instead of one of my garters, and I chewed that for twenty-four hours. It saved me from thirst and hunger, oddly enough. It was not possible to get a drink from my pan, for it was far too salty. But anyhow that thought did not distress me much, for as from time to time I heard the cracking and grinding of the newly formed slob, it seemed that my devoted boat must inevitably soon go to pieces.

At last the sun rose, and the time came for the sacrifice of my shirt. So I stripped, and, much to my surprise, found it not half so cold as I had anticipated. I now re-formed my dogskins with the raw side out, so that they made a kind of coat quite rivaling Joseph's. But, with the rising of the sun, the frost came out of the joints of my dogs' legs, and the friction caused by waving it made my flagpole almost tie itself in knots. Still, I could raise it three or four feet above my head, which was very important.

Now, however, I found that instead of being as far out at sea as I had reckoned, I had drifted back in a northwesterly direction, and was off some cliffs known as Ireland Head. Near these there was a little village looking seaward, whence I should certainly have been seen. But, as I had myself, earlier in the winter, been night-bound at this place, I had learnt there was not a single soul living there at all this winter. The people had all, as usual, migrated to the winter houses up the bay, where they got together for schooling and social purposes.

I soon found it was impossible to keep waving so heavy a flag all the time, and yet I dared not sit down, for that might be the exact moment someone would be in a position to see me from the hills. The only thing in my mind was how long I could stand up and how long go on waving that pole at the cliffs. Once or twice I thought I saw men against their snowy faces, which, I judged, were about five and a half miles from me, but they were only trees. Once, also, I thought I saw a boat approaching. A glittering object kept appearing and disappearing on the water, but it was only a small piece of ice sparkling in the sun as it rose on the surface. I think that the rocking of my cradle up and down on the waves had helped me to sleep, for I felt as well as I ever did in my life; and with the hope of a long sunny day, I felt sure I was good to last another twenty-four hours— if my boat would hold out and not rot under the sun's rays.

Each time I sat down to rest, my big dog "Doc" came and kissed my face and then walked to the edge of the ice pan, returning again to where I was huddled up, as if to say, "Why don't you come along? Surely it is time to start." The other dogs also were now moving about very restlessly, occasionally trying to satisfy their hunger by gnawing at the dead bodies of their brothers.

I determined, at mid-day to kill a big Eskimo dog and drink his blood, as I had read only a few days before in "Farthest North" of Dr. Nansen's doing—that is, if I survived the battle with him. I could not help feeling, even then, my ludicrous position, and I thought, if ever I got ashore again, I should have to laugh at myself standing hour after hour waving my shirt at those lofty cliffs which seemed to assume a kind of sardonic grin, so that I could almost imagine they were laughing at me. At times I could not help thinking of the good breakfast that my colleagues were enjoying at the back of those same cliffs, and of the snug fire and the comfortable room which we call our study.

I can honestly say that from first to last not a single sensation of fear entered my mind, even when I was struggling in the slob ice. Somehow it did not seem unnatural; I had been through the ice half a dozen times before. For the most part I felt very sleepy, and the idea was then very strong in my mind that I should soon reach the solution of the mysteries that I had been preaching about for so many years.

Only the previous night (Easter Sunday) at prayers in the cottage, we had been discussing the fact that the soul was entirely separate from the body, that Christ's idea of the body as the temple in which the soul dwells is so amply borne out by modern science. We had talked of thoughts from that admirable book, "Brain and Personal-

ity," by Dr. Thompson of New York, and also of the same subject in
the light of a recent operation performed at the Johns Hopkins Hospital by Dr. Harvey Cushing. The doctor had removed from a man's
brain two large cystic tumors without giving the man an anæsthetic,
and the patient had kept up a running conversation with him all the
while the doctor's fingers were working in his brain. It had seemed
such a striking proof that ourselves and our bodies are two absolutely
different things.

Our eternal life has always been with me a matter of faith. It
seems to me one of those problems that must always be a mystery
to knowledge. But my own faith in this matter had been so untrou-
bled that it seemed now almost natural to be leaving through this
portal of death from an ice pan. In many ways, also, I could see how
a death of this kind might be of value to the particular work that
I am engaged in. Except for my friends, I had nothing I could think
of to regret whatever. Certainly, I should like to have told them the
story. But then one does not carry folios of paper in running shorts
which have no pockets, and all my writing gear had gone by the
board with the komatik.

I could still see a testimonial to myself some distance away in my
khaki overalls, which I had left on another pan in the struggle of
the night before. They seemed a kind of company, and would possibly be picked up and suggest the true story. Running through my
head all the time, quite unbidden, were the words of the old hymn:

> "My God, my Father, while I stray
> Far from my home on life's dark way,
> Oh, teach me from my heart to say,
>   Thy will be done!"

It is a hymn we hardly ever sing out here, and it was an unconscious memory of my boyhood days.

It was a perfect morning—a cobalt sky, an ultramarine sea, a
golden sun, an almost wasteful extravagance of crimson over hills of
purest snow, which caught a reflected glow from rock and crag.
Between me and the hills lay miles of rough ice and long veins of
thin black slob that had formed during the night. For the fore-

ground there was my poor, gruesome pan, bobbing up and down on the edge of the open sea, stained with blood, and littered with carcasses and débris. It was smaller than last night, and I noticed also that the new ice from the water melted under the dogs' bodies had been formed at the expense of its thickness. Five dogs, myself in colored football costume, and a bloody dogskin cloak, with a gay flannel shirt on a pole of frozen dogs' legs, completed the picture. The sun was almost hot by now, and I was conscious of a surplus of heat in my skin coat. I began to look longingly at one of my remaining dogs, for an appetite will rise even on an ice pan, and that made me think of fire. So once again I inspected my matches. Alas! the heads were in paste, all but three or four blue-top wax ones.

These I now laid out to dry, while I searched about on my snow pan to see if I could get a piece of transparent ice to make a burning-glass. For I was pretty sure that with all the unraveled tow I had stuffed into my leggings, and with the fat of my dogs, I could make smoke enough to be seen if only I could get a light. I had found a piece which I thought would do, and had gone back to wave my flag, which I did every two minutes, when I suddenly thought I saw again the glitter of an oar. It did not seem possible, however, for it must be remembered it was not water which lay between me and the land, but slob ice, which a mile or two inside me was very heavy. Even if people had seen me, I did not think they could get through, though I knew that the whole shore would then be trying. Moreover, there was no smoke rising on the land to give me hope that I had been seen. There had been no gun-flashes in the night, and I felt sure that, had anyone seen me, there would have been a bonfire on every hill to encourage me to keep going.

So I gave it up, and went on with my work. But the next time I went back to my flag, the glitter seemed very distinct, and though it kept disappearing as it rose and fell on the surface, I kept my eyes strained upon it, for my dark spectacles had been lost, and I was partly snowblind. I waved my flag as high as I could raise it, broadside on. At last, beside the glint of the white oar, I made out the black streak of the hull. I knew that, if the pan held on for another hour, I should be all right.

At last there could be no doubt about it: the boat was getting nearer and nearer. I could see that my rescuers were frantically waving, and when they came within shouting distance, I heard someone cry out, "Don't get excited. Keep on the pan where you are." They were infinitely more excited than I. Already to me it seemed just as natural now to be saved as, half an hour before, it had seemed inevitable I should be lost, and had my rescuers only known, as I did, the sensation of a bath in that ice when you could not dry yourself afterwards, they need not have expected me to follow the example of the apostle Peter and throw myself into the water.

As the man in the bow leaped from the boat on to my ice raft and grasped both my hands in his, not a word was uttered. I could see in his face the strong emotions he was trying hard to force back, though in spite of himself tears trickled down his cheeks. It was the same with each of the others of my rescuers, nor was there any reason to be ashamed of them. These were not the emblems of weak sentimentality, but the evidences of the realization of the deepest and noblest emotion of which the human heart is capable, the vision that God has use for us his creatures, the sense of that supreme joy of the Christ—the joy of unselfish service. After the handshake and swallowing a cup of warm tea that had been thoughtfully packed in a bottle, we hoisted in my remaining dogs and started for home. To drive the boat home there were not only five Newfoundland fishermen at the oars, but five men with Newfoundland muscles in their backs, and five as brave hearts as ever beat in the bodies of human beings.

So, slowly but steadily, we forged through to the shore, now jumping out on to larger pans and forcing them apart with the oars, now hauling the boat out and dragging her over, when the jam of ice packed tightly in by the rising wind was impossible to get through otherwise.

My first question, when at last we found our tongues, was, "How ever did you happen to be out in the boat in this ice?" To my astonishment they told me that the previous night four men had been away on a long headland cutting out some dead harp seals that they had killed in the fall and left to freeze up in a rough wooden store they had built there, and that as they were leaving for home, my pan of ice had drifted out clear of Hare Island, and one of them, with his keen fisherman's eyes, had seen something unusual. They at once returned to their village, saying there was something alive drifting out to sea on the floe ice. But their report had been discredited, for the people thought that it could be only the top of some tree.

All the time I had been driving along I knew that there was one man on that coast who had a good spyglass. He tells me he instantly got up in the midst of his supper, on hearing the news, and hurried over the cliffs to the lookout, carrying his trusty spyglass with him. Immediately, dark as it was, he saw that without any doubt there was a man out on the ice. Indeed, he saw me wave my hands every now and again toward the shore. By a very easy process of reasoning on so uninhabited a shore, he at once knew who it was, though some of the men argued that it must be someone else. Little had I thought, as night was closing in, that away on that snowy hilltop lay a man with a telescope patiently searching those miles of ice for *me*. Hastily they rushed back to the village and at once went down to try to launch a boat, but that proved to be impossible. Miles of ice lay between them and me, the heavy sea was hurling great blocks on the landwash, and night was already falling, the wind blowing hard on shore.

The whole village was aroused, and messengers were despatched at once along the coast, and lookouts told off to all the favorable points, so that while I considered myself a laughing stock, bowing with my flag to those unresponsive cliffs, there were really many eyes watching me. One man told me that with his glass he distinctly saw me waving the shirt flag. There was little slumber that night in the villages, and even the men told me there were few dry eyes, as they thought of the impossibility of saving me from perishing. We are not given to weeping overmuch on this shore, but there are tears that do a man honor.

Before daybreak this fine volunteer crew had been gotten together. The boat, with such a force behind it of will power, would, I believe, have gone through anything. And, after seeing the heavy breakers through which we were guided, loaded with their heavy ice batter-

ing-rams, when at last we ran through the harbor-mouth with the
boat on our return, I knew well what wives and children had been
thinking of when they saw their loved ones put out. Only two years
ago I remember a fisherman's wife watching her husband and three
sons take out a boat to bring in a stranger that was showing flags
for a pilot. But the boat and its occupants have not yet come back.

Every soul in the village was on the beach as we neared the shore.
Every soul was waiting to shake hands when I landed. Even with
the grip that one after another gave me, some no longer trying to
keep back the tears, I did not find out my hands were frost-burnt—a
fact I have not been slow to appreciate since, however. I must have
been a weird sight as I stepped ashore, tied up in rags, stuffed out
with oakum, wrapped in the bloody skins of dogs, with no hat, coat,
or gloves besides, and only a pair of short knickers. It must have
seemed to some as if it were the old man of the sea coming ashore.

But no time was wasted before a pot of tea was exactly where I
wanted it to be, and some hot stew was locating itself where I had
intended an hour before the blood of one of my remaining dogs
should have gone.

Rigged out in the warm garments that fishermen wear, I started
with a large team as hard as I could race for the hospital, for I had
learnt that the news had gone over that I was lost. It was soon painfully impressed upon me that I could not much enjoy the ride, for I
had to be hauled like a log up the hills, my feet being frost-burnt so
that I could not walk. Had I guessed this before going into the
house, I might have avoided much trouble.

It is time to bring this egotistic narrative to an end. "Jack" lies
curled up at my feet while I write this short account. "Brin" is once
again leading and lording it over his fellows. "Doc" and the other
survivors are not forgotten, now that we have again returned to the
less romantic episodes of a mission hospital life. There stands in our
hallway a bronze tablet to the memory of three noble dogs, Moody,
Watch, and Spy, whose lives were given for mine on the ice. In my
home in England my brother has placed a duplicate tablet, and has
added these words, "Not one of them is forgotten before your Father
which is in heaven." And this I most fully believe to be true. The

boy whose life I was intent on saving was brought to the hospital a day or two later in a boat, the ice having cleared off the coast not to return for that season. He was operated on successfully, and is even now on the high road to recovery. We all love life. I was glad to be back once more with possibly a new lease of it before me. I had learned on the pan many things, but chiefly that the one cause for regret, when we look back on a life which we think is closed forever, will be the fact that we have wasted its opportunities. As I went to sleep that first night there still rang in my ears the same verse of the old hymn which had been my companion on the ice, "Thy will, not mine, O Lord."

TO THE MEMORY OF
THREE NOBLE DOGS.
MOODY.
WATCH.
SPY.
WHOSE LIVES WERE GIVEN
FOR MINE ON THE ICE.
April 21st 1908.
WILFRED GRENFELL,
ST. ANTHONY.

# THE RACE FOR THE SOUTH POLE

*By WALTER B. HAYWARD*

*Illustrations by Warren Chappell*

ROALD AMUNDSEN, conqueror of the South Pole, lies in the peaceful depths of the seas that wash the coast of Norway, his native land. Captain Scott, who reached the Pole a few weeks after Amundsen, sleeps beneath a cairn on the Ross Ice Barrier, close to the scene of his triumphs. The story of their race for the coveted goal has no parallel in polar annals. It is a drama of hopes achieved and hopes shattered, of gallantry, of self-sacrifice and tragedy. And it is a story that will live to stir the blood of generations of men.

Amundsen deliberately chose his career. As a lad he was fascinated by the works of Sir John Franklin, who had sought the fabulous Northwest Passage. He determined to be an explorer, and his reading taught him that in the wilderness a man must have not only a stout heart but a strong body. So Amundsen, the boy, set himself a rigorous course of mental and physical self-discipline. He schooled himself to undergo hardship, slept with his window open in winter —an unheard of thing in the Norway of that day—took long walks over rough country, became an expert ski runner, and built up a set of muscles that caused the army doctors to marvel when he presented himself for his period of military training.

His mother had other ideas for Amundsen. She wanted him to be a physician. Actually he gave two years to his medical course, which ended with the death of his mother. Free to choose for himself, he went to sea before the mast, believing that an explorer should also be a master mariner, capable of commanding his own ship. At the age of twenty-five his first chance came. He went to the Antarctic regions as mate of the *Belgica,* which was to undertake a variety of scientific work. The account of that expedition, which came close to disaster, has been briefly related in a previous chapter. It was a difficult and hazardous adventure for all hands; Amundsen returned filled with self-confidence. He had successfully passed his novitiate.

Amundsen dreamed great dreams and usually succeeded in translating them into actualities. His first dream was of a voyage to the Arctic for the purpose of fixing anew the location of the North Magnetic Pole and finding the long sought Northwest Passage. To be sure, he had no ship and no funds and without a sound scientific program he could expect no financial backing. Still he had the encouragement of Dr. Fridtjof Nansen, the hero of many polar exploits, and Amundsen went to Hamburg to consult George von Neumayer, an eminent scientist, to whom he explained his urgent wish to study methods of taking magnetic observations. When Professor von Neumayer heard of Amundsen's ambition to make conclusive observations of the true location of the Magnetic Pole, he remarked that if the young man succeeded he would be the benefactor of mankind for ages to come.

So Amundsen pursued his course of study and became a magnetician. Then he prepared for his adventure with that meticulous care which characterized every one of his expeditions. "Man's triumph over nature is not the victory of brute force, but the triumph of the mind." This belief guided him in all his journeys into the unknown. He left nothing to chance.

Amundsen purchased the fishing smack *Gjoa,* pursued scientific societies for funds and was in turn pursued by angry creditors. All through his life the burden of debt pressed upon him. Every penny that he earned went into his expeditions and still there was always a shortage somewhere. Debt, an expedition, lecture tours to discharge his obligations—that was Amundsen's life. He called himself a "penniless explorer."

At last he took the *Gjoa* to sea to outwit one persistent creditor. She was only seventy-two feet long and manned by "seven as lighthearted pirates as ever flew the black flag." The voyage took three years. From the Atlantic to the Pacific by way of the Arctic coast of North America the *Gjoa* went. She found and passed through the Northwest Passage and her master brought home a mass of scientific data that the pundits took twenty years to digest. It was a notable exploit for a man of thirty-three, giving Amundsen high rank among the explorers of all time.

Another man might have been satisfied with this measure of glory. Not so Amundsen. He was young, he was seasoned; he wanted to go to the North Polar Basin and to plant Norway's flag at the top of the globe. He bought the *Fram,* Nansen's old ship—one of the best ever built for ice navigation—and chose his companions for the voyage. Suddenly Peary, the American admiral, came out of the Arctic wastes and announced to the world that he had reached the North Pole in April, 1909. The supreme prize of the Arctic had been won, so Amundsen turned to the Antarctic, with the South Pole as his single objective. He told no one of his plans, except his brother and the *Fram's* master. His financial backers were kept in darkness. Amundsen wanted no public discussion of his change of program, for fear that the project might be "stifled at its birth."

When the *Fram* left Norway in August, 1910, she carried 97 Eskimo dogs, purchased in Greenland. Oddly enough, no one raised the question why dogs should be taken to the Arctic regions, although it was customary for explorers to buy their animals after they had reached the north. There was, in fact, no suspicion that Amundsen had anything in view except an Arctic voyage. It was not until the *Fram* reached Funchal, Madeira, that he saw fit to disclose his secret. The world was astonished and so was Amundsen's crew; but his sailors readily agreed to go south instead of north and the *Fram* slipped away on her long voyage to the Ross Barrier.

The Norwegian's change of program made him the target of severe criticism. He was well aware of the fact that Captain Scott had organized a private expedition and was even then on his way to the Antarctic. He argued quite reasonably that although Scott aimed to reach the Pole, the Englishman's chief purpose was scientific research while his (Amundsen's) purpose was merely a quick dash to the Pole. Amundsen believed that the field was free and open to all and that he was not poaching on Scott's preserves. As a matter of courtesy he notified Scott of his intentions before the latter left civilization. The Norwegian never forgot the charge of unsportsmanlike conduct leveled against him by British explorers, but it is certain that many of those who felt most keenly about the matter finally agreed that Amundsen had not actually violated the code of sportsmen.

It will be recalled that Shackleton intended to make his base on the Ross Barrier at the Bay of Whales and that upon his arrival at this position he found that a large section of the Barrier face had calved away since 1902. He concluded, therefore, that the Barrier was unsafe and reluctantly changed his plan, going to a base in McMurdo Sound. Amundsen, on the other hand, was convinced that the Barrier about the Bay of Whales was securely anchored by shoals and islets in shallow water. His examination of all the records from the time of Ross satisfied him that any recession of the Barrier at this point was insignificant, and that he could safely winter there. Amundsen was correct in his judgment. During his sojourn at the Bay of Whales the Barrier remained firm; he never had the slightest anxiety on this score.

The Bay of Whales offered several important advantages to Amundsen. It was nearer to the Pole than any other base a ship could reach and, moreover, Amundsen felt certain that the Barrier surface would be much smoother than Scott's route along the ice shelf along the western mountains. Another advantage was that the Amundsen party would have their home, their stores and their dogs on the Barrier itself, while Scott, based on McMurdo Sound, would have to cross sea ice to reach the shelf. Furthermore, Scott's distance to the Pole was sixty miles or more longer than Amundsen's route.

The bay was filled not only with whales but with seals. Thus Amundsen had at hand an unlimited supply of fresh meat for dog and man. No other Antarctic explorer had been similarly favored, and this fact enabled the Norwegian to keep his dogs in superb condition for the polar journey. The dogs had increased to 116 by the time he reached the Barrier, and he had with him trained dog drivers and adequate sledging equipment. In fact, everything was planned to make the polar dash a success. No thought of scientific exploration entered into Amundsen's calculations; he was satisfied to leave that to Scott.

Every item of equipment that Amundsen took with him—food, clothing, boots, tents, skis, sledges, dog harness—bore the test of a man with years of Arctic experience to guide him. Moreover, the Norwegian had plotted his polar route—a pioneer journey—long before he left Norway, and determined the extent of the preliminary work of depot-laying. He had even worked out a time schedule, which set January 25, 1912, as the day he would return to the Bay of Whales from the Pole. That was the day he returned.

On September 5, 1910, the *Fram* was at Funchal Roads. Four days afterward she was ready for the long voyage. Amundsen called the crew to quarters, explained his mission, and asked each man if he would go to Antarctia. The ceremony was soon over; Amundsen knew then he had a crew that would go anywhere with him. His only worry concerned the effect of the heat upon the dogs while passing through the tropics, but as events turned out there was no cause for worry. Nature corrected with good measure the losses of dogs at sea.

The Antarctic Circle was crossed on January 2 and a week later the *Fram* was in Ross Sea, having been in the ice pack only four days. Soon the ice blink told Amundsen that the Barrier was not far away. Captain Nilsen, master of the *Fram,* had calculated that the voyage of 16,000 geographical miles from Norway would end at the Bay of Whales on January 15. He was only a trifle wrong. The *Fram* lay in the bay alongside the edge of the sea ice on January 14. Amundsen and some of his men started off at once to investigate what he called the "mystic Barrier." They walked a little more than a mile, climbed a snow slope, and were at the top. "Without striking a blow we had entered into our kingdom." The Barrier cliff was only twenty feet high at this point.

Now came the selection of a site for the hut. Amundsen had thought it might be necessary to make his base ten miles from the sea edge of the Barrier, in order to avoid the possibility of being carried out to sea on an iceberg. He gave up that idea as soon as he came to two pressure ridges about 100 feet high. A skilled ice craftsman, Amundsen saw at a glance that these were old formations, securely anchored. They had held for ages; he felt certain that they would hold much longer. In a basin near the ridges, named Mounts Nelson and Ronniken, he marked out a place for the hut. It all seemed very simple, and on the morrow the *Fram's* crew began to discharge the ship.

Men and dogs lost no time in sledging the stores to the Barrier. The distance from ship to hut site was short, and before the end of the month the shore party moved into their Barrier home, which they called Framheim. The hut is still there, buried beneath the snowdrifts. On February 4, the Norwegians had a surprise visit from the *Terra Nova,* Scott's ship, which reported her unsuccessful attempt to reach King Edward VII Land, having been blocked by the ice pack. The *Terra Nova* came into the bay on her way back to McMurdo Sound. Campbell, whom the British leader had put in charge of this exploring party, heard enough about Amundsen's plans to realize that in the Norwegian Scott had a worthy rival for polar honors. The Norwegian's dog transport was superb; moreover, he would get away for the south sooner than Scott, who was relying on ponies to carry his stores across the Barrier and would necessarily travel the whole distance on foot.

Priestley, who accompanied Campbell, was deeply impressed with the hardy, genial Norwegians, recognizing them as men of wide experience in snow traveling. He watched with admiration the way Amundsen handled his dogs while crossing the sea ice to the *Terra Nova.* As Amundsen ranged alongside he whistled and the team came to a dead halt. Then he turned the sledge upside down, leaving the dogs to themselves. They did not move until his visit ended. Priestley's opinion was that good dogs were the best draught animals for polar work—a belief shared by Amundsen. The Norwegian could not understand why a polar explorer should use any other form of transport. He was convinced that his animals would take him across the Barrier and through the mountains and bring him back again without difficulty.

The dogs were put to their first severe test within the next week, when Amundsen and three men started south to lay the first food depot. Three sledges, heavily loaded, each drawn by six dogs, were used, and bamboo poles with black flags were carried along to mark the route, for they were going into the unknown and no man could tell exactly what they would encounter. Prestrud, the "forerunner," as Amundsen called him, walked in front to give the direction. The dog drivers, each with a compass, checked his direction.

Amundsen admitted that his first inland trip was "undeniably exciting." He knew nothing of the surface conditions; there was no experience to guide him, and not a landmark on the undulating plain. Men had never before trod this end of the great Barrier. The weather was mild and pleasant, except for fog, but with the dogs pulling strongly, they pushed ahead and at 80 degrees south they laid the depot.

Returning, the dogs traveled very fast, doing sixty-two miles the last day. Amundsen was well satisfied. The equipment was right and the dogs were willing. Before they got to Framheim the *Fram* had sailed to carry on oceanographical work in the South Atlantic. Amundsen had with him eight men—Prestrud, Johansen, Hanssen, Hassel, Bjaaland, Wisting, Stubberud and Lindstrom, the cook.

Two depots were next laid, at 81 and 82 degrees south. This work was accomplished by eight men with seven sledges and forty-two dogs. It was a much more difficult task. Bitterly cold weather and hard pulling among crevassed areas exhausted the dogs and cut their feet. Several dogs were lost or killed on the trail, most of the others returning in poor condition.

The last journey of the season was made to the first depot, where seal meat was deposited for the dogs, for here Amundsen promised to give his animals a full feed before the final dash south in the spring. The men had collected about sixty tons of seal meat—a supply more than ample for the winter. Seal steak and cutlets were placed on the Framheim bill of fare regularly; men as well as dogs relished it. Thus, with such a large supply of fresh meat available, Amundsen had no fear of scurvy.

Framheim was a tiny hut, 26 feet long by 13 wide. It had only two rooms, one a dormitory and dining room, the other a kitchen. The house was securely anchored to the Barrier and was snug and comfortable in all respects. To offset the lack of space in the hut, Amundsen's men dug into the snowdrifts surrounding Framheim and made several large compartments, all linked together by tunnels. Here the work of preparing the sledges and gear for the spring campaign was carried on through the winter. Near the hut were the dog tents and a maternity hospital—a much needed affair if the newly born puppies were to be saved from the jaws of predacious males. The dogs ran loose in winter and some of them wandered away and were gone for days. Most of the wanderers returned; a few only were lost in crevasses.

There were not many idle hours at Framheim during the winter. Although the autumn journeys had proved that the equipment was suitable, Amundsen found room for improvement. Sledges were rebuilt and considerably lightened without sacrificing strength; clothing and tents were overhauled; and for once Amundsen was provided with roomy boots fitted with inner wooden soles. He could wear as many pairs of socks as he pleased and did not intend to suffer the misery of frozen feet. He had discovered that the Barrier was cold, for a temperature as low as minus 74 degrees had been registered.

On September 8 Amundsen started for the Pole with seven men and ninety dogs—a caravan on runners. The dogs were "on the verge of exploding." They fought and were beaten by the drivers, and they fought again. It was a wild start and a false start. The caravan got to the first depot and was driven back to Framheim by the cold. The dogs could not stand it, the men were frost bitten. Amundsen decided to wait for milder weather. He also determined to split his party. One would go to the Pole, the other would attempt to reach King Edward VII Land.

The polar party started again on October 19 in good weather. Amundsen had with him four men—Hanssen, Wisting, Hassel and Bjaaland—and four sledges each pulled by thirteen dogs, the strongest and most capable animals in the pack. Four marches took them to the first depot, ninety-nine miles south of Framheim—fast traveling. It had been a dangerous journey. In fact, through some miscalculation during a blizzard, the men got themselves into a veritable ice trap and nearly lost a sledge in a deep crevasse. At the depot the dogs were allowed to gorge themselves on seal meat, while the sledges were repacked.

There is no doubt that Amundsen introduced a new technique in Antarctic exploration. He was fortunate in having a single objective, the Pole, with no side issues to complicate his program. To make certain of success he provided himself with a surplus both of dog-power and food. Within reason he could afford to lose dogs and, unlike Shackleton and Scott, he had no reason to fear a food shortage in the event of undue delay on the journey. In addition to the food carried on the sledges there were three tons of stores in the three depots—pemmican for dogs and pemmican for men, also biscuits, chocolate, milk powder and oil for the primus stoves.

When the course was laid for the second depot each loaded sledge weighed nearly 900 pounds. There was more than sufficient food to carry the party to the Pole and back to the depot at 80 degrees. Some of this food was to be cached along the trail; moreover, Amundsen intended to kill the larger number of his dogs when the Polar Plateau was reached, retaining enough to bring him home. The dead animals would be fed to the living, and the men would have their share of meat.

The dogs pulled the heavy sledges with ease, so easily in fact that Amundsen and the drivers were towed on skis. The chief did not have to use his own legs at all, and was actually out of condition when the mountains were reached. Soon after leaving the first depot the work of building snow beacons was begun. Each beacon contained a slip of paper giving the distance and direction of the preceding one. Thus the course for the return journey was accurately marked. The depot at 81 degrees and the next one at 82 degrees were reached without mishap. Each had been marked with a ring of flags, which were flying as bravely as the day they had been set up months before.

Leaving the depot at 82 degrees south, Amundsen said the journey had now begun "in earnest." Between the dog caravan and the Pole lay tall and rugged mountain chains—at least that was the supposition, based on Shackleton's observations of the direction of the high land surrounding the Polar Plateau. The dogs ran along a smooth surface and on November 8 the land was showing distinctly in the distance. It was the mountainous mass which Shackleton had observed extending southeastward from the Beardmore Glacier. In two days the land was definitely outlined. Amundsen had never seen "a wilder or more beautiful landscape." The peaks took many forms. Some rose to heights of 15,000 feet, glistening white in the sunlight; others had bare cliff faces. Amundsen found names for many of the peaks, among them Mount Fridtjof Nansen, "crowned by a mighty hood of ice," and Mount Don Pedro Chris-

*Warren Chappell*

*The peaks took many forms.*

tophersen, a bulky monarch. He gave the name Queen Maud Range to this massive land, honoring the queen of his native country.

Somewhere between the mountains he would have to find a route to the Polar Plateau. As he drew nearer to the land the flat Barrier surface changed to long undulations, like giant waves. Up went the dogs, then down into a valley, then up again. The Barrier ended at 85 degrees south. Amundsen had been towed 340 miles on skis. There supplies for thirty days were put into a depot, together with a record of the proposed route through the mountains. If Amundsen did not return a relief party would at least know where he had begun his climb. He had forty-two dogs left; some had deserted, the weaklings had been killed. There were no longer any female dogs in the pack. Amundsen was rather glad of that, for they had been a source of dissension. The distance from the 85-degree depot to the Pole and back to this point was 683 miles. With food for two months on the sledges, Amundsen felt serene, although the critical phase of the journey lay ahead.

The climb began on November 17 after a reconnaissance of the terrain. Old glacier courses took them to a height of 2,000 feet, where they camped, two parties going out to explore ahead. They found that after another steep ascent they must descend, which was rather disconcerting. Up and down and up again went men and dogs. It was hard pulling going up; going down brakes were put on the sledges to ease the pace. A height of 4,500 feet was reached and from a snow plateau the men saw a new highway, the Axel Heiberg Glacier—an imposing ice stream fed by tributary glaciers which came through the mountains from all sides. Axel Heiberg, built in terraces, was reached with difficulty, and when reached it proved to be anything but a smooth highway. Indeed, it presented a region of chaos which seemed to block the way completely.

These Norwegians were hardy, determined men, not the kind to be beaten by yawning crevasses, deep chasms and valleys filled with gigantic blocks of ice. Bred in a land of ice and snow, they were bold alpinists, and first-rate ski runners, with an inborn knowledge of how to surmount obstacles in such a country as Antarctica. Amundsen sought a way out of the inferno of ice and he found it, despite the fact that avalanches were thundering down the surrounding slopes. At night the explorers listened to the crash of ice and snow, as the mountains freed themselves of their load.

Then they climbed and descended and finally reached a height of 10,920 feet, beginning now to feel the effects of the high altitude. So far the weather had favored them; on some days the sun was so hot that they shed their polar garments. This new camp was the Butcher's Camp, so named because here twenty-four dogs were killed. "It was hard—but it had to be so," wrote Amundsen. "We had agreed to shrink from nothing in order to reach our goal." The surviving dogs feasted until they could eat no longer; the men had dog cutlets. There would be meat for all when they returned to this camp among the clouds a few weeks later.

The Butcher's Camp was a blizzard area. The party had arrived there on November 21 and was not able to leave until November 25. Even then they marched in the face of a violent storm. One sledge was left behind; the remaining dogs were harnessed to three sledges, six to a team. Amundsen had thought he was on the Plateau, or very close to it. He was mistaken. The course he followed took the explorers downhill. On the following day they were at a height of 9,475 feet, going blind in a blizzard. Here they were in a treacherous, unknown country and unable to see. Still they went ahead and reached the Devil's Glacier. Once or twice they caught a fleeting glimpse of the land. Mount Helmer Hanssen stood alone. Mounts Oscar Wisting, Sverre Hassel and Olav Bjaaland were grouped. Mount Thorvald Nilsen "took our breath away, so formidable did it appear."

The Devil's Glacier was appropriately named by Amundsen. He said it resembled a battleground, the ammunition being great blocks of ice piled up in the utmost confusion. Amundsen was thankful that he had not been here while the battle was raging. He thought it must have been "a spectacle like doomsday." There were many times when the men roped themselves together while going through the mountains—this was one of them. They got away from the Devil's Glacier and came to Hell's Gate, a narrow path between tall pressure ridges. From this point a smoother route could be seen.

The instruments showed the altitude to be 8,450 feet, much lower than the Butcher's Camp. "It was, in fact, an extraordinary journey we were undertaking," said Amundsen. Only the surface was visible; the landmarks had been blotted out by fog. He expected to rely on his beacons to guide him on the homeward trek.

At last the sun broke through and unveiled the land. Some of the mountains had sharp peaks, others were rounded; glaciers poured down the slopes of all. The ice sheet of Mount Helmer Hanssen bristled "like the quills of a porcupine." The coloring was superb. Amundsen called it a "fairy landscape."

More crevassed areas, if not worse than the others, at least as hazardous. A large number of formations like haycocks were seen; each covered a bottomless hole in the ice. It was hard going, every foot of it, and there was a renewal of blizzard weather. Ascents, descents, detours—they were all in the day's work. Out of the rough they toiled and into the Devil's Ballroom, a unique part of the glacier. It was a thin, glasslike ice floor through which men, dogs and sledges broke again and again. Here they said good-bye to the glacier without regret, for they were on the Plateau. The date was December 4, the height 10,100 feet. They drove on over high waves of sastrugi, and through thick weather, with snow. The dogs were going strong, but their appetites were voracious. They would eat anything from sledge lashings to whips and boots.

The Plateau was monotonous and the light bad. It was difficult to take observations. Shackleton's "farthest south," at 88 degrees 23 minutes was passed on December 7. Amundsen was deeply moved to see the Norwegian flag snapping in the cold breeze, but he did not forget Shackleton, whom he admired as a man and as a determined explorer. Going on a short distance, they made their last depot, lightening their sledges for the final stretch. The Pole was less than 100 miles away; they were almost certain of their goal.

A splendid surface awaited the Norwegians when they started from the last depot. The weather could hardly have been better. Two marches of twenty-eight miles were put behind them; three shorter marches took them to the Pole—on December 14, 1911, a glorious day for the Norwegians, but a wearisome one for Scott, who was climbing the lower reaches of the Beardmore Glacier, a beaten man unconscious of his defeat. Amundsen in "The South Pole" describes the last eventful hours of the march:

"On the morning of December 14 the weather was of the finest, just as if it had been made for arriving at the Pole. I am not quite sure, but I believe we despatched our breakfast rather more quickly than usual and were out of the tent sooner, though I must admit that we always accomplished this with all reasonable haste. We went in the usual order—the forerunner, Hanssen, Wisting, Bjaaland, and the reserve forerunner. By noon we had reached 89 degrees 53 minutes by dead reckoning, and made ready to take the rest in one stage. At 10 A.M. a light breeze had sprung up from the southeast, and it had clouded over, so that we got no noon altitude; but the clouds were not thick, and from time to time we had a glimpse of the sun through them. The going on that day was rather different from what it had been; sometimes the skis went over it well, but at others it was pretty bad.

"We advanced that day in the same mechanical way as before; not much was said, but eyes were used all the more. Hanssen's neck grew twice as long as before in his endeavor to see a few inches farther. I had asked him before we started to spy out ahead for all he was worth, and he did so with a vengeance. But, however keenly he stared, he could not descry anything but the endless flat plain ahead of us. . . .

"At three in the afternoon a simultaneous 'halt' rang from the drivers. They had carefully examined their sledge meters, and they all showed the full distance— our Pole by reckoning. The goal was reached, the journey ended. I cannot say—though I know it would sound much more effective—that the object of my life was attained. That would be romancing rather too barefacedly. I had better be honest and admit straight out that I have never known any man to be placed in such a diametrically opposite position to the goal of his desires as I was at that moment. The regions around the North Pole—well, yes, the North Pole itself—had attracted me from childhood, and here I was at the South Pole. Can anything more topsy-turvy be imagined?

"We reckoned now that we were at the Pole. Of course, every one of us knew that we were not standing on the absolute spot; it would be an impossibility with the time and instruments at our disposal to ascertain that exact spot. But we were so near it that the few miles which possibly separated us from it could not be of the slightest importance. It was our intention to make a circle around this camp, with a radius of twelve and a half miles (20 kilometers), and to be satisfied with that. After we had halted we collected and congratulated each other. We had good grounds for mutual respect in what had been achieved, and I think that was just the feeling that was expressed in the firm and powerful grasps of the fist that were exchanged. After this we proceeded to the greatest and most solemn act of the whole journey—the planting of our flag.

"Pride and affection shone in five pairs of eyes that gazed upon the flag as it unfurled itself with a sharp crack and waved over the Pole. I had determined that the act of planting it—the historic event—should be equally divided among us all. It was not for one man to do this; it was for all who had staked their lives in the struggle, and held together through thick and thin. This was the only way in which I could show my gratitude to my comrades in this desolate spot. I could see that they understood and accepted it in the spirit in which it was offered. Five weather-beaten, frostbitten fists they were that grasped the pole, raised the waving flag in the air, and planted it as the first at the geographical South Pole. 'Thus we plant thee, beloved flag, at the South Pole, and give to the plain on which it lies the name of King Haakon VII's Plateau.' That moment will certainly be remembered by all of us who stood there."

Polar explorers are never presentable after a hard journey. The faces of the Norwegians were covered with sores, the result of frost bite, cutting winds and hot sun. But their feet were good, they had suffered little from snow blindness, and altogether they were fit and well-fed. The weather was fair; there was no reason to hurry observations.

The encirclement of the camp was undertaken by Wisting, Hassel and Bjaaland—a rather hazardous task, for they went out in

*Warren Chappell*

*Planting of the Norwegian flag at the South Pole.*

different directions without compasses to guide them over the plain. One of the flags they planted was found later by Scott. It told him that the race had been won by the Norwegians.

Amundsen fixed his position with characteristic thoroughness. A series of hourly observations covering twenty-four hours was taken.

It was, he said, strange to find the sun apparently always at the same altitude, no matter what the hour, but at the bottom of the world the sun could not behave otherwise. The readings told him that although they were not absolutely on the polar center, they were as near to it as possible. A few feet one way or the other made no difference. The altitude was 10,260 feet above sea level; at 88 degrees the instruments had registered 11,070 feet.

The final ceremony was to set up the spare tent and to record their names. Here they left spare instruments and gear, also letters from Amundsen to King Haakon and to Captain Scott. The Englishman found the tent intact on Jan. 18 and admired its workmanship.

Amundsen said good-bye to Polheim and 90 degrees south on December 17. He was homeward bound with two sledges and sixteen dogs. One dog had been killed at the Pole, another, worn out, had wandered away to die. The slaughtered dog was fed to his mates. They left nothing of him but his teeth and the brush of his tail—the custom of the pack. Sometimes even the teeth disappeared.

Night marches, each a trifle more than seventeen miles long, were the order on the Plateau. Amundsen did not want to overwork the dogs; moreover, the rarefied air made breathing an effort for the men. Inasmuch as the sun was almost as bright at night as in the daytime, and the weather good, each beacon showed up boldly on the white plain. Rations had been increased and all was going well, although the men were somewhat bored by the long hours of rest between marches. Christmas Day passed, and the next day they were on the 88th parallel, with land in sight. Going south the thick weather had veiled the mountains except on occasions, and even then their outlines were indistinct. But now the land appeared in all its majesty. It was a series of mountain ranges, far greater in extent than Amundsen had imagined. He thought the mountains must stretch across the continent. In the full light the appearance of the land was so changed that the old peaks seen on the outward journey could not be recognized. It was odd, but true.

Three days after Christmas the descent from the Plateau began and Amundsen was at last able to spot an old friend, Mount Helmer Hanssen, with its ice cap of many points. Then he knew he was on the right course leading to the Devil's Glacier. This time the Ballroom was avoided. The party missed a depot, found it again after some trouble, and began to descend rapidly. Luck was traveling with Amundsen and his men, for they passed over the worst surface of the glacier with ease.

At the Butcher's Camp on January 4 the dogs feasted again on the bodies of the animals killed there on the way up. The avalanches were still crashing from the mountains about this camp, a fearsome locality. Amundsen and his comrades did not linger. They flew down with the sledges to Heiberg Glacier, and hence to the Ross Barrier, which was reached on January 6. The party had been on the land fifty-one days. They left the 85-degree depot with eleven dogs, ample food, and more supplies in depots ahead of them, this being the last stage of the journey.

Amundsen had experienced enough Antarctic weather to appreciate its peculiarities and variability. The sun shines, fog descends, a blizzard bursts out of the heavens—all within the space of a few hours. On the Barrier the changes were rung frequently. Despite the weather, Amundsen traveled rapidly north. One day the dogs would do seventeen miles, the next day the distance would be doubled. The schedule was maintained rigidly.

Three occurrences caused Amundsen astonishment. At about the 84th parallel he saw two skua gulls—life amid desolation. What were they doing so far from the coast and their feeding ground, and where were they going? It was a mystery, except to the gulls. Possibly they had a route across the mountains to the other side of the continent. At any rate, they flew south. Amundsen had another surprise when he reached the 82-degree depot and found that it had been raided. Some of the dog deserters had gorged there, but the loss of food did not worry the men; they had sufficient. The third surprise was an appearance of land. When Amundsen reached the crevassed region near the 81st parallel he saw in the distance what seemed to be mountainous country southeast of his position, and he called it Carmen Land, though he hesitated to put it on his chart. Eighteen years afterwards, Dr. Gould disposed of Carmen Land, which proved to be large pressure ridges.

January 21 marked the arrival at the 80-degree depot—the last one. Amundsen found there a note from Prestrud saying that he had halted at this point while on his way to King Edward VII Land. January 25 was the date set for the arrival at Framheim. That day Amundsen stumbled into the hut; Scott, disheartened by the fact that he had been forestalled at the Pole, was then homeward bound on the Plateau.

The good old *Fram* was lying in the Bay of Whales waiting to take the Norwegians home, having kept her appointment faithfully. Amundsen's journey had been faultless. Everything had moved with precision, not a cog in the machine had slipped. He had been out ninety-nine days and had covered about 1,860 miles. Amundsen had found a new route through the mountains, attained the South Pole, and ascertained more fully the extent and character of the Ross Barrier. Moreover, he proved conclusively that dog transport was far more efficient than the old British method of man-hauling sledges.

In May, 1925, Amundsen, Ellsworth and four men started from Spitsbergen in two airplanes for the North Pole. After a flight of eight hours they came down into a water lead, being short of the fuel necessary to carry them to their goal and to return. They had drifted off the course, which accounted for fuel shortage. Before the planes could rise again the water lead closed, and they were imprisoned in the ice. Twenty-five days of gruelling work followed, and then one plane was released, taking the air with the six men in it. They had had a narrow shave, but when they returned to Spitsbergen all were convinced that polar exploration by aircraft was feasible.

The following year (1926) Amundsen and Ellsworth set out upon a much more important venture, sailing from Spitsbergen in the dirigible airship *Norge,* built in Italy from the design of Umberto Nobile. Colonel Nobile accompanied the expedition, also Oscar Wisting, who had been to the South Pole with Amundsen. The ship sailed on May 11, arrived at the North Pole, and then laid a course which took her over the unknown area of the Arctic regions, landing at the trading post of Teller. ninety-one miles northwest of

Nome, Alaska. The voyage of 3,393 miles had lasted seventy-two hours. When the *Norge* landed she was covered with an ice-film weighing a ton—sufficient evidence of the perilous nature of the journey.

After that Amundsen was satisfied. He had sailed through the Northwest Passage, visited the two poles, and flown over the north polar seas; there was little more for him to do. No longer a young man, he realized that the time had come for him to retire gracefully. A new weapon of exploration—the airplane—had come into use; the dog and sledge had become accessories. "Their place now," he said, "is in the museum and the history books." Younger men, using the new weapon, would blaze new trails through the hidden spaces. Amundsen was content to rest and grow old. He was then fifty-four.

The fates had other plans in store for him. The month is June, the year 1928. The scene is the frozen waste north of Spitsbergen. Nobile's airship *Italia,* carrying an Italian polar expedition, has been wrecked and burned on the ice floes. The radio is sending frantic calls for aid. There was no love lost between Nobile and Amundsen; they had quarreled and it seemed that their paths might never cross again. But the thought of men stranded on the ice quickened the heart of Amundsen; he had been in a similar plight only three years before. He answered the call—and it was his last adventure. He flew from Tromsö, Norway, in a French airplane, with Major René Gilbaud as pilot, and a crew of four men, hoping to reach Spitsbergen and help in the work of rescue. The plane never reached its destination, but months later a fragment of it was found in the sea.

So passed into the great unknown the conqueror of the South Pole. "The end, no doubt," wrote Ellsworth, "was as he himself would have wished it, for Amundsen often told me that he wanted to die in action. He could bear the thought of no other way. . . . His old life had been one long uphill struggle in the face of terrific odds—mental as well as physical. . . . Roald Amundsen had acquired a philosophy of life that had taught him to accept with equal equanimity whatever the day brought forth. I cannot see him other than the great leader he was—a man inspired by the highest ideals and responsive to all the finer and nobler things of life, beloved and admired by all those with whom he came in contact; his supreme effort, while it cannot be measured in terms of human lives, will go down through the ages as one of the finest examples of human sacrifice ever made. He gave of his best, and God grant that in doing so he may receive of the best."


## II


Amid the solitudes of the Ross Ice Barrier, many miles from land, is a lonely grave—perhaps the loneliest grave in all the world. Its marker is a snow cairn within which lie the bodies of three heroic men. A metal cylinder holds this record and tribute:

> "November 12, 1912. Lat. 79 degrees, 50 minutes south. This cross and cairn are erected over the bodies of Captain Scott, C.V.O., R.N., Dr. E. A. Wilson, M.B.B.C., Cantab., and Lieutenant H. R. Bowers, Royal Indian Marine—a slight token to perpetuate their successful and gallant attempt to reach the Pole. This they did on January 17, 1912, after the Norwegian expedition had already done so. Inclement weather with lack of fuel was the cause of their death. Also to commemorate their two gallant comrades, Captain L. E. G. Oates of the Inniskilling Dragoons, who walked to his death in a blizzard to save his comrades about eighteen miles south of this position; also of Seaman Edgar Evans, who died at the foot of the Beardmore Glacier.
>
> " 'The Lord gave and the Lord taketh away; blessed be the name of the Lord.' "

The date, November 12, is the day on which the tragedy of the Barrier was fully revealed. Scott's comrades at the base had realized months before that the polar party was lost; where, they could not tell, for the Antarctic night had prevented a search of the polar trail. When spring returned they traveled south on the Barrier until they came to a tent pitched eleven miles beyond One Ton Depot, where food for Scott had been cached. Within the tent were Scott,

Wilson and Bowers, lying in their sleeping bags, and among their possessions were thirty-five pounds of geological specimens gathered from the moraines of the Beardmore Glacier. These they had treasured even when death stalked them, a fine example of devotion to science. Scott's diaries, the letters he had written to relatives and friends, and his "message to the public," told the grim story of success, misfortune and self-sacrifice, and finally of death by starvation. The last entry in Scott's journal—"For God's sake look after our people"—was made on March 29, 1912. He may have died that day while the blizzard shook his frail tent.

The *Discovery* expedition left Scott with the desire to visit Antarctica again, but his naval duties intervened and it was not until the summer of 1909 that his plans for a new venture matured. His announcement brought private subscriptions and grants from the British Government and from the Governments of Australia, New Zealand and South Africa. The *Terra Nova,* one of the best of the old Scottish whalers, was purchased and equipped, the ship sailing in June, 1910, for South Africa, where Scott joined her for the voyage to New Zealand.

Shackleton had failed by a narrow margin to reach the Pole; that coveted goal was therefore one of Scott's objectives. He also hoped to explore King Edward VII Land, which he had discovered, and to pursue extensive scientific work. For this reason he gathered a strong staff of scientists. Some of his men had served with the *Discovery* expedition and with Shackleton. Wilson, Day, Priestley, Lashly and Edgar Evans were the veterans. It was, in fact, an unusual body of men, well equipped for the work in hand.

Scott intended to follow Shackleton's example and use pony transport, reinforced by dogs and motor sledges. He had nineteen ponies and thirty-three dogs aboard the *Terra Nova* when the ship sailed for the south from Port Chalmers, New Zealand, on November 29. The *Terra Nova* was deeply laden, her deck being piled high with bags of coal and packing boxes. After two days at sea she ran into a strong gale, which played havoc with the deck cargo, and made life miserable for ponies and dogs, to say nothing of the men who had to make fast the broken lashings. Then the pumps choked, and it was even necessary to bail the ship before the suction pipes were cleared. Two ponies and one dog were lost in the gale—not a happy beginning for the voyage.

At the end of winter Scott made a short journey to the Ferrar Glacier, one of many that flow through the western mountains to the sound. His purpose was to get into training for the southern journey. He examined the coast line for some distance and at Cape Bernacchi discovered copper ore. It was in this sector that Professor Edgeworth David, one of Shackleton's scientists, found many minerals. By the end of September Scott was back at Cape Evans, ready to organize the polar party.

The southern journey began on November 1. "We are going away with high hopes of success," wrote Scott; "I am lucky in having with me the right men for the work." Although Scott could not know it, Amundsen had started from the Bay of Whales on October 19 and was even then well on his way across the Barrier. The Scott plan of action was somewhat different from that which Shackleton had been obliged to follow. Scott had ten ponies available, two dog teams and two motor sledges. He intended to make full use of his supporting parties. They were to build depots along the trail with food and fuel sufficient for their own needs and for the needs of the polar party on its return. Some of the men in support were to go up the Beardmore Glacier to the summit of the Polar Plateau. The first setback occurred when the cylinders of both motor sledges cracked under the cold, after traveling only a few miles on the Barrier. Their loads were then man-hauled.

The weather Scott met on the Polar Plateau was on the whole favorable, but the surface proved to be an increasingly difficult problem. There were belts of snow that was almost like fine loose sand, and areas of sastrugi, covered with ice crystals. The difficulties of pulling were multiplied by the effects of the high altitude. "It takes it out of us like anything," wrote Scott. "None of us ever had such hard work before."

They traveled on skis, then on foot in finnesko, alternating as the surface changed.

On January 10 they made another depot, called One-and-a-Half

Degree Depot and pushed on with a lighter load. The going was no better, but five days later Scott believed that he would reach his goal. He wondered whether Amundsen had already won through; the next day would tell the story. It did. The race was lost.

Bowers was the first man to detect what seemed to be a cairn on the frozen plain, then a black object came into view—a flag. Next, the remains of a camp were found, and about it sledge and ski tracks and the impressions of dogs' paws. There was no longer doubt; the prize was Amundsen's.

That day Scott made this entry in his log: "It is a terrible disappointment and I am very sorry for my loyal companions. Many thoughts come and much discussion have we had." He believed the Norwegians had found "an easy way up." Weary in body and spirit, the men marched to the Pole, following the tracks of the Norwegians for some distance. At the end of fourteen miles, their observations indicated that they were one mile beyond the Pole and three miles to the right of it. Scott's record for January 17 said: "The Pole. Yes, but under very different circumstances from those expected."

That day Amundsen was driving his dogs among pressure ridges on the Barrier, nearly at the end of his journey. His distance to Framheim was eight days' march.

January 18 was the Englishman's last day at the bottom of the world. They visited the tent left by the Norwegian party and read the record signed by Roald Amundsen, Olay Olavson Bjaaland, Hilmer Hanssen, Sverre H. Hassel, Oscar Wisting. The date was December 16, 1911. The Norwegians had left behind odds and ends of clothing, navigating instruments and hypsometers. There was also a note from Amundsen asking Scott to forward a letter to King Haakon of Norway. Scott left a letter to say he had visited the tent with his companions.

Additional sights gave the position as one-half to three-quarters of a mile from the Pole. They did not linger, for the temperature was minus 21 degrees.

Scott gives this account of the last hours:

"We built a cairn, put up our poor slighted Union Jack, and photographed ourselves—mighty cold work all of it. Less than one-half a mile south we saw stuck up an old underrunner of a sledge. This we commandeered as a yard for a floor cloth sail. I imagine it was intended to mark the exact spot at the Pole as near as the Norwegians could fix it. (Height, 9,500.) A note attached talked of the tent as being two miles from the Pole. Wilson keeps the note. There is no doubt that our predecessors have made thoroughly sure of their mark and fully carried out their program. I think the Pole is about 9,500 feet in height; this is remarkable considering that in latitude 86 degrees we were about 10,500.

"We carried the Union Jack about three quarters of a mile north with us and left it on a piece of stick as near as we could fix it. I fancy the Norwegians arrived at the Pole on the 15th December and left on the 17th, ahead of a date quoted by me in London as ideal, viz., December 22. . . . Well, we have turned our back on the goal of our ambition and must face our 800 miles of solid dragging—and good-bye to most of the day dreams!"

Facing north again, Scott knew that a desperate struggle would ensue. Could he lead his party home? He would be thankful when they had crossed the cold and desolate Plateau, with its blanket of snow—the snow of ages, carried to and fro by punishing blizzards. Indications of what lay ahead were apparent before many marches had been logged. Oates, the "soldier" as his comrades called him, was feeling the cold; Evans, with fingers and nose frostbitten, his face covered with sores, was out of sorts and an anxiety; Wilson had strained a tendon; footgear, cut by ice, was wearing out. They plodded forward on skis, all except Bowers, who had left his pair at a depot farther north. Not only were the winds harassing, but they piled the drift over their old tracks—an erratic course now hard to follow. Follow it they must, else they could not pick up their guiding mounds, built on the way south, and their food depots. Again and again, as they approached the head of the glacier, the party got into disturbed ice conditions—immense waves of pressure that were difficult to navigate. Scott was injured by a fall and later both Scott and Evans went into a crevasse. Evans had had an ugly fall on a previous day and was becoming "rather dull and incapable."

It is unnecessary to give more than a brief outline of the journey down the glacier. The log makes references to fog, deep snow pockets, crevasses, fearful traps of broken ice which blocked the trail. Evans was "nearly broken down in brain"; Bowers and Wilson were snowblind; rations and sleep reduced. It was at the foot of the Beardmore, near Lower Glacier Depot, that the end came to Evans. He had fallen behind on the march, and the party had waited for him. Then he dropped out again and was a long distance behind when camp was pitched for lunch. This time he failed to come in, and his companions went back to fetch him. They found Evans down in the snow, incoherent and utterly helpless. That day, February 17, he died in the tent. Wilson thought that the seaman had suffered an injury to his brain in one of his falls on the ice.

The month of March opened—would they get home before it ended? Scott said that his companions were unendingly cheerful, "but what each man feels in his heart I can only guess." The task of making camp at night—unpacking the sledge, erecting the tent, cooking—had become a burden, and each day it took longer to put on frozen foot gear and get under way. Food was in hand, but there was the nightmare of fuel shortage. If the oil gave out completely, there would be no hot meals and thirst would soon follow. By March 4 Oates was in a sorry plight. Wilson was doctoring the soldier's feet, though Scott admitted that little could be done to help him. "We cannot help each other; each has enough to do to take care of himself." Under ordinary conditions the heavy work had kept them warm, but no longer did they possess the vitality of strong men. They were cold on the march and cold in the tent, and Oates had become "a terrible hindrance, though he does his utmost and suffers much, I fear."

Mount Hooper lay ahead. It was not far away on March 7, the day that Amundsen arrived at Hobart, Tasmania, to announce his discovery of the South Pole. The contrast is strikingly tragic. Amundsen, his journey ended, receiving the acclamation of the world; Scott, worried to the point of desperation, trudging over the snow wastes with three companions, one of them close to death. The world knew nothing of the grim drama which was approaching its climax on the Barrier; its interest for the moment was absorbed by the new hero who had come out of the south.

At Mount Hooper Depot Scott hoped to find that dog teams from the base had reinforced his supplies, but when he got to this depot on March 9 he had to record: "Cold comfort. Shortage on our allowance all around. I don't know that anyone is to blame. The dogs, which would have been our salvation, have evidently failed."

The succeeding days were stern and bitter. The men were going "steadily downhill." Oates had no chance. On March 11 Scott wrote that Oates had practically asked for advice, after discussing the situation. He was urged to march. "One satisfactory result to the discussion: I practically ordered Wilson to hand over the means of ending our troubles to us, so that any of us may know how to do so. Wilson had no choice between doing so and our ransacking the medicine case."

They went on, making some distance with great effort. Every man was "deadly cold" after camp was pitched. Another entry:

> "Friday, March 16 or Saturday, 17. Lost track of dates but think the last correct. Tragedy all along the line. At lunch the day before yesterday poor Titus Oates said he couldn't go on; he proposed we should leave him in his sleeping bag. This we could not do, and we induced him to come on, on the afternoon march. In spite of its awful nature for him he struggled on and we made a few miles. At night he was worse and we knew the end had come.
>
> "Should this be found I want these facts recorded. Oates's last thoughts were of his mother, but immedi-

ately before he took pride in thinking that his regiment would be pleased with the bold way in which he met his death. We can testify to his bravery. He has borne intense suffering for weeks without complaint, and to the very last was able and willing to discuss outside subjects. He did not—would not—give up hope till the very end. He was a brave soul. This was the end. He slept through the night before last, hoping not to wake; but he woke in the morning—yesterday. It was blowing a blizzard. He said, 'I am just going outside and may be some time.' He went out into the blizzard and we have not seen him since.

"I take this opportunity to say that we have stuck to our sick companions to the last. In case of Edgar Evans, when absolutely out of food and he lay insensible, the safety of the remainder seemed to demand his abandonment, but Providence mercifully removed him at this critical moment. He died a natural death and we did not leave him till two hours after his death.

"We knew that poor Oates was walking to his death, but though we tried to dissuade him, we knew it was the act of a brave man and an English gentleman. We all hope to meet the end with a similar spirit, and assuredly the end is not far.

"I can only write at lunch and then only occasionally. The cold is intense, minus 40 degrees at midday. My companions are unendingly cheerful, but we are all on the verge of serious frostbites, and though we constantly talk of fetching through, I don't think any one of us believes it in his heart.

"We are cold on the march now, and at all times except meals. Yesterday we had to lay up for a blizzard and today we move dreadfully slowly. We are at No. 14 pony camp, only two pony marches from One Ton Depot. We leave here our theodolite, a camera, and Oates's sleeping bags. Diaries, etc., and geological specimens carried at Wilson's special request, will be found with us or on our sledge."

They were within twenty-one miles of One Ton Depot on March 18, and were halted by wind. Scott's log for that date reads:

"My right foot has gone, nearly all the toes—two days ago I was the proud possessor of best feet. These are the steps of my downfall. Like an ass I mixed a spoonful of curry powder with my melted pemmican—it gave me violent indigestion. I lay awake and in pain all night; woke and felt done on the march; foot went and I didn't know it. A small measure of neglect and have a foot which is not pleasant to contemplate.

"Bowers takes first place in condition, but there is not much to choose after all. The others are still confident of getting through—or pretend to be—I don't know. We have the last half fill of oil in our primus and a very small quantity of spirit—this alone between us and thirst."

When camp was made on the afternoon of March 19—the last camp—One Ton Depot was eleven miles away. They had started in the morning with food for two days and barely a day's fuel. All three were severely frostbitten. "There is no chance to nurse one's feet till we get hot food into us. Amputation is the least I can hope for now, but will the trouble spread?" Scott said that the weather did not give them a chance. The temperature was forty degrees below zero. A raging blizzard swept down upon them. On the 21st Wilson and Bowers were going to the depot for fuel, but they did not go. They could not face the blinding drift. In his journal for the 22nd and 23rd, Scott set forth their plight:

"Blizzard bad as ever—Wilson and Bowers unable to start—tomorrow last chance—no fuel and only one or two of food left—must be near the end. Have decided it shall be natural—we shall march for the depot with or without our effects and die in our tracks."

The last desperate march which Scott thought they might make was never attempted. On March 29 he finished his journal, a remarkable record of a remarkable journey. Despite cold, hunger and anxiety, he had filled out his log with fidelity, missing but a few dates. The last few words were written in a steady hand:

> "March 29—Since the 21st we have had a continuous gale from W.S.W. and S.W. We had fuel to make two cups of tea apiece, and bare food for two days on the 20th. Every day we have been ready to start for our depot eleven miles away, but outside the door of the tent it remains a scene of whirling drift. I do not think we can hope for any better things now. We shall stick it out to the end, of course, and the end cannot be far.
> "It seems a pity, but I do not think I can write more.
> > "R. SCOTT.
> "Last entry.
> "For God's sake look after our people."

In his "message to the public" Scott set forth the chain of circumstances which led up to the final tragedy:

> "The causes of the disaster are not due to faulty organization, but to misfortunes in all risks which had to be undertaken.
> "1. The loss of pony transport in March, 1911, obliged me to start later than I had intended, and obliged the limits of stuff transported to be narrowed.
> "2. The weather throughout the outward journey, and especially the long gale in 83 degrees S. stopped us.
> "3. The soft snow in lower reaches of glacier again reduced pace.
> "We fought these untoward events with a will and conquered, but it cut into our provision reserve.
> "Every detail of our food supplies, clothing and depots made on the interior ice sheet and over that long stretch of 700 miles to the Pole and back, worked out

to perfection. The advance party would have returned to the glacier in fine form and with surplus of food but for the astonishing failure of the man whom we had least expected to fail. Edgar Evans was thought the strongest man of the party.

"The Beardmore Glacier is not difficult in fine weather, but on our return we did not get a single completely fine day; this with a sick companion enormously increased our anxieties.

"As I have said elsewhere we got into frightfully rough ice and Edgar Evans received a concussion of the brain—he died a natural death, but left us a shaken party with the season unduly advanced.

"But all the facts above enumerated were as nothing to the surprise which awaited us on the Barrier. I maintain that our arrangements for returning were quite adequate, and that no one in the world would have expected the temperatures and surfaces which we encountered at this time of year. On the summit in lat. 85 degrees, 86 degrees we had—20 degrees—30 degrees. On the Barrier in lat. 82 degrees, 10,000 feet lower, we had —30 degrees in the day—47 degrees at night pretty regularly, with continuous head wind during our day marches. It is clear that these circumstances came on very suddenly, and our wreck is certainly due to this sudden advent of severe weather, which does not seem to have any satisfactory cause. I do not think human beings ever came through such a month as we have come through, and we should have got through in spite of the weather but for the sickening of a second companion, Captain Oates, and a shortage of fuel in our depots for which I cannot account, and finally, but for the storm which has fallen on us within 11 miles of the depot at which we hoped to secure our final supplies. Surely misfortune could scarcely exceed this last blow. We arrived within 11 miles of our old One Ton Camp with fuel for one last meal and food for two days. For four days we have been unable to leave the tent—the gale howling about us. We are weak, writing is difficult, but for my own sake I do not regret this journey, which has shown that Englishmen can endure hardships, help one another and meet death with as great a fortitude as ever in the past. We took risks, we knew we took them; things have come out against us, and therefore we have no cause for complaint, but bow to the will of Providence, determined still to do our best to the last. But if we have been willing to give our lives to this enterprise, which is for the honor of our country, I appeal to our countrymen to see that those who depend on us are properly cared for.

"Had we lived, I should have had a tale to tell of the hardihood, endurance and courage of my companions which would have stirred the heart of every Englishman. These rough notes and our dead bodies must tell the tale, but surely, a great rich country like ours will see that those who are dependent on us are properly provided for.

"R. Scott."

# THE LONE VOYAGERS

## By JAMES B. CONNOLLY

*Illustration by Henry O'Connor*

GLOUCESTER is a far-famed port. It is also a cosmopolitan port. Men of many racial strains have long been coming there. They came in the beginning to have a look at a place they had been hearing so much about. Having had a look they quite often settled down there, and usually became good citizens: an adventurous and virile lot, take them full and by, as men should be who go in for the fishing out of Gloucester.

It was the Centennial Year, the one hundredth anniversary of the Declaration of Independence, and Gloucester, always a militantly patriotic port, was preparing for what was to be her greatest of all Fourth of July celebrations.

Alfred Johnson, not such a great while in this country, and just then fresh in from a Grand Banks halibut trip, got a whiff of the overpowering contagion of the year and decided right there that he would do a little celebrating on his own account, show them that he was as good an American as anybody.

The best thing he could think of to do was to get a banker's dory, name her the *Centennial,* and sail her across the Atlantic alone.

A banker's dory is between fifteen and sixteen feet over all, with a flat bottom and flaring sides. They are made flat-bottomed so that they may be nested one inside the other and compactly stowed on the vessel's deck; otherwise there wouldn't be room to stow so many of them properly inboard and lash them securely against a hard passage.

Most shore people, and many seafaring people, would never pick a flat-bottomed small craft for safety at sea; but Gloucestermen will tell you that there is no small boat like it in heavy weather—when she is handled right. She has to be handled right, of course. They

can spin you scores of tales of the men of the fleet who have lived
through great gales in a dory.

Johnson got himself a regular dory, just such a dory as he had
hauled hundreds of skates of halibut gear into on the Banks. Ocean
liner passengers may see just such dories while crossing the Grand
Banks; that is, if their ship happens to lie close aboard. Passengers
would be very apt to overlook them at any distance, because they
are tiny craft, sitting low in the water. Johnson's dory was sixteen
foot over all, and the gunnel of it sat about two feet above the water
when empty.

He decked over the forward half of her for dry stowage for his
stores, which were largely canned goods, with a proper allowance
of sugar, tea, and hard bread; also a small cask of fresh water. With
himself and his stores aboard, the gunnel of Johnson's *Centennial*
was twelve inches, possibly fourteen inches, above the water.

He chose a fine day to sail; and the older Gloucester folk still
speak of how they stood on the cap-logs to see that lone figure
sailing out past old Cape Ann Light in his little dory. Every soul
there that day wished him fair wind, even as many a soul there,
Gloucester folk though they were with all of Gloucester's faith in
dories, said to his neighbor, "We've probably seen the last of him,
poor man."

Johnson believed he was in for a dangerous trip, not a fatal trip.
He was young, of course, just the age when a man thinks nothing
is going to happen to him. It's somebody else that will have things
happen to him. His chief problem, as he judged it, would be to
keep his dory from capsizing in heavy weather, which was no more
than what he had to do many a time while hauling trawls on the
fishing banks.

He set sail.

It was slow going and a long road.

A dory isn't a bad little sailer with a fair wind, but let the wind
be anywhere forward of the beam and off to loo'ard she slides on
her flat bottom like a sled on ice. A keel would have helped her
wonderfully against the wind, but with a keel in her she wouldn't
have been a dory.

After ninety-six days Johnson made England. An introspective person could have written eight hundred pages easily of that dory trip across, but no introspective person would ever have made such a trip. A man of meager courage would never have got over the wonder of his marvelous escapes, but Johnson would never admit a single marvelous escape; nor even a moderately close call. He admitted that he did come near to being washed out of the dory and overboard once; but after that, whenever it looked bad, he rigged a life line from his waist to the butt of the mast, and there was no more of that.

Henry O'Connor

*A dory isn't a bad sailer with a fair wind.*

He may have denied all danger because of the fear, which so many fishermen hold, that somebody might be trying to make a hero of him. It is against all bank fleet traditions to be a hero. You can be a high line skipper, a sail carrier till all is blue, a smart hand aboard a vessel, a dory mate to depend on till the last sea rolls high and low—but a hero? No hero.

Johnson says that all he did all the way across was to sit in the stern and steer her, just let her go along the road. Oh, yes, of course, once in a while he paid out or hauled a sheet, or shortened sail or gave her a bit more sail. Three times a day he stopped, without stopping the boat's way, to eat, except of course now and then when it was too lumpy to do anything except keep yourself from being hove overboard. He stayed awake daytimes, and nighttimes he slept—heaving the dory to, when it was all right to do so. He could sleep pretty good in the stern of the dory—a little cramped up, but all right—except of course when it was rough.

Was there much rough weather? N-n-not so much as you'd maybe think. Two or three good breezes of wind that would've been nothing to mind in a big vessel, though—yes—in a dory, of course, it was pretty lively at some times. With a high sea running there was nothing of course to do then but put her head to it and let her ride 'em.

One day when things looked bad he rigged a drogue (floating sea anchor) and paid it out over her bow with all the spare line he had. She rode 'em like a gull then—a brown gull, man, atop of the heaving waters. Why wouldn't she—so tight and light she was?

One day a German steamer ran down and spoke him. She had come out of her way to rescue him. (Steamers were always sailing out of their way to rescue him.) When he refused to be rescued this day they asked if there was anything they could do for him. Johnson yelled up at them to ask if they had anything to drink. He was no rum hound, but a nip of good liquor after you have been soaking for a day or two in sea water does help to dry a man out. Also it would help to kill the germs which people ashore had warned him might be getting into his drinking water after being kept for a long time in a small cask out at sea, and he was at this time more than a month at sea. The steamer people lashed a bottle of whiskey to a plank and hove it down at him.

"And would you believe it of me, me thinking I knew how to behave in a dory?"—this is Johnson's comment and excuse later—"I all but capsized her reaching over the gunnel for the bottle. I must've been a bit stiff from living so long in the stern of the dory. No chance to supple up a man's legs in a dory. No."

No man had ever crossed the Atlantic in anything like so small a craft before, alone or in company. No man has since crossed in a dory, alone or in company. After his return to Gloucester, Johnson had offers to go traveling around the country as a wonder man, a great hero. He did allow his dory to be exhibited at the Centennial

Exposition in Philadelphia, which of course she should have been—a wonder of a dory.

Johnson went back to his fishing, rose to be master of a vessel, made a name as a halibut killer, and was able to retire before that age when bank fishing becomes a hard task for even a tough-fibred Gloucesterman.

Johnson is now in his eightieth year; and a solid block of a man he still is, with deepset eyes under eyebrows that curl like young mustachios when he is in deep thought. He is still a citizen of Gloucester and comes regularly of fine afternoons to the Master Mariners' quarters.

Some readers may be interested to know what the super-sailorman, Johnson, does for excitement after his rough-water life. He plays cards, almost any game of cards; but his passion is for auction bridge, and Lord help the partner who makes a foolish original bid on him! The first time I ever sat in to a game with Johnson I was dealt eight spades to a king, jack, ten. Instantly and blithely I bid three spades. Johnson, my partner, went three no trump. I went four spades, Johnson four no trump. The bidding stopped, and the enemy took us for a cruise. It was a wreck. The ace and queen of spades lay to my left. My king and jack were blown out of water, the other six sank quietly one after the other to their moorings. What a blasting Johnson gave me then!

"You make an original bid without the tops? You bid three spades and the ace and queen layin' up to wind'ard of you? An original bid without the tops! Such a damn fool chance to take! I bet you'd expect to climb up on the bottom of a capsized dory and not get your feet wet?"

Centennial Johnson was not to remain Gloucester's lone voyager across the Atlantic.

I have written of the man who went astray in a dory and had his dory mate freeze to death on him. With all his fingers and toes and half of one foot gone, Howard Blackburn was tending patiently to his little business in Gloucester.

All kinds of people were coming and going in his place; hearty seafaring people, mostly, with great talk of outdoor things. One day there came into his place a group of men who talked of going gold-hunting in the Klondike. They wound up by buying an old fishing schooner, fitting her out, and sailing for San Francisco. Howard thought he had done with the sea, but he found himself one of the ship's company when she sailed.

They met with no great adventures on the voyage around South America. There was much wind and high seas at times, but nothing truly stirring. They arrived safely in San Francisco, where those of the company who were still for it went on to Alaska. Blackburn was for Alaska, but before he could be on his way he had his knee smashed in an accident. He came back to Gloucester and there for eight months he hobbled around on crutches. People who did not know him said, "Surely he'll stay home now."

He stayed home long enough to get rid of the crutches. Then his mind took to wandering again; and when a born adventurer's mind takes to wandering his body is soon likely to be on the way. With a few dollars he had saved he built himself a thirty-foot sloop, being not certain just where he was going to sail her to, but feeling sure that he was going to sail her somewhere. She was a great little vessel to look at, with a bunk in her. He named her the *Great Western*.

Somebody told him that to sail the little boat from Gloucester in New England to Gloucester in Old England would be a good stunt. The man who sold him the idea thought that of course two or three men would be taken along to help out; such a thing as a man going it alone was beyond his thought: a man without fingers and toes going it alone was beyond his conception.

But Blackburn was not strong for taking anybody along. There had been dissension among the company with whom he had sailed to San Francisco and he wanted no more of that—men arguing through whole watches about nothing at all. He put a man in charge of his place of business and set out all alone in his thirty-footer for England. The waterfront of Gloucester was jammed to hail him Godspeed.

He made Gloucester, England, without accident, and was there given his first taste of high life. Officials passed him through the

Customs free of cost, refused to let him pay dock dues, gave him free towage for his boat; men stood on drawbridges and cheered him, women showered him with roses—he sitting at the wheel of his little sloop and wondering half the time what it was all about. There was a procession, with the Lord Mayor and the High Sheriff in the front rank and himself between them; and out in front of all was the town crier, ringing a bell and proclaiming sonorously the arrival in Gloucester, Old England, of the lone voyager from Gloucester in New England.

All this was a pleasant change from hauling a halibut trawl on the winter Grand Banks. Howard decided to travel farther, to sail on to London. Having stayed awake for nineteen hours a day while crossing the Atlantic, he shipped a man to stand the night watches while he would be catching up on sleep on the trip to London. He was a very fat man.

Away they sailed and all was well until one night when Howard was awakened from a fine sleep by the shout that the boat was hove down in the breakers of Goodwin Sands. "We're lost! We're lost!" shouted his man, who had been standing watch.

Howard hurried on deck. The boat was on her beam ends, her stern almost into the breakers. His man, who weighed two hundred and seventy pounds, was helpless. Getting him into the little cabin and out of the way of further harm was a tougher job than working the sloop out of the breakers.

Next morning he put the fat one ashore. He made London alone, sold his boat there and returned to the United States like a gentleman; that is, as a passenger on a regular steamer. He arrived in Gloucester with a feeling of refreshment and a stronger conviction than ever that, except with a gang of fishermen, the only way to sail the ocean was to sail it alone.

He was showered with praises for what people termed his daring venture, which praises he did not take too seriously. He had sailed her leisurely across, taking sixty-eight days for the passage—where was the great daring? Loafing, pure loafing, all the way it was. He made up his mind that when next he sailed across the Atlantic he would make better time.

For his next voyage Blackburn built himself a smaller boat than the *Great Western*. She was also a sloop, twenty-five feet over all, and a great little vessel, too. He named her the *Republic,* and issued a challenge to race any man in the world across the Atlantic in a boat up to thirty feet, each man to sail his own boat alone. He received several acceptances through the newspapers, but on the appointed day for the start none of them showed up. One sporting editor wished to claim for him the one-man ocean sailing championship of the world by default, but Blackburn wasn't that kind of a champion. He would race his boat across anyway, and see what time he could make of it.

He had laid in his ship's stores, mostly canned corned beef, beans, peas, lobster, and salmon, and bolted a fifty-gallon tank of fresh water to the bottom of the boat. Hard bread, tea, sugar, coffee, and butter he stored in a locker built especially for them. He lashed a little oil cookstove so it wouldn't go drifting all over the cabin in heavy weather, laid in a five-gallon can of oil, and a good supply of tobacco, chewing and smoking. She had a tiny cabin, to hold the stores and afford him sleeping shelter. The bunk was a bit narrow for a full-sized man, but no use expecting too much comfort in a twenty-five-footer.

He planned to sail nights and sleep days; that is, when he had to sleep. He figured that it would be best to keep a lookout nights; in the daytime his boat would be in less danger of being run down. As for heaving to his boat while he was asleep—no, no. If he was to make any kind of time across he would have to keep her going always.

His schedule was to stay awake from six o'clock of the evening of each day to noon of the next day; and that schedule he stuck to for most of the way across. When it came time to turn in he would usually set the riding sail and jib, lash the wheel, and let her go, she making what speed she could of it by herself. If bad weather should come on while he was asleep he counted on his sailor's instinct to awaken him before any great damage was done.

It was when he turned out at five in the afternoon after his daily sleep that he did his cooking for the next twenty-four hours, preparing his supper, breakfast, and dinner all at one time; that is, if the weather allowed. When it didn't allow he opened up a can of beef, and with a biscuit and a little water made a cold meal of it.

A man crossing the ocean by himself in a twenty-five-foot boat meets with little adventures that are denied to passengers in big steamers. One afternoon it came foggy. According to his schedule he should have been in his bunk; but knowing he was in the steamship lane he had decided to stick close to the wheel and keep the foghorn handy. The fog stretched out into the second day and night, he pretty much all the time sitting on his tiny wheel-box with the foghorn in his lap. It was calm, the boat barely making headway, and he was growing sleepy. "No use tryin' to stay awake forever," thought Howard, and into his bunk he turned, taking the foghorn inside with him for safety. He was awakened by a steamer's whistle. He had learned to adjust himself to his cramped bunk when awake, but not always when asleep. In his hurry to get out of his bunk he bumped his head against a beam and fell on to the foghorn, damaging it so that he could get no sound out of it when he reached the deck. It would have done him no good if he could—the steamer, a huge bulk, was already on top of him.

She did not run him down, but she came so close that he could have hove the foghorn at her and hit her high steel side going by. She swept on by, an enormous shadowy hull with pale yellow eyes blinking through the fog. Twenty knots at least she was going and she was all of twenty thousand tons. Her bow waves rolled high over his little boat. The swash from her filled his cockpit and open cabin.

Well, no harm was done, but no sense letting it happen again. He decided to get clear of the steamer lane as soon as he could.

Next morning while taking down his sidelights, his port (red) light slipped overboard. He put a white light in its place. That same night his starboard (green) light would not burn; in pure disgust he threw it overboard and put another white light in its place. That made a white light to port and starboard, contrary to all maritime regulations for sailing ships, but in no way to be helped that he could see. It rained hard that night, the boat was going along by

herself, and Blackburn was in the cabin trying to do a little cooking on his oil stove, he having missed his regular cooking session
that afternoon. He heard the rumble of a steamer blowing off steam.
"She's handy enough," thought Howard, and had a look out on
deck. He made out red and green side lights of some craft, and
then the hull of a big steamer, she less than her length from the
*Republic* and directly in his course.

"This one must be tryin' to run me down too," he thought, and
took his stand under one of his white lights. He waved his hand,
hoping he would be seen before they ran him down. A voice hailed
back that they had seen two white lights and, thinking it meant a
wreck, had slowed down their steamer to take the people off. Howard waved to let them know he heard. They made steam and put
off to the west'ard.

The next afternoon he was awakened from a sound sleep by another steamer's whistle. He grabbed the foghorn, which he had in
the meantime repaired, and hurried on deck, thinking thick weather
had set in. He found the weather clear and fine. The whistle came
from a steamer that was hove to close by. They hailed him to know
if he was all right. He answered that he was all right. They gave
him three whistles and steamed off.

"Too many steamers around here—I guess I better get farther
away," thought Howard, "or they'll keep on waking me up when
I ought to be sleepin'." When a breeze sprang up he shifted his
course.

For more than one reason Blackburn was glad to get away from
the steamer people. The sound of his own voice answering their
hail was so harsh and disagreeable to himself that he made up his
mind he would not let another hour pass without using it. So thereafter when a thing had to be done, he would give orders to himself.
"Reef the mains'l!" he would shout, and hop to the reefing of it;
or "Take in that outer jib. . . . Time to rig her sailin' lights," and
so on.

One night he cooked a beef stew of canned corned beef, potatoes,
tomatoes, and so on—a lovely stew. He had been awake for sixty
hours of watching in a fog and after having a meal off the stew he

rolled into his bunk. Next morning he was rolling out of his bunk when he heard a noise from the stew pot, which was sitting up on the cabin floor with its cover on. The cover started to slide off. He shoved it back in place, thinking the pitching of the boat was displacing it. A cheeping noise came from inside the pot. Blackburn was startled. He gave the pot a kick. The pot upset and out hopped a Mother Cary's chicken, she all dressed up in beef stew gravy.

The little thing was terribly frightened. He took her up on deck, soothed her and talked to her and tossed her into the air. She flew off a little way and fluttered to the water. He was tempted to put back and stand by her, to make sure she would wash the gravy off her feathers and fly free again; but he had to be on his way sailing for a small boat record across the Atlantic. The thought that the little thing might not have risen from the sea troubled him for days.

Blackburn tried to plot his position every day on his chart, but he had doubts at times as to just where he was; so one day when a steamer came up from astern of him—he was well clear of the passenger steamer lane now, but this was a freighter—and she hailed him, asking if he needed any help, he hailed back to ask if they would give him his position. They replied that they had not worked it out yet, but they would do it now and let him know. She was an English steamer, and going three miles to Blackburn's one at the time; yet they put her wheel over and steamed around in a circle miles wide and as the circle brought them under Blackburn's stern again they called out his position, gave him a whistle and sailed on. Blackburn was grateful to her, but he was also regretful for putting a big steamer to so much trouble: he made up his mind that he would never ask another vessel for his position.

He had passed the Azores when he saw a steamer turning off her course and heading his way. She steamed all around him as if to look him over. By and by the watch officer yelled across to ask him if he wasn't the man who had previously sailed the little boat to Gloucester, England. Howard answered that he was the man.

"Thought so! Anything you want?"

"I'd like a little wind," answered Howard.

Soon after that he got all the wind he wanted. He had had a few breezes of wind before that, but this turned out to be a breeze worth talking about. The wind began to freshen at daylight. By ten o'clock in the forenoon it was blowing a gale. He took in his mainsail and set the storm trysail (a small triangular sail of heavy canvas used in place of the mainsail in heavy weather). He hauled down his jib and let her lay to while he reefed the jib. She buried herself, sending him under to his neck several times while he was at the work of reefing the jib, but the water being warm he did not mind it. With jib and trysail set, and cabin closed up tight, he put her on her course again. It was a fair wind for Lisbon way and he held her to it. There was so much water rolling over her that for two days and nights he dared not open the cabin except once to wind the chronometer, and again to grab a bit of cold grub and swallow a drink of water; and neither time did he do any loafing opening and closing the cabin door.

His little vessel was making great headway now, but he began to fear that perhaps she was carrying too much sail for moderate safety. He hove her to and hauled half his trysail down on deck. To his mind she lay like a duck, and he went into the cabin for a mouthful of water. He was gone no more than half a minute, but that was long enough; a sea broke aboard and filled the cabin solid.

Presently a steamer came along and blew her whistle. She was in ballast and a sight to look at, rolling and pitching heavily. They came as near to him as they dared and asked him if he wanted to be taken off. "No, thank you," answered Howard.

"You may change your mind," they roared back at him through a megaphone. "We'll wait here a while."

"She's like one of those fellows that were all the time wanting to rescue *Centennial* when he sailed across," thought Howard.

The steamer remained close at hand, waiting for Howard to change his mind. When he saw that she was not leaving him, he swayed up storm trysail, set his reefed jib and put the *Republic* on her course. The steamer followed him.

"They act as if they thought I don't know what to do with a boat in a breeze," thought Howard. "I'll keep her going now if I lose her."

He had a wild time of it keeping the little boat right side up in the gale; but she stayed up, and after an hour of it the steamer gave him three whistles and went on about her business, which she should have in the first place; as she would have, no doubt, if she knew what a sight she looked to him, rolling her decks under, first one rail and then the other.

Howard had intended to heave to again as soon as the steamer was out of sight, but the great little craft was making such good headway on her course and such good weather of it besides, despite all the seas breaking over her, that he kept her to it. He drew rapidly near to land.

When it moderated he found himself in the company of schools of flying fish, turtles, and Portuguese men-o'-war. Some of the turtles were as beamy almost as the *Republic*. He sailed alongside one especially able-looking one, placed his hand under its side and flopped it over on to its back. It was comical to see him claw upward with his flippers, right himself and paddle off.

That same day the wind went flat. The sun was very hot. Howard stretched himself across the cabin house and was staring sleepily into the water, his arms folded on the rail, when he was startled by the nose of a shark within a few inches of his face. He had an enormous mouth, which he closed with a snap as he flashed by. Without stirring, Howard watched him. He swam onward, rubbing his belly against the entire length of the side of the boat, and disappeared under the bow. Soon he reappeared, coming from under the after end of the boat, again turning on his back and snapping at the shadow of Howard's head on the water.

A rising breeze ended any further studies of the way of sharks. The breeze developed into a gale. He had to get down to reefed jib and storm sail and once more lock up his cabin. For three days and two nights the seas crashed into and over his little boat, he making the best of it in his cockpit, which was just big enough to hold him and his wheel. Once he seized a chance to get into the cabin and wind up his chronometer and to grab a pocketful of hard bread and a bottle of water.

The incessant battering eventually loosened up the top of his cabin house, forcing much water between the house and deck into his cabin; but he could do nothing about it until the weather should moderate. If the cabin house carried away he would be in a bad fix— his boat would probably go down under him. As it was, her shipping so much water was making her logy, slowing down her sailing. However, she slid along pretty well with the northeaster abeam.

When Blackburn sailed from Gloucester, he was told that he would be doing well if he made any part of Europe in fifty days. On the thirty-eighth day out of Gloucester he made his landfall at Cape Espichel, Portugal. This was fifteen miles farther south than he had aimed at, not so bad a shot after three thousand-and-odd miles, dead reckoning. He ran the fifteen miles up the coast to Cape Rocca, hauled to beside a fishing boat with three men and two boys in it. He laid a tin of kerosene oil, a tin of biscuit, a hunk of salt pork, a plug of smoking tobacco, two cans of tomatoes, two of corned beef, and four of salmon in a row atop of the cabin house, unrolled a chart and said: "Pilot me up the river to Lisbon and you can have these."

"They did not know what I said, but they understood me," said Howard.

A fresh breeze and a good tide were behind them as up the Tagus River they went in style, the American flag to her peak, while down in the cabin Howard scrubbed the floor and lockers, shaved, washed and dressed himself all fresh for the shore.

While in Lisbon, he stripped his great little boat, stowed sails, rigging, and compass below, nailed up her cabin and saw to her being safely hoisted on the deck of a steamer for New York. She was smaller than the smallest of the steamer's lifeboats.

He saw the sights in Portugal, France, and England, being every-where treated royally, and came back to New York on the steamer *Columbus,* which he thought a good name for a ship, Columbus also being a sailor.

# AN ADVENTURE WITH A WHALE

## By FRANK T. BULLEN

*Illustration by Rockwell Kent*

THROUGH all the vicissitudes of this strange voyage I had hitherto felt pretty safe, and as the last thing a man anticipates (if his digestion is all right) is the possibility of coming to grief himself, while fully prepared to see everybody else go under, so I had got to think that whoever got killed I was not to be—a very pleasing sentiment, and one that carries a man far, enabling him to face dangers with a light heart which otherwise would make a nerveless animal of him.

In this optimistic mood, then, I gayly flung myself into my place in the mate's boat one morning, as we were departing in chase of a magnificent cachalot that had been raised just after breakfast. There were no other vessels in sight—much to our satisfaction—the wind was light, with a cloudless sky, and the whale was dead to leeward of us. We sped along at a good rate toward our prospective victim, who was, in his leisurely enjoyment of life, calmly lolling on the surface, occasionally lifting his enormous tail out of water and letting it fall flat upon the surface with a boom audible for miles.

We were, as usual, first boat; but, much to the mate's annoyance, when we were a short half-mile from the whale, our mainsheet parted. It became immediately necessary to roll the sail up, lest its flapping should alarm the watchful monster, and this delayed us sufficiently to allow the other boats to shoot ahead of us. Thus the second mate got fast some seconds before we arrived on the scene, seeing which we furled sail, unshipped the mast, and went in on him with the oars only. At first the proceedings were quite of the usual character, our chief wielding his lance in most brilliant fashion, while not being fast to the animal allowed us much greater freedom in our evolutions; but that fatal habit of the mate's—of allowing his boat to take care of herself so long as he was getting in some good home-thrusts—once more asserted itself. Although the whale was exceedingly vigorous, churning the sea into yeasty foam over an enormous area, there we wallowed close to him, right in the middle of the turmoil, actually courting disaster.

He had just settled down for a moment, when, glancing over the gunwale, I saw his tail, like a vast shadow, sweeping away from us toward the second mate, who was laying off the other side of him. Before I had time to think, the mighty mass of gristle leapt into the sunshine, curved back from us like a huge bow. Then with a roar it came at us, released from its tension of Heaven knows how many tons. Full on the broadside it struck us, sending every soul but me flying out of the wreckage as if fired from catapults. I did not go because my foot was jammed somehow in the well of the boat, but the wrench nearly pulled my thigh bone out of its socket. I had hardly released my foot, when, towering above me, came the colossal head of the great creature, as he plowed through the bundle of *débris* that had just been a boat. There was an appalling roar of water in my ears, and darkness that might be felt all around. Yet, in the midst of it all, one thought predominated as clearly as if I had been turning it over in my mind in the quiet of my bunk aboard— "What if he should swallow me?" Nor to this day can I understand how I escaped the portals of his gullet, which of course gaped wide as a church door. But the agony of holding my breath soon over- powered every other feeling and thought, till just as something was going to snap inside my head I rose to the surface. I was surrounded by a welter of bloody froth, which made it impossible for me to see; but oh, the air was sweet!

I struck out blindly, instinctively, although I could feel so strong an eddy that voluntary progress was out of the question. My hand touched and clung to a rope, which immediately towed me in some direction—I neither knew nor cared whither. Soon the motion ceased, and, with a seaman's instinct, I began to haul myself along by the rope I grasped, although no definite idea was in my mind as to where it was attached. Presently I came butt up against something solid, the feel of which gathered all my scattered wits into a com- pact knub of dread. It was the whale! "Any port in a storm," I murmured, beginning to haul away again on my friendly line. By dint of hard work I pulled myself right up the sloping, slippery bank of blubber, until I reached the iron, which, as luck would have it, was planted in that side of the carcass now uppermost. Carcass I said— well, certainly I had no idea of there being any life remaining within the vast mass beneath me; yet I had hardly time to take a couple of turns round myself with the rope (or whale line, as I had proved it to be), when I felt the great animal quiver all over, and begin to forge ahead. I was now composed enough to remember that help could not be far away, and that my rescue, providing that I could keep above water, was but a question of a few minutes. But I was hardly prepared for the whale's next move. Being very near his end, the boat, or boats, had drawn off a bit, I supposed, for I could see nothing of them. Then I remembered the flurry. Almost at the same moment it began; and there was I, who with fearful admira- tion had so often watched the titantic convulsions of a dying. cach- alot, actually involved in them. The turns were off my body, but I was able to twist a couple of turns round my arms, which, in case of his sounding, I could readily let go.

Then all was lost in roar and rush, as of the heart of some mighty cataract, during which I was sometimes above, sometimes beneath, the water, but always clinging, with every ounce of energy still left, to the line. Now, one thought was uppermost—"What if he should breach?" I had seen them do so when in flurry, leaping full twenty feet in the air. Then I prayed.

Quickly as all the preceding changes had passed came perfect peace. There I lay, still alive, but so weak that, although I could feel the turns slipping off my arms, and knew that I should slide off the slope of the whale's side into the sea if they did, I could make no effort to secure myself. Everything then passed away from me, just as if I had gone to sleep.

I do not at all understand how I kept my position, nor how long, but I awoke to the blessed sound of voices, and saw the second mate's boat alongside. Very gently and tenderly they lifted me into the boat, although I could hardly help screaming with agony when they touched me, so bruised and broken up did I feel. My arms

Rockwell Kent

*The mighty mass of gristle leapt into the sunshine.*

[See page 363]

must have been nearly torn from their sockets, for the strands of the whale line had cut deeply into their flesh with the strain upon it, while my thigh was swollen enormously from the blow I received at the onset. Mr. Cruce was the most surprised man I think I ever saw. For full ten minutes he stared at me with wide-open eyes. When at last he spoke, it was with difficulty, as if wanting words to express his astonishment. At last he blurted out, "Whar you bin all de time, ennyhaow? 'Cawse ef you bin hangin' on to dat ar wale ev' sence you boat smash, w'y de debbil you hain't all ter bits, hey?" I smiled feebly, but was too weak to talk, and presently went off again into a dead faint.

When I recovered, I was snug in my bunk aboard, but aching in every joint, and as sore as if I had been pounded with a club until I was bruised all over. During the day Mr. Count was kind enough to pay me a visit. With his usual luck, he had escaped without the slightest injury; neither was any other member of the boat's crew the worse for the ducking but myself. He told me that the whale was one of the largest he had ever seen, and as fat as butter. The boat was an entire loss, so completely smashed to pieces that nothing of her or her gear had been recovered. After spending about a quarter of an hour with me, he left me considerably cheered up, promising to look after me in way of food, and also to send me some books. He told me that I need not worry myself about my inability to be at work, because the old man was not unfavorably disposed toward me, which piece of news gave me a great deal of comfort.

When my poor, weary shipmates came below from their heavy toil of cutting in, they were almost inclined to be envious of my comfort—small blame to them—though I would gladly have taken my place among them again, could I have got rid of my hurts. But I was condemned to lie there for nearly three weeks before I was able to get about once more. In my sleep I would undergo the horrible anticipation of sliding down that awful, cavernous mouth over again, often waking with a shriek, and drenched with sweat.

While I lay there, three whales were caught, all small cows, and I was informed that the skipper was getting quite disgusted with the luck. At last I managed to get on deck, quite a different-looking man to when I went below, and feeling about ten years older. I found the same sullen quiet reigning that I had noticed several times before when we were unfortunate. I fancied that the skipper looked more morose and savage than ever, though of me, to my great relief, he took not the slightest notice.

The third day after my return to duty we sighted whales again. We lowered three boats as promptly as usual; but when within about half a mile of the "pod" some slight noise in one of the boats gallied them, and away they went in the wind's eye, it blowing a stiffish breeze at the time. It was from the first evidently a hopeless task to chase them, but we persevered until recalled to the ship, dead beat with fatigue. I was not sorry, for my recent adventure seemed to have made quite a coward of me, so much so that an unpleasant gnawing at the pit of my stomach as we neared them almost made me sick. I earnestly hoped that so inconvenient a feeling would speedily leave me, or I should be but a poor creature in a boat.

# THE VOYAGE OF THE "BOUNTY"

*Anonymous*

*Illustrations by J. WHYMPER and WARREN CHAPPELL*

T HIS is the story of a man who, when in command of his ships and when everything went prosperously with him, was so overbearing and cruel that some of his men, in desperation at the treatment they received, mutinied against him. But the story shows another side of his character in adversity, which it is impossible not to admire.

In 1787, Captain Bligh was sent from England to Tahiti in charge of the *Bounty,* a ship which had been especially fitted out to carry young plants of the breadfruit tree for transplantation in the West Indies.

"The breadfruit grows on a spreading tree about the size of a large apple tree; the fruit is round, and has a thick, tough rind. It is gathered when it is full-grown, and while it is still green and hard; it is then baked in an oven until the rind is black and scorched. This is scraped off, and the inside is soft and white, like the crumb of a penny loaf."

The Tahitians use no other bread but the fruit kind. It is, there-fore, little wonder that the West Indian planters were anxious to grow this valuable fruit in their own islands, as, if it flourished there, food would be provided with little trouble for their servants and slaves.

In the passage to Tahiti, Captain Bligh had several disturbances with his men. He had an extremely irritable temper, and would often fly into a passion and make most terrible accusations, and use most terrible language to his officers and sailors. On one occasion he ordered the crew to eat some decayed pumpkins, instead of their al-lowance of cheese, which he said they had stolen from the ship's stores. The pumpkin was to be given to the men at the rate of one pound of pumpkin to two pounds of biscuits.

The men did not like accepting the substitute on these terms. When the captain heard this, he was infuriated, and ordered the first man of each mess to be called by name, at the same time saying to them, "I'll see who will dare refuse the pumpkin or anything else I may order to be served out." Then, after swearing at them in a shocking way, he ended by saying, "I'll make you eat grass, or anything else you can catch, before I have done with you," and threatened to flog the first man who dared to complain again.

While they were at Tahiti, several of the sailors were flogged for small offenses, or without reason, and on the other hand, during the seven months they stayed at the island, both officers and men were allowed to spend a great deal of time on shore, and were given the greatest possible liberty.

Therefore, when the breadfruit plants were collected, and they weighed anchor on April 4, in 1787, it is not unlikely they were loath to return to the strict discipline of the ship, and to leave an island so lovely, and where it was possible to live in the greatest luxury without any kind of labor.

From the time they sailed until April 27, Christian, the third officer, had been in constant hot water with Captain Bligh. On the afternoon of that day, when the captain came on deck, he missed some coconuts that had been heaped up between the guns. He said at once that they had been stolen, and that it could not have happened without the officers knowing of it. When they told him they had not seen any of the crew touch them, he cried, "Then you must have taken them yourselves!" After this he questioned them separately; when he came to Christian, the latter answered, "I do not know, sir, but I hope you do not think me so mean as to be guilty of stealing yours."

The captain swore terribly, and said, "You must have stolen them from me, or you would be able to give a better account of them!" He turned to the others with much more abuse, saying, "You scoundrels, you are all thieves alike, and combine with the men to rob me! I suppose you'll steal my yams next, but I'll sweat you for it, you rascals! I'll make half of you jump overboard before you get through Endeavor Straits!"

Then he turned to the clerk, giving the order to "give them but half a pound of yams tomorrow: if they steal *them,* I'll reduce them to a quarter."

That night, Christian, who was hardly less passionate and resentful than the captain, told two of the midshipmen, Stewart and Hayward, that he intended to leave the ship on a raft, as he could no longer endure the captain's suspicion and insults. He was very angry and excited, and made some preparations for carrying out his plan, though these had to be done with the greatest secrecy and care.

It was his duty to take the morning watch, which is from four to eight o'clock, and this time he thought would be a good opportunity to make his escape. He had only just fallen into a restless slumber when he was called to take his turn. He got up with his brain still alert with the sense of injury and wrong, and most curiously alive to seize any opportunity which might lead to an escape from so galling a service.

On reaching the deck, he found the mate of the watch had fallen asleep, and that the other midshipman was not to be seen. Then he made a sudden determination to seize the ship, and rushing down the gangway ladder, whispered his intention to Matthew Quintal and Isaac Martin, seamen, both of whom had been flogged. They readily agreed to join him, and several others of the watch were found to be quite as willing.

Someone went to the armorer for the keys of the arm chest, telling him they wanted to fire at a shark alongside. Christian then armed those men whom he thought he could trust, and putting a guard at the officers' cabins, went himself with three other men to the captain's cabin.

It was just before sunrise when they dragged him from his bed, and tying his hands behind his back, threatened him with instant death if he should call for help or offer any kind of resistance. He was taken up to the quarter-deck in his night clothes, and made to stand against the mizzenmast with four men to guard him.

Christian then gave orders to lower the boat in which he intended to cast them adrift, and one by one the men were allowed to come up the hatchways, and made to go over the side of the ship into it.

Meanwhile no heed was given to the remonstrances, reasoning, and prayers of the captain, saving threats of death unless he was quiet.

Some twine, canvas, sails, a small cask of water, and a quadrant and compass were put into the boat, also some bread and a small quantity of rum and wines. When this was done the officers were brought up one by one and forced over the side. There was a great deal of rough joking at the captain's expense, who was still made to stand by the mizzenmast, and much bad language was used by everybody.

When all the officers were out of the ship, Christian said, "Come, Captain Bligh, your officers and men are now in the boat, and you must go with them; if you make the least resistance you will be instantly put to death." He was lowered over the side with his hands still fastened behind his back, and directly after the boat was veered astern with a rope. Someone with a little pity for them threw in some pieces of pork and some clothes, as well as two or three cutlasses; these were the only arms given.

There were altogether nineteen men in this pitiful strait. Although much of the conduct of the mutineers is easily understood with regard to the captain, the wholesale crime of thrusting so many innocent persons out to the mercy of the winds and waves, or to the death from hunger and thirst which they must have believed would inevitably overtake them, is incomprehensible.

As the *Bounty* sailed away, leaving them to their fate, those in the boat cast anxious looks to the captain, wondering what should be done. At a time when his mind must have been full of the injury he had received, and of the loss of his ship at a moment when his plans were so flourishing and he had every reason to congratulate himself as to the ultimate success of the undertaking, it is much in his favor that he seems to have realized their unfortunate position and to have been determined to make the best of it.

His first care was to see how much food they had. On examining it, they found there was a hundred and fifty pounds of bread, thirty-two pounds of pork, six quarts of rum, six bottles of wine, and twenty-eight gallons of water.

As they were so near Tofoa they determined to put in there for a supply of breadfruit and water, so that they might keep their other provisions. But after rowing along the coast for some time, they only discovered some coconut trees on the top of a stony cliff, against which the sea beat furiously. After several attempts they succeeded in getting about twenty nuts. The second day they failed to get anything at all.

However, some natives came down to the boat and made inquiries about the ship; but the captain unfortunately told the men to say she had been lost, and that only they were saved. This proved most disastrous; for the treacherous natives, finding they were defenseless, at first brought them presents of breadfruit, plaintains and coconuts, rendering them all more hopeful and cheerful by their kindness. But toward night their numbers increased in a most alarming manner, and soon the whole beach was lined with them.

Presently they began knocking stones together, by which the men knew they intended to make an attack upon them. They made haste to get all the things into the boat, and all but one, named John Norton, succeeded in reaching it. The natives rushed upon this poor man and stoned him to death.

Those in the boat put to sea with all haste, but were again terribly alarmed to find themselves followed by natives in canoes from which they renewed the attack. Many of the sailors were a good deal hurt by stones, and they had no means at all with which to protect themselves. At last they threw some clothes overboard; these tempted the enemy to stop to pick them up, and as soon as night came on they gave up the chase and returned to the shore.

All the men now begged Captain Bligh to take them toward England; but he told them there could be no hope of relief until they reached Timor, a distance of full twelve hundred leagues; and that, if they wished to reach it, they would have to content themselves with one ounce of bread and a quarter of a pint of water a day. They all readily agreed to this allowance of food, and made a most solemn oath not to depart from their promise to be satisfied with the small quantity. This was about May 2.

After the compact was made, the boat was put in order, the men divided into watches, and they bore away under a reefed lug-foresail. A fiery sun rose on the 3d, which is commonly a sign of rough weather, and filled the almost hopeless derelicts with a new terror. In an hour or two it blew very hard, and the sea ran so high that their sail was becalmed between the waves; they did not dare to set it when on the top of the sea, for the water rushed in over the stern of the boat, and they were obliged to bale with all their might.

The bread was in bags, and in the greatest danger of being spoiled by the wet. They were obliged to throw some rope and the spare sails overboard, as well as all the clothes but what they wore, to lighten the boat; then the carpenter's tool chest was cleared and the bread put into it. They were all very wet and cold, and a teaspoonful of rum was served to each man, with a quarter of a breadfruit which was so bad that it could hardly be eaten; but the captain was determined at all risks to keep to the compact they had entered into, and to make their provisions last eight weeks.

In the afternoon the sea ran even higher, and at night it became very cold; but still they did not dare to leave off baling for an instant, though their legs and arms were numb with fatigue and wet.

In the morning a teaspoonful of rum was served to all, and five small coconuts divided for their dinner, and everyone was satisfied.

When the gale had subsided they examined the bread, and found a great deal of it had become mouldy and rotten; but even this was carefully kept and used. The boat was now near some islands, but they were afraid to go on shore, as the natives might attack them; while being in sight of land, where they might replenish their poor stock of provisions and rest themselves, added to their misery. One morning they hooked a fish, and were overjoyed at their good fortune; but in trying to get it into the boat it was lost, and again they had to content themselves with the damaged bread and small allowance of water for their supper.

They were dreadfully cramped for room, and were obliged to manage so that half their number should lie down in the bottom of the boat or upon a chest, while the others sat up and kept watch; their limbs became so stiff from being constantly wet, and from want of space to stretch them in, that after a few hours' sleep they were hardly able to move.

About May 7, they passed what the captain supposed must be the

Fiji Islands, and two large canoes put off and followed them for some time, but in the afternoon they gave up the chase. It rained heavily that day, and everyone in the boat did his best to catch some water, and they succeeded in increasing their stock to thirty-four gallons, besides having had enough to drink for the first time since they had been cast adrift; but the rain made them very cold and miserable, as they had no dry clothes. The next morning they had

*J. Whymper*

*Captain Bligh's diary, water gourd, and water measure.*

an ounce and a half of pork, a teaspoonful of rum, half a pint of coconut milk and an ounce of bread for breakfast, which was quite a large meal for them.

Through fifteen weary days and nights of ceaseless rain they toiled, sometimes through fierce storms of thunder and lightning, and before terrific seas lashed into foam and fury by swift and sudden squalls, with only their miserable pittance of bread and water to keep body and soul together.

In this rain and storm the little sleep they got only added to their discomfort, save for the brief forgetfulness it brought; for they had to lie down in water in the bottom of the boat, and with no covering but the streaming clouds above them. The captain then advised them to wring their clothes through sea water, which they found made them feel much warmer for a time.

On May 17 everyone was ill and complaining of great pain, and begging for more food; but the captain refused to increase their allowance, though he gave them all a small quantity of rum.

Until the 24th they flew before the wild seas that swept over stem and stern of their boat and kept them constantly baling. Some of them now looked more than half dead from starvation, but no one suffered from thirst, as they had absorbed so much water through the skin.

A fine morning dawned on the 25th, when they saw the sun for the first time for fifteen days, and were able to eat their scanty allow, ance in more comfort and warmth. In the afternoon there were numbers of birds called boobies and noddies near, which are never seen far from land. The captain took this opportunity to look at the state of their bread, and found if they did not exceed their allowance there was enough to last for twenty-nine days, when they hoped to reach Timor.

That afternoon some noddies came so near the boat that one was caught. The birds are about the size of a small pigeon; it was divided into eighteen parts and given by lot. The men were much amused when they saw the beak and claws fall to the lot of the captain. The bird was eaten, bones and all, with bread and water, for dinner.

Now they were in calmer seas, they were overtaken by a new trouble. The heat of the sun became so great that many of them were overcome by faintness, and lay in the bottom of the boat in an apathetic state all day, only rousing themselves toward evening, when the catching of birds was attempted.

On the morning of the 28th the sound of breakers could be heard plainly; they had reached the Great Barrier Reef, which runs up much of the east coast of Australia. After some little time a passage nearly a quarter of a mile in width was discovered through the reef, and they were carried by a strong current into the peaceful waters which lie within the Barrier.

For a little time they were so overjoyed that their past troubles were forgotten. The dull blue-gray lines of the mainland, with its white patches of glaring sandhills, could be seen in the distance, and that afternoon they landed on an island. They found the rocks around it were covered with oysters and huge clams, which could easily be got at low tide. Some of their party sent out to reconnoiter returned greatly pleased at having found plenty of fresh water. A fire was made by help of a small magnifying glass. Among the things thrown into the boat from the ship was a small copper pot; and thus with a mixture of oysters, bread and pork a stew was made, and everyone had plenty to eat.

The day after they landed was the 29th of May, the anniversary of the restoration of King Charles II, and as the captain thought it applied to their own renewed health and strength, he named it Restoration Island.

After a few days' rest, which did much to revive the men, and when they had filled all their vessels with water and had gathered a large supply of oysters, they were ready to go on again. As they were about to start, everybody was ordered to attend prayers, and as they were embarking about twenty naked savages came running and shouting toward them, each carrying a long barbed spear, but the English made all haste to put to sea.

For several days they sailed over the lakelike stillness of the Barrier reef-bound waters, and past the bold desolations of the Queensland coast, every headland and bay there bearing the names Cook gave them only a few years before, and which still tell us by that nomenclature each its own story of disappointment and hope. Still making way to the north, they passed many more islands and keys, the onward passage growing hot and hotter, until on June 3, when they doubled Cape York, the peninsula which is all but unique in its northward bend, they were again in the open sea.

By this time many of them were ill with malaria; then for the first time some of the wine which they had with them was used. But the little boat still bravely made its way with its crew, whose faces were so hollow and ghastly that they looked like a crew of specters, sailing beneath the scorching sun that beat down from the pale blue of the cloudless sky upon a sea hardly less blue in its greater depths. Only the hope that they would soon reach Timor seemed to rouse them from a state of babbling delirium or fitful slumber.

On the 11th the captain told them they had passed the meridian of the east at Timor; and at three o'clock on the next morning they sighted the land. It was on Sunday, June 14, when they arrived at Company Bay, and were received with every kindness by the people.

Thus ended one of the most remarkable voyages that have ever been made. They had been sent out with provisions only sufficient for their number for *five* days, and Captain Bligh had, by his careful calculation and determination to give each man only that equal portion they had agreed to accept, made it last for *fifty* days, during which time they had come three thousand six hundred and eighteen nautical miles.

There had been days when the men were so hunger-driven that they had besought him with pitiful prayers for more to eat, and when it was his painful duty to refuse it; and times, as they passed those islands where plentiful food could be got, when he had to turn a deaf ear to their longings to land. He had to endure the need of food, the cramped position, the uneasy slumber, as did his men; as well as the more perfect knowledge of their dangers. There had been days and nights while he worked out their bearings when he had to be propped up as he took the stars or sun.

It was, therefore, Captain Bligh's good seamanship, his strict discipline and fairness in the method of giving food and wine to those who were sick, that enabled them to land at Timor with the whole of their number alive, with the exception of the one man who was stoned to death by the savages at Tofoa.

# ROUNDING CAPE HORN IN A WINDJAMMER

### By *ALAN J. VILLIERS*

*Illustrations by Warren Chappell*

## I

W ITH a young reporter-photographer friend, I conceived the idea of once more rounding the Horn to get a cinema record of it while the chance remained. It was a stirring opportunity which no film-producing corporation seemed inclined to tackle. We kept our ideas to ourselves, thinking that if we sought to interest some great film concern they would be more inclined to charter a ship and send some expert cameramen and a gang of scene-shifters and whatnot out to sea for a week or two, rather than to commission us to go after the real thing in our own way.

We had spent a lifetime looking at bad sea films, at impossible and ridiculous ship pictures that showed anguished heroines and dashing heroes aboard all sorts of ships except any that ever sailed; at so-called sea classics made by cameramen and directors the real sea would have drowned. If this picture was to be made as we wanted it made, we had to make it ourselves. We got what money we could, which was very little; we resigned our jobs, sold our homes, and went across to the little South Australian grain port of Wallaroo and there we shipped before the mast of the Finnish ship *Grace Harwar,* for her passage round the Horn to the English Channel for orders, scupper-deep with grain.

We went aboard late at night, with our cameras and film in our sea bags, but saying nothing to anybody of our intentions. We signed as sailors, to do the ship's work. We considered, then, that it was not the ship's business what else we might intend to do. We knew about the conservatism of sailing-ship masters, and feared that if we opened

our mouths about this film, other able seamen might be found and
we should lose our job. There also was the possibility of the captain
cabling to his owner and raising the question of film rights and such
things. It is the film producers' own fault that there exists a world-
wide impression that the outpouring of gold unlimited is a necessity,
and even a pastime, to anyone concerned with the making of "pictures"; but we were not ordinary film producers and we had no
gold.

So we joined the ship and did our work with the others and said
nothing. In the course of time the *Grace Harwar* sailed. She was a
lovely full-rigged ship, of 1,760 tons, ideal for our purpose. She was
Clyde-built, more than forty years old; she had an open wheel and
none of those labor-saving devices—brace winches, halyard winches,
and the like—of later days. She was a genuine sister of the Horn of
forty years ago—one of the last, if not the very last, full-rigger
actually to round the Horn.

## II

We had a Frenchman, a Londoner, four Australians, and the rest
were Finns—Swedish-speaking Finns, mostly from the Åland
Islands, where the ship belonged. Only two of the crew had been
round the Horn before, the Londoner and I.

The Londoner and I had been in more ships under the Finn flag
than any of the Finns aboard. He had sailed in *Olivebank;* I in
*Lawhill* and *Herzogin Cecilie.* The Finns were all first-voyage boys,
some deserters from other ships, two or three members of the original crew who had joined the *Grace Harwar* in Swansea nearly two
years before. The average age of our crew was about 19. Three had
never been to sea before.

But they were all fine boys and settled down manfully. They
were strong and willing, which is a lot. There was an entire absence
of that old bickering spirit which was so evident in sail's heyday,
when every forecastle had its boss, its bloodshed, and its undercurrent
of cliques and jealousies. We had no fight the whole voyage. I have
not seen a fight in a Finnish ship.

We began the voyage well. We knew that it was coming on winter then and prayed for a quick run to the Horn. The Horn is bad enough in summer, and we did not want to prolong our passage of the west winds getting there. In six days we passed to the south of Tasmania. That was good. We had a strong west wind the whole time, with a big sea. It was piercingly cold and the little *Grace Harwar* was inclined to throw the sea about her decks a lot.

We blew out a sail or two. The first night out the mizzen-top-gallantsail blew out of its boltropes, and we set no sail upon that yard thereafter because the ship had none. There was no square topgallantsail fit to stand down there. The mizzen-topgallant yard had to go bare until a new sail was cut and sewn. That took some time.

We did not mind the cold. We did not mind the ceaseless wet at the cold wheel, the seas that slopped over us at brace and buntline, the teeth-chattering peril of the work aloft. We laughed at the big seas and thought it a joke when a larger one than usual fell aboard with a shock that made the whole ship tremble and threatened to do her serious damage. What did we care, while the wind was fair and we came quickly toward Cape Horn?

From Wallaroo to Cape Horn is, roughly speaking, about 6,000 miles. If we ran nine knots before the strong west winds, we should make it in 30 days—say, 35 or 38, allowing for some spells of lesser winds and maybe some days hove to, when there was too much wind to use. We went that way, as all sailing ships do, in the hope of getting strong west winds, in order that if we had to suffer acute discomfort, and cold and wet, and ceaseless work, at least it would not last long and we should be quickly round. The sailing ship does not mind strong wind, so long as it is fair. We had nothing to fear from westerly gales, which would help us on; it was wind from the east we feared.

The wind came from the east. It hauled around to southeast and hurled itself upon us with all the sting of the Antarctic ice, in its frigid and unwelcoming blast. We could do nothing with the strong east wind. We shortened down and hove to. This was in the southern waters of the Tasman Sea, between Tasmania and New Zealand, across which we had been making to pass to the south of New Zealand on our way to the Horn. The Tasman Sea is storm-lashed and furious in winter time. We knew that, but we expected at least that we would have west wind.

The wind refused flatly to go back toward any point west. We held on, giving the ship the full mainsail in the hope that it would hold her head up a little, decrease her leeway, and give us some longitude toward Cape Horn. The newcomers to the sea were sick and utterly fed up with it. They wondered why, if once one ship had sailed that road and met with such conditions, any others were ever foolhardy enough to follow after. The sea froze where it touched the steel of the bulwarks; one of our pigs was drowned; the rain and the sleet froze into the serving of the footropes.

We tried our best to beat those easterly winds, hoping always they would stop, believing that the Wind God would take pity on us and at least let us come to the Horn, no matter what torment he wreaked on us on the way. But it was not fair to delay us so, with this accursed east wind.

The east wind continued, with no slightest sign of ever giving up. Gale succeeded gale. Constantly the open decks of the old full-rigger were awash; one had to look lively to the lifelines going to the wheel. At night the lookout man could not go on the forecastle head, for the seas came over there green, and if he had gone there he would have been drowned. We began to notice how short-handed we were, with six in one watch and seven in the other.

In the end, Captain Svensson got fed up with the east wind and put up the helm to run for Cook Strait, that separates the two islands of New Zealand, intending to pass through that way into the South Pacific beyond, if the east wind would not allow us to pass south of that Dominion. We reached Cook Strait after three weeks at sea, and then it fell calm and we could not get through.

Four days we lay there, wallowing stagnantly, with Mount Egmont on the one hand and the rocky northern shores of the south island on the other. We were about to up helm and stand on northward to pass right round the northern extremity of New Zealand, when a west wind came at last and saw us through.

Warren Chappell

*The "Grace Harwar."*

[See page 378]

## III

We saw the lights of Wellington, capital of New Zealand, and reported the ship all well. The west wind kept with us for a day or two and saw us clear of the Chatham Islands. We began to think it meant to stay, and that we would come to the Horn without further undue misery.

But then the wind faltered and stopped again. When it returned it was from the east, with fog and rain and gale in miserable succession. Day succeeded day in sodden gale and cold misery. We went out to so many alternate watches on deck, hoping that while we slept the wind had changed, and were disappointed, that we gave up hoping any more. We accepted what was in store for us with sullen indifference.

Oilskins were long since useless; there was no dry spot in the ship, nor dry rag. The hutch of a forecastle was washed out time and time again by great seas that swept joyously through the inefficient doors. When the forecastle doors were shut, the atmosphere was stifling. When they were open, the sea swept in. We kept them shut, preferring to die of suffocation rather than exposure.

There was often no warm food. The seas put the galley fire out, and because the water stormed so incessantly across the main deck, where the fresh-water pump was, we could not work the inefficient pump for fear of mingling salt water with the fresh, and went thirsty. We were cold, wet through, and hungry. There is no heating system in a full-rigged ship. The very cockroaches and the bugs in the bunks retired from active service and might all have died, for all we saw of them.

I give an extract or two from the diary of poor Ronald Walker, my reporter friend, scrupulously kept until the day he died, the better to describe this section of the voyage. He brought new eyes to it and a new mind. I had been that way before and had described it before, and did not see it with the same freshness.

"May 16, 29 days out," he wrote. "Looking back, those 29 days seem an interminable age. Many strange things have happened in them. . . . Frenchman and I were sent aloft to make fast the fore upper topgallantsail this morning, in a hard squall which showed every sign of developing into a real Cape Horn snorter. We climbed into the shrouds at 6 a. m., in pitch darkness. It was raining steadily and big seas were coming aboard. The wind had a cold sting in it which gradually froze us to the marrow, in spite of heavy clothing, oilskins, and sea boots.

"We were up there for nearly two hours, while a cold and cheerless dawn broke over the wind-torn sea, and we fought with the sodden sails until the work became a pain and a purgatory. The rain persistently drove at us, making our caps sodden and our oilskins sodden; the cold water trickled down through crevices which nothing but water could find. Our fingers were stiff and blue with the cold and red with blood from tears with the jagged wire gear....

"At first we shivered when an icy finger of water found its way down our backs or up a sleeve, but soon we were so wet and cold we ceased to care. Get wet and stay wet is the best policy for sailing ships. The greatest agony of mind comes when you change into comparative dry, only to know with horrible certainty that as soon as you go on deck again everything will be sodden through and through once more. . . .

"May 19, 32 days. You stand a miserable lookout on the forecastle head for hours, with plenty of time for thought, but the antidote for depression lies just behind you, towering into the darkness, sweeping on and on along the rolling road, heaving or stumbling as she meets a sea, rushing on again and on, indomitable, insuperable as fate.

"Great seas come up to meet the ship, thrusting at her, shouldering one another to get at her, like footballers in a mad footer 'scrum.' Up and up they heave, gathering for the blow. You turn to watch them. The wind howls in your face and the sea spits at you spitefully, driving its spray above and around. A great sea, a liquid mountain of menace, hangs poised above the ship. Up, up it leaps, shouldering its smaller children aside, the splendid crest whitening where it breaks, lending a touch of color like the plume of a warrior's helmet.

"Down, down, sinks the ship, shuddering already at the impending blow. A hundred lesser blows she has avoided; this mighty one she cannot beat. She writhes like a living thing, in fear and trembling. She heels over heavily; she hovers frighteningly. . . .

Warren Chappell

*At the capstan.*

"The stars shoot suddenly past the spars—not so bad with them out—careening madly across the sky. The ship receives the blow full, staggering at the impact. A tremor runs through the laboring hull. . . .

"But the shattered sea crest has met its match. The warrior's plume has dropped; the ship rises again, tumbling hundreds of tons of roaring, fighting water from her gushing wash ports. The sea sweeps her furiously end to end, murderously intent upon human prey. Balked of that, it shifts whatever is movable and snarls and hisses at the hatch breakwaters, maddeningly intent upon breaking them down. . . .

"But the ship wins. Under her load of hundreds of tons of seething water, she rolls on, recovering her poise, steadying herself to meet the next onslaught, and the next, and the next after that. For forty years and more now she has been doing that. Beautiful and game old ship! . . ."

## IV

On the 38th day Walker was killed at his work in the rigging.

It was very simple. Just one of those ordinary everyday accidents that nine hundred times kill nobody and on the 901st wreak vengeance on some innocent for their previous failings.

We were setting the fore upper topgallantsail, which had not been loosed since its getting in, described in his diary. The wind, which for so long had been from something east, had at last something of west in it, and we were giving the ship a little more sail to help her on—not that the fore upper topgallantsail would make much difference, really, but the psychological effect was not to be scorned.

Walker, with a small boy named Finila, went up to loose the sail. It was a little after 4 o'clock in the morning, the worst time of the day. We had so few in a watch that it was bad to send two men into the rigging; but there were reasons for that. We had coffee at 5:30, and the tradition of the sea is, that if there is any work afoot and it is not finished before the coffee bells, then whatever time is taken up with finishing the work is lost. The coffee hour is not extended merely because some of it has been given up to the ship's work. A good mate will see that his watch receives its coffee time unbroken.

That was why our second mate sent both Walker and young Finila to loose the fore upper topgallant that fateful morning. It was very securely made fast with many gaskets to stand against the Cape Horn gale. Since it had been made fast it had become sodden with rain and the canvas had swollen. Ice had formed in the gaskets, and any sailor knows it may take an hour to get a sail loose in such conditions. With the two of them at it, they managed in half an hour, and then we on deck—five of us with the second mate—began the painful process of heaving the yard aloft by the capstan.

When it was halfway up, the second mate saw that a gasket was foul on the weather clew. The sail would not hoist properly. He yelled aloft to Walker, through the rain, to go out on the lower topgallant yard to clear the gasket. Walker went and cleared it. He called down to us that everything was clear. We began to heave again. The halyards carried away and the yard came tumbling down.

It fell on Walker, beneath it, and killed him there.

We did not know that he was dead when we rushed up the mast and found him unconscious between the yards. We thought he was merely senseless. There was no sign of wound, save for some blood oozing slowly from his mouth.

It never occurred to us that he was dead; we were too much concerned with bringing him to and getting him to the deck that we might see the extent of his injuries and what we could do about them. I tried to bring him to with cold water that had been brought from the deck. I did not know how hopeless it was. We wanted to restore him to his senses in order that he might help us with the difficult task of getting him, from high on that swaying mast, to the deck. It was not easy to bring a senseless body down that slippery and pitching rigging.

But he did not come to. We rigged a gantline and lowered him down, gently, carefully.

When we got to the bottom, Captain Svensson took one look.

"He is dead," he said.

Dead! The shock was stunning. We did not, could not, believe it. Nowhere is the awfulness of death more painfully apparent than at sea. Ashore there are diversions; one forgets. There are other people to see, other people to talk to. One is not missed so much. But at sea, in a full-rigged ship, there is only the one little band, and always the wind moans in the rigging and the sea rolls on. When one is gone, no one comes to take his place; there are no diversions; nothing happens to deaden sorrow and make up for the loss of the one who is gone.

We buried him from the poop next day, with the Finnish ensign at half-mast and the crew white-faced and deeply moved. I do not know of anything more moving than sea burial—not the committal of some poor corpse of steerage passenger from high on the steamship's promenade deck, in the dead of night, lest the saloon passengers be put off their dancing for a moment, but the last sad rites over a shipmate's bier in a Cape Horn windjammer.

We all had known him so well. At sea, like that, you see the utmost "innards" of a man—what he is made of. No subterfuges, no pretense of city life, no masking of real intents and real character, will pass here; you see all. We knew poor Walker and we liked him well. And this was his end!

The captain read some prayers; we sang Swedish and English hymns. There was a short address. The ship was hove to, sadly wallowing, with the moan of the wind in her rigging now quieted by her deadened way, the surly wash of the sea about her decks now softened. We carried him to the rail, tilted the hatch; there was a dull "plop" and it was over.

We put the ship before the wind again and sailed on.

## V

It was the 57th day before we came to the Horn. It was June then. We had a gale from the west, and though the sea ran huge and the cold was almost overpowering, the old ship ran on and we were glad.

We wanted to come round the Horn now more quickly than ever, that we might forget something of the tragedy of the other side of it. Death is a worrying thing at sea, especially when its cause is bad gear that might have killed another of us. At the wheel, on the lonely lookout, aloft on the yards, sleeping in the wet, cold forecastle, we remembered the one who had died, turned the details of that tragedy over and over in our minds until it was not good for us longer to remain in that saddening belt of the wild ocean. A boy screamed in his sleep; he had dreamed of Walker's wraith coming in the forecastle to call us.

The ship began to leak in the height of a gale; the pumps jammed; the water seeped in, and we could do nothing about it. Through a night of storm and snow-squall fury we were huddled on the poop, not certain that the ship would live to see the morning.

The next day one of the boys was swept overboard by a big sea, and there were no falls rove off in the lifeboats to try to save him. What could we do? Many had gone like that, and the wind ships could only run on.

But the wind was a little quieter then. We did not run on, though it seemed futile to try to save him. We jammed the wheel hard down and brought her, shivering and groaning, into the wind. We rove off new ropes into the lifeboat tackle blocks with mad speed. One of us was aloft in the mizzen-top, seeing where the floating figure had gone. It was coming on nightfall then, with rain squalls and gale in the offing. We saw he had grasped a life buoy flung to him, and still lived. But for how long?

We got the boat over and six volunteers quickly leaped into it, the mate in charge. Nobody was asked to go; nobody hung back.

We dropped astern and the boat seemed a futile thing, rising and falling in the big seas. It was queer to see the green bottom of the old ship, when we rose on a crest, lifted almost bodily from the swirling water. When we dropped in a trough her royal yards swept wild arcs through the gray sky, and we saw little else. Soon we could not see her at all, when the boat sank deep in the valleys between the big seas. We had no idea where the boy was. We could not see him. How could we? We could see nothing there, not even the ship. Maybe it was madness to look.

We pulled this way and that, hopelessly; yet we could not go back. It began to rain heavily. None of us had oilskins. Frenchman was in his underpants, just as he had come from his bunk. (It was our watch below.) Sjöberg, from Helsinki, had been laid up with neuralgia. But now he pulled at his oar, coatless, wet through, hungry and tired, yet not noticing any of those things and intent only on the saving of this second life. We did not want to lose one more.

One was enough to give to Cape Horn—more than enough.

The mate, at the steering oar in the stern sheets, swept the sea with his sharp eyes, this way and that. There was a chance we would not find the ship again, if the squall came down heavily and shut her out. That had happened with the Swedish bark *Staut,* in much the same circumstances. She put out a boat to save a man fallen into the sea from the main yard, and a squall came down and she lost everybody—man overboard, those who went to rescue him, boat and everything. We remembered that. There was nothing in the boat to sustain life. We had thrown the water cask and the bread barrels out to lighten her.

Then, in the last moment of light, we saw him. It was a sea miracle, if ever there was one. He was on the crest of a sea, only three seas away from us! We had been on the point of giving up. We lay to heartily and soon had the boy back aboard. We pulled him in over the stern and went back to the ship, which had been watching us and now ran slowly downwind toward us. The boy was unconscious and nearly frozen to death, but he lived. He was among the lucky ones.

A few days afterward we were around the Horn, and immediately the temperature rose about 20 degrees and our spirits with it. In reality we ran into a nasty snowstorm off the Falkland Islands, which was every bit as bad as anything the Pacific side of the Horn had given us, but we were in the Atlantic now and did not mind.

Blow on, old gale! We did not mind. We knew that we should quickly come to warmer latitudes and southeast trades, and so to the Line, the northeast trades, the Azores, and home. But we did not count upon too much just now.

We took advantage of the Cape Horn currents to pass between the Falklands and the mainland of South America, which is an unusual way for sailing ships. Once past the Horn, we made good progress. It seemed that the Pacific had wreaked the ocean's wrath on us and delivered us to the Atlantic with the gruff greeting: "Here, these dogs have had enough. Treat them well."

# SOURCES OF STORIES IN VOLUME IX

*Stover Plays Football,* from The Varmint, by Owen Johnson. Little, Brown & Company.

*The Winning Bug,* from Split Seconds, by Jackson Scholz. William Morrow & Company, Inc.

*The Fight,* from Tom Brown's School Days, by Thomas Hughes. The Macmillan Company.

*Billy Topsail and the Devilfish,* from The Adventures of Billy Topsail, by Norman Duncan. Fleming H. Revell Company.

*The Two-Twenty Low Hurdle Race,* from The Human Comedy, by William Saroyan. Harcourt, Brace and Company, Inc.

*Head Over Heels,* from Shift to the Right, by B. J. Chute. The Macmillan Company.

*Knapsack of Salvation,* from I'll Take the High Road, by Wolfgang Lange-wiesche. Harcourt, Brace and Company, Inc.

*Chased by the Trail,* by Jack London. *The Youth's Companion.* Perry Mason Company.

*The Prospector,* from They of the High Trails, by Hamlin Garland. Harper & Brothers.

*Tom Chist and the Treasure Chest,* from Howard Pyle's Book of Pirates. Harper & Brothers.

*Dick Turpin,* from Highwaymen, by Charles J. Finger. Robert M. McBride & Company.

*The Red-Headed League,* from The Adventures of Sherlock Holmes, by A. Conan Doyle. Doubleday, Doran & Company, Inc.

*New York to Paris,* from We, by Charles A. Lindbergh. G. P. Putnam's Sons.

*Flying Over the North Pole,* from Skyward, by Richard E. Byrd. G. P. Put-nam's Sons.

*Dawn Over Zero,* first chapter of Dawn Over Zero, by W. L. Laurence. Al-fred A. Knopf, Inc.

*The Making of an Explorer,* from Ends of the Earth, by Roy Chapman Andrews. Doubleday, Doran & Company, Inc.

*With Helmet and Hose,* from Exploring with Beebe, by William Beebe. G. P. Putnam's Sons.

*Summit of the World: The Fight for Everest,* from High Conquest, by James Ramsey Ullman. J. B. Lippincott Company.

*Adrift on an Ice Pan,* by Wilfred T. Grenfell. Houghton Mifflin Company.

*The Race for the South Pole,* from The Last Continent of Adventure, by Walter B. Hayward. Dodd, Mead & Company, Inc.

*The Lone Voyagers,* from The Book of the Gloucester Fishermen, by James B. Connolly. John Day Company, Inc.

*An Adventure with a Whale,* from The Cruise of the Cachalot, by Frank T. Bullen. D. Appleton-Century Company.

*Rounding Cape Horn in a Windjammer. The National Geographic Magazine,* February, 1931.